Elaine Williams, author and prizewinning poet, has covered India extensively as a travel journalist. She began her career as a magazine editor, and wrote articles for many major magazines and newspapers.

She is the author of "MAHARANI, *Memoirs of a Rebellious Princess*" - republished in 2000. *The New Yorker* called MAHARANI "An unusual biography, a fantastic and anachonistic kind of life. It can hardly fail to hold your interest."

In her new novel, SEEKING THE TAJ, Elaine Williams has drawn on her travels throughout India as a background for the story of a young poet who finds healing in India from her painful past.

Seeking the Taj

A Tale of Love and Awakening in a Far Country

Elaine Williams

Rupa & Co

First Published 2001
First in Rupa Paperback 2003

Published by
Rupa & Co
7/16, Ansari Road, Daryaganj,
New Delhi 110 002

Sales Centres:

Allahabad Bangalore Chandigarh Chennai
Dehradun Hyderabad Jaipur Kathmandu
Kolkata Ludhiana Mumbai Pune

ISBN 1-4010-3462-4

This edition is for sale in the Indian subcontinent only.

Printed in India by
Rekha Printers Pvt. Ltd.,
A-102/1, Okhla Industrial Area,
Phase-II, New Delhi-110 020

Contents

Ode to Taj Mahal's Paradise Gardens
Emperor Shah Jahan

Prayers here are answered,
It is in fact, the very spot where worship
Meets with a favorable reception.

The roses of pardon bloom throughout the gardens,
Their perfume intoxicates the brains of the pure.
Should a sinner enter this abode,
He will be cleansed from his sins.

I

INDIA Taj Mahal, Agra

I have seen starry archipelagoes! and islands
Whose raving skies are opened to the voyager.

I have bathed in the poem of the sea . . .
Devouring the green azores.

I have seen the sunset
stained with mystic horrors,
Illumine the rolling waves with long purple forms.

I have embraced the summer dawn . . .

Arthur Rimbaud

*"Happy is the one who like Ulysses,
makes a glorious voyage."*

i

The *Desert Queen* snaked its way around a clump of black mountains, puffing and snorting steam as it lurched along the narrow-gauge rails imbedded in India's great *Thar* Desert. A bleak stretch of wasteland, five hundred miles blasted by heat. A clay oven of a desert, more suitable for *tandoori* grilling than human existence.

A young woman moved restlessly on the wooden seat of the rail-car trying to ease the ache of her back and hips. There seemed no air left to breathe in the third-class carriage and the odors steaming up from huddles of unwashed bodies were making her ill. She sprinkled a few drops of cologne on a handkerchief, covered her nose and breathed through the cloth, praying for sleep.

From time to time, she glanced anxiously toward a young man resting against a grimy window, his thin frame hunched into a corner, his face pressed white into the glass. It had been a wretched night and she was relieved his eyes were still closed.

The young woman was the object of much curiosity, a rare sight to bedraggled passengers jammed into a third-class rail car. Some had never seen an American girl before, much less a fair-haired one, and were drawn by the sight of tawny blonde hair tumbling over her shoulders, glistening silk in the sun as she leaned over the boy she was tending.

Two middle-aged Indian women in worn and stained saris, plumply self-satisfied types, were seated across the aisle chattering in Hindi at breakneck speed, their high-pitched voices rising above the din of the train as they watched the young woman. They followed her every move as she cared for a bone-thin boy with gaunt cheeks and dark-shadowed eyes. They'd seen her nursing him through the night, surprised at the tenderness of such a young girl, observing the way she gave him pills and held the cup of water to his lips, rubbed his forehead and clasped his hand as she whispered in his ear. They gossiped and speculated about the pair, there was little else to occupy them on the train. Were they brother and sister, lovers? Obviously not husband and wife. The girl wore no ring and didn't look old enough to be married.

The women guessed at her age. Fifteen or sixteen? They clucked their tongues - too young to be responsible for a sick boy. In reality, the girl was twenty-five.

As they watched, the younger woman studied her and pondered the question. "She may not be as young as she looks - Americans don't age like we do."

Her friend snorted in derision. "If we had their life of ease, we wouldn't age either," she retorted.

"What do you think is wrong with him?" the woman whispered, her hand shielding her mouth, as if the young Americans might understand Hindi.

The older woman narrowed her eyes and thought for a moment. "Cancer," she replied, her manner decisive, like a doctor reaching a diagnosis.

The two women nodded in agreement, closed their eyes, and resting against each other fell back to sleep.

The young woman across the aisle dozed off as well but slept fitfully, disturbed by dreams, fighting them in her sleep, afraid to surrender to the murky world of nightmare which could linger in her head for days. But there was no way to break the *film loop* as she swam through the chilly New England sea of her childhood, gasping for breath, unable to touch land. When the dream image shifted she was struggling in the heat of a yellow desert where sand burned her feet, thirst scalded her throat and her legs were leaden as she climbed over dunes towards an oasis shimmering on the horizon.

As she neared, the lagoon melted into sand, the palm trees faded, and the blinding whiteness of the Taj Mahal glistened against the horizon. But Niles' angry eyes glared through the minarets, his face distorted like a bad closeup in a photo, hair slicked against chalk-chill skin, lips a sneer of blackened red, growing larger and larger until the vision of the Taj Mahal was pushed into oblivion.

Half awake, she saw him lying next to her. Observing his thinness and fragility as he slept she felt a twinge of tenderness, the old urge to protect and restore him. But Niles was burnt out by tragedy, his early crazy brilliance dimmed and deadened, leaving him listless and resistant to making an effort. Any attempts she made on his behalf infuriated him and he snarled at words of encouragement.

"*You can save yourself, Niles!*" he mocked, in high-pitched falsetto, "*Make a better life, blah, blah, blah*. Give it up! The *Prince of Darkness* will never live up to his potential."

As an adolescent she'd been drawn to his suffering, recognizing her buried anguish as a link between them. His intellect was impressive and his relentless misery evoked her battle with darkness. She wrote in her journal . . .

A specter of my hidden self has appeared . . . a flash of recognition that this wretched creature is a manifestation of me, mirroring all I conceal from the world. His gaunt face and skeletal body are a metaphor for the pain and hurt I can't express. I am drawn to his desolation, and his willingness to be his appalling self at any cost.

At fifteen, her pity and mistaken identification with him had nearly destroyed her. Now she'd made a huge mistake by bringing him with her to India. But after ten years of avoiding contact some inane compassion let her yield to his pleas after his sister abandoned him. *Love your enemies, do good to those who despitefully use you? Or no good deed ever goes unpunished?* The sad thing was that despite the suffering he'd brought her in the past she still pitied him. She knew he couldn't keep his promises to be reasonable and cooperative on the trip. He was too disturbed for that. But she hadn't realized just how bad his moods and tantrums would be when she agreed.

When the train jolted to a stop at a small way station, she woke in a daze of heat and perspiration. Niles was still asleep, his head thrown back against the window. She touched his hand but he didn't move. His skin felt hot and dry and he looked ill. She tried not to panic but realized there'd be no help on the train if his condition became serious. She opened the bottle of purified water, soaked her handkerchief, and began to bathe his face. He stirred, moaning at her touch, his eyes shuttering.

"It's too hot, Garnet," he whimpered. "I'm dying of heat." She folded the handkerchief, drenched it with more water and laid the wet cloth across his forehead. Then she leaned over and pressed her cheek against his.

"Try to be patient, Niles," she whispered.

"The t-t-train isn't moving," he stammered. "Is it time to get off?"

He made an attempt to lift himself up from the seat, then grimaced in pain, holding his head. "My head is exploding. I c-can't . . . I can't get up."

"Shhh, we're not there yet," she said, rummaging through her purse for his pill box. "This will help you sleep." She filled a paper cup with water and handed him two capsules which he swallowed with difficulty before he fell back and began to drowse again.

After the train left the station she waited to be sure the drug had taken effect and Niles was deeply asleep, then jostled her way through the crowd to the platform between the cars and leaned out into the stream of air to cool her face. A rising sun scattered amber as it trailed a sash of carnelian across a lavender sky. For a moment, she forgot about Niles and surrendered to a rush of pure joy. She was in India at last.

It was 1969 and men had just landed on the moon, clumping around the craters in great boots and floating fuzzily across the TV screen. The magnitude of their accomplishment shrank Garnet's sense of distance and she took it as an omen of encouragement to pursue her childhood longing. After all, compared to the moon India was barely on the other side of the world.

Nor was she unique in her desire. India swarmed with hippies, long-haired ghosts in white kurtahs seeking salvation, squatting on dusty earth, faces upturned to the heavens in rapture, blissed out on drugs and the call of the spirit, breathing o-o-o-ohm to the shrill twang of the sitar, as soothing to Aquarian-age ears as Bach's meticulous rhythms were to an earlier century.

The sun burned into her hair and scalp as it ballooned above the horizon. She pulled her head back into the shade of the train and leaned against the iron frame of the platform squinting to see more clearly as the train approached a village. She looked for the women of the village and was surprised to see them emerge from thatched adobe huts dressed in colorful saris with bracelets jangling on brown arms as if going to a party. *Safeguarding treasures by wearing them*, she thought. *Fearful of thieves and anxious to hold onto what little they owned.*

The train moved slowly, raising swells of dust as it cut through the barren village and she studied the women going about their chores, swinging buckets of water across the fields, stooping to pick up lumps of cow dung to burn for fuel. Two young women, nubile beauties whose long black hair gleamed like Chinese silk, crouched on the ground straining to break rocks with pick axes.

She tried to examine the expressions on their faces, curious about survival on that level of existence but the women revealed little emotion, neither happiness or unhappiness. Perhaps their lives required only surrender.

The train lumbered beyond the village into an uninhabited expanse of desert. She was tired but couldn't face returning to the crowded rail-car with its hard wooden seats. She sighed and tried to rest by slumping into the iron brace of the platform.

"Why do they make the seats so damn uncomfortable?" she muttered under her breath.

"Why not?" someone whispered behind her head. "Who but the poor sit in such seats?"

The voice had the timbre of a fine old cello and she turned to see its owner. An elderly Sikh gentleman stood behind her, tall and spare in a scarlet turban and narrow tunic tracing his bones down to his knees. His white moustache was waxed and curled and his goatee meticulously groomed with the ritual Sikh side-strings of hair tucked under the chin. An elegant portrait, betrayed only by the shabbiness of his sandals and threadbare cuffs.

As he spoke, he gazed into her eyes with a scrutiny as intense as a laser beam but the words came slowly as if thoughts traveled into his head from a far place.

"It's no secret. The powerful enjoy torturing the powerless. Impoverished masses are despised simply because they exist and the more wretched their existence the greater the mistreatment, revenge being the means by which the mighty appease their guilt. As our revered poet Tagore asked, *who but God visits the poor*? I ask, who but God loves them?"

Who but God loves anyone? she thought. She'd known little enough love as a child and not much more when she grew up. All too often, a young man's so-called *love* was a carrot held before a girl's nose in exchange for sexual favors. But even love and betrayal didn't count for much pitted against the wretchedness of poverty in a country like India where the poor survived only by chance and Mahatma Gandhi asserted *God would not dare to appear to the starving masses except in the form of food.*

He saw her glance at his frayed sleeves and nodded his head.

"It's true, my worn-out garments and I are the remnants of a former existence. But have no pity. We are grateful companions who embrace a more joyous life."

The Sikh turned and stared into the desert as the train whipped its tail around the mountain. He was silent and she was reluctant to intrude. Instead she, too, peered into the dark mountains, strangely comforted by the desolate landscape.

It's the pull of darkness, the comfort of the familiar, she told herself. *But you don't have to sink into the gloom or drag it on your shoulders like a backpack. Take a lesson from trains and keep moving. Leave the bleakness in the desert where it belongs.*

Too bad it wasn't that easy. Darkness could cling to you like blue jellyfish, stick on your skin and prick you with poison if you tried to pull it off.

ii

The Sikh remained silent. Garnet immersed herself in the shifting landscape as the train zigzagged beyond the mountains to a plateau where streams of light stained the desert silver and bronze, and shadows danced over the arid land like slivers of smoke. She disagreed with St. Teresa of Avila. *Answered* prayers *were* best - they gave you what you wanted.

She'd been envious of all the seekers who managed to get to India; even the Beatles took their turn sitting at the feet of the Maharishi, breathing out his mantras and strumming the *sitar* with Ravi Shankar. That later they returned to refute the experience and negate the Maharishi while retaining the sitar didn't cut into her yearning one bit.

Now it was her turn to savor the *shining and shifting spectacle of India,* Mark Twain's image of *the most extraordinary country the sun visits on his rounds . . . the one land all men desire to see.* And at least one woman, she thought, resenting nineteenth century *zeitgeitz* which gave men license to roam the world while compelling women to sit by the fire.

When the Sikh spoke it was to ask about Niles.

"Are you traveling with the young man?" His voice was low, coming from a place of stillness unfamiliar to her.

"Yes," she answered, her tone deliberately curt to fend off further questions. She didn't know how to explain Niles to a stranger. Strangers could be intrusive. Sometimes it didn't matter because you never saw them again but on a long train trip it was difficult to escape unwanted attentions or involvement in your affairs.

Of course, she was worried about Niles, anxious about the journey ahead and the problems he might present. Along with his physical difficulties, everything disturbed him, his sensitive system experienced discomfort as acute pain and Garnet's efforts to keep him comfortable were wearing her out.

She had her own delicate constitution to contend with but refused to allow her body or emotions to dominate her life and survived by force of will, accepting the residual exhaustion as a small price for the ability to *rev* up some power. But Niles had neither the will nor the health to save himself.

The Sikh gazed off into the desert and spoke again without turning to her. The measured beat of his voice, its monotony of tone was hypnotic, like a medicine man drumming in a jungle luring with potions to cure her life . . .

"The Bhagavad-Gita says *that which is non-existent can never come into being, and that which is can never cease to be. No weapon can pierce the soul, no fire can burn it, no water can moisten it, nor can any wind wither it. The soul is birthless, deathless, unchanging forever. If so, how can it die the death of the body?*"

He stopped for a moment and turned to face her.

"Illusion tricks us into believing we can salvage the life of another but such power is not ours to command."

She didn't know how to respond or if an answer was necessary. Was the Sikh saying she was deluded to believe Niles' life was in her hands? Months earlier when his sister, Imelda, begged her to take him in she questioned whether agreeing to care for Niles was an act of compassion on her part or a way to salve her conscience from the pain of lingering guilt. For it was Niles' involvement with her when she was fifteen that led to his destruction.

Ten years had elapsed since then and the tragic events of the past had recast his adolescent terrors into reality. Now there were serious reasons for anxiety over his health, especially on a sweltering, swarming train rattling through the Indian desert.

The Sikh said it all. She had no power. And he was telling her she had no obligation. Still, there was no way of avoiding the problem of Niles until this long journey was over. She nodded toward the Sikh as she slipped back to the rail car but he didn't seem to notice.

Luckily, sedatives kept Niles asleep for most of the day. Moments when he stirred from his drugged slumber Garnet bathed his face and did what she could to keep him cool but the desert sun beat down relentlessly on the metal roof, elevating the temperature inside the rail car where ceiling fans were ineffectual, air fluttering through open windows was hot and dusty and the squalor exacerbated by throngs of raggedy Indian families pushing against each other to squeeze a bit more space on the floor of the train.

Traveling third-class on an Indian train with Niles was a serious blunder. Alone, she could have roughed it but clearly conditions were too arduous for him and there was another day to go before the train arrived at Agra. But her concern over money, the financial constraints of a grant funding her India journey, forced her to settle for the cheapest tickets.

iii

Niles grew restless toward evening as the train clattered relentlessly through the desert, but Garnet was afraid to give him more sedation.

"I'm feeling quite ill," he whispered, his voice barely audible, as if he'd lost the strength to speak.

Garnet was shaken. She had no idea how to find help on the train.

"Don't be scared," he murmured, squeezing her hand. "I've survived worse than this. Put me to sleep with a story, the one about the sad prince."

Garnet mopped up the perspiration on Niles' forehead, and let him grip her hand while she whispered a tale she invented about a young prince of such beauty that his jealous King-father snuffed out the light in his eyes, sentenced away his smiles and locked him up in the Tower of Misery. All was lost until the prince was rescued by a beautiful princess who restored his smiles and the light in his eyes. Niles insisted on tales with happy endings and Garnet complied, aware there might never be one for him.

When she finished, Niles rubbed the back of her hand across his eyes and lips as if her touch could restore him.

"You're my beautiful princess . . . ," he breathed, taking strands of her hair in his fingers and rubbing them into his cheek as he closed his eyes.

He slept on and off for some hours, his head resting on her shoulder, his hand clutching hers. Worn out by heat and exhaustion, Garnet fell asleep as well. But in the middle of the night, Niles gave a sharp cry and she felt him convulse against her. Rousing herself from a shadowy cave of sleep she reached out but when she touched him he was in the throes of a seizure, his body rigid and twisted.

His anti-convulsive medicine was in her purse but first she forced open his mouth, pulled his tongue forward so he wouldn't choke and placed a rubber depressor on his tongue to hold it in place. She waited until the convulsion subsided to dribble medication down his throat but despite her efforts his seizures continued with only brief intervals of respite.

She panicked. The conductor rarely came through the car and there was little chance of finding a doctor on a third-class train. Then she thought of the Sikh. He might know how to get help. She was afraid to leave Niles but realized it was urgent he receive medical attention. She soaked a cloth in water, spread it across his forehead, then pushed her way through the rail-car, stepping gingerly over bodies wrapped in rags, mounds of men, women and children huddled in sleep on the floor of the aisles.

The Sikh was nowhere to be seen and as she reached the end of the car she decided to take a moment and step out to the platform between the cars to breathe in fresh air and think about what to do next. But as she pulled open the door she saw a man sitting cross-legged on the platform and realized it was the Sikh. She crouched beside him, touching him gently on the shoulder.

"I'm sorry to disturb you but my friend needs a doctor."

He opened his eyes slowly and gazed at her distraught face for a moment without speaking.

"Has the young man taken a turn for the worse?"

"Yes, yes," Garnet answered, stumbling over the words in her distress. "He's having seizures and his medication isn't stopping the convulsions. Is it possible to find a doctor on the train?"

The Sikh spoke softly, his manner calm. "Let me take a look at him. "Don't be frightened, I have some knowledge in such things. Come, let us see what can be done."

Garnet hesitated, then followed him through the rail car as the Sikh stepped lightly and quickly over the mass of bodies as if he were walking on air. But she was unable to stop herself from whispering nervously at his back as they moved.

"He has epilepsy from a head injury, and an attack of migraine for two days - the pain is excruciating."

The Sikh did not turn or reply.

Niles was sprawled against the window when they reached him. Garnet moved to the outer edge of the wooden bench as the Sikh stepped in and stood over him quietly, remaining silent as

he gazed down at him without comment or touch, watching Niles'
face contort as his body stiffened into another convulsion.

The Sikh took a small vial from his pocket, sprinkled some
drops of a cloudy liquid on Niles' tongue, and began to speak to
him in a low voice. Garnet could not define the words or even the
sounds. *Mumbo, jumbo?* she wondered. *Another Indian fakir out
to pick up a little change?* She thought of interrupting but decided against it. What difference did it make? It was unlikely
other help was available and if it distracted Niles or soothed his
brain for a few minutes it was worth a try.

She watched the man lay the palm of his hand across Niles'
eyes and forehead, barely touching the skin while his lips moved
continuously. He might have been repeating a mantra, but only
a dull hum was audible to her. Niles sighed, his eyelids flickered
and closed. But his body was limp, no longer convulsed. Probably a form of hypnosis. *Fakirs* were good at that sort of thing.

As the hum of sound continued, she had the curious feeling
she was being drawn in to whatever spell the Sikh was casting
over Niles. She felt drowsy and it was difficult to keep her eyes
open. *At least I'll get some rest*, she thought. *It's been a long time
since I slept without interruption.*

But as she began to slide into a heavy torpor she was shaken
awake, torn from reality as if she were soaring above the train in
a cool translucent sky. She let herself experience the pleasure of
flying without trying to define it, recapturing old dreams where
she sailed through space over tree tops and was surprised how
easy it was to fly, wondering in her sleep why she couldn't soar in
life when it felt so natural in dreams.

Now, in air lucid as crystal she glided into infinite space
where nothing existed, but the nothing was everything. No ties,
no bonds. A blue hush radiated from the sky and she saw it was
possible to breathe this stillness of spirit into herself. She breathed
deeply, again and again, as if these breaths were the source of

life for her soul, then rested in the unfamiliar silence. Was this *Samadhi*, the bliss of bliss, union with God as the all-pervading reality? Had she stumbled on Nirvana through the hocus pocus of a weird Sikh?

When she opened her eyes, the old Sikh had straightened up and was moving toward her. He put his fingers to his lips, motioning her to be quiet.

"Don't disturb him. Let him sleep as long as possible. Sleep will aid his recovery."

He lifted his folded hands to his chin, palms together, in traditional Indian greeting and bowed slightly, "Namaskar, my child, may the Divine Powers be with you."

Before she could thank him he'd slipped through the crowded car and vanished like a puff of smoke.

When she bent over Niles she saw his face was peaceful, his breathing quiet and his lips turned up as though the smiles of the sad prince had rippled across them.

Some healing had taken place. It was hard to decide about the Sikh and his powers but she was grateful. No point in trying to discern the reality. This was the East and she'd come for its mysteries. It would be unwise to attempt unraveling the inscrutable so early in the game. She was tired but no longer exhausted, as if she could sleep and be rested for the first time since the trip began.

For the rest of the night and several hours into the heat of the morning, they slept the deep and dreamless sleep of children, *Hansel and Gretel in the forest*, with Niles' head resting on her shoulder, her arm flung protectively across his chest.

iv

They didn't awaken until the train pulled into Agra and a scramble of travelers pushed their way off the train while waiting crowds on the platform shoved back in their anxiety to squeeze aboard. Garnet whispered to Niles to hurry, not wanting to shock him as he woke, then climbed on the seat and reached up for the suitcases in the wire mesh holder above. To her surprise, Niles smiled at her when he opened his eyes.

"I feel good this morning. Let me help with the luggage."

She shook her head and piled the bags under her arms.

"Take it easy, Niles," she pleaded. "Forget the baggage. You were very ill last night."

Niles looked pleased. "You were worried about me, weren't you?"

"Of course," she replied, with a wan smile as she hurried Niles toward the exit.

When they disembarked at the station, she tried to find the Sikh to thank him but with hordes of people pressing against her, swarming onto the platform like a herd of rampaging buffalos, only the tops of heads were visible. Impossible to pick out one Sikh among dozens of scarlet turbans.

Niles was limping badly, his lame leg cramped from days of sitting in tight quarters. Garnet tried not to get impatient but had to hurry him along to secure places on the bus taking them into the city of Agra.

She breathed a sigh of relief at finding two seats together, settled Niles in and tried to relax as the bus rumbled along the muddy waters of the Yamuna River. She peered through the dusty window hoping for a glimpse of the Taj Mahal, then caught her breath at the sudden sight of its marble dome gleaming ivory in the sun.

The Taj Mahal is as exquisite as an ice-storm, nature's supreme achievement in the domain of the superb and the beautiful, wrote Mark Twain. And *beauty can pierce like a pain*, she thought, craning her neck at the pearly dome as the bus moved along the river, feeling a pang of guilt for her intense pleasure and the tears in her eyes.

The bus swayed away from the Taj toward the city, rocking

her into a half sleep as she thought back to her eighth birthday when her uncle, returning from his travels in India, brought her a tiny replica of the Taj Mahal. She pulled the miniature out of the tissue paper with care and held it in her hands but her face paled and tears lurched down her cheeks.

"What's wrong, *l'il darlin'*?"

Garnet stared at him, helpless to explain the pain stirring inside her. She fingered the delicate carving of domes and minarets.

"Don't be afraid to tell me," he said, patting her hand.

"It hurts to look at it," she whispered. "It's too beautiful."

Winslow shook his head and laughed in amazement. "You're an enigma, my dear Garnet," he said, pinching her cheek. "An amazement. Such a funny little thing - part waif, part tiger cub and as sensitive as the *Princess and the Pea*. Clothes itch you, smells make you ill but you remain an interesting anomaly in an impossible family."

Her mother sniffed and turned her head away. Francesca disliked Winslow, tolerating him only for the estate she hoped her husband, Edward, would one day inherit. Certainly, his fuss over Garnet was irritating. No one else in the family shared Winslow's inflated opinion of her. Mostly, they ignored the existence of the little creature, although her mother mocked her when she cried over beauty.

Winslow comforted her. "Beauty is sacred, a panacea sent by God, an antidote for the pain of existence."

Despite her age, Garnet understood Winslow's barbs at her family, secretly agreeing with a critique she overheard waiting outside his study when he was on the phone; the beauteous Francesca was *vain and self-absorbed*, her father (his brother, Edward) was *a snobbish bore*, and her sister, Valerie, *a disagreeable brat*. At eight, Garnet longed to escape, fantasizing about the far-off lands frequented by her uncle, praying for journeys with no return.

She treasured the miniature, setting it on her window sill

where the waking sun shimmered opalescence over the fragile shrine. Pleased by the delight Garnet took in his gift, Winslow gave her a leather-bound volume of *The Book of Knowledge* with a full-page photo of the Taj Mahal. She dreamed over the pearly luminosity of the tomb for hours and begged her uncle to tell her more about India.

Winslow invited her to tea, serving tiny cups of India *Assam* grown in the Himalayan mountains sweetened by Madras honey and stuffed her with cakes and Indian sweets. Later, he showed her photos of his trips to India, on tiger shoots, safaris, in palaces and playing polo with his maharaja friends. Then he burned sticks of incense in a hammered-brass holder while she curled in his lap listening to Kipling's '*Jungle Stories*,' breathing in spirals of musky smoke and imagining herself an adventurer in that remote land of magic and mystery.

v

The Rajmahal, despite its regal name, was a rundown inn where a dingy and stained floral-papered entryway served as lobby. Mr. Chaturvedi, the manager, round-cheeked and balding, his stomach bulging against the vest of his dark European suit, leaned across a makeshift reception desk and greeted them effusively, then turned with annoyance to a boy in rumpled tunic slouching against the glass doorway. Clapping his hands, the manager called out in a sharp voice.

"Look smart, and run for the luggage - be quick. Quick, quick, I say!"

Garnet ordered lunch sent up to the room, rice and curry for her and something plain for Niles' sensitive stomach, yoghurt and paratha bread. But before they were halfway through the meal, Niles turned pale and ran into the bathroom to throw up.

It wasn't surprising. No matter what precautions you took in

India it was difficult to stay healthy. She'd felt queasy on the train herself. Since food wasn't available on third class trains one had to buy from stands in railway stations or lean out of train windows trying to catch a vendor with a cart. God only knew under what conditions it was prepared, the bacteria carried by the food or the diseases of cooks breathing on it. And no matter how carefully you avoided drinking tap water there was no guarantee mineral water was bottled under sanitary conditions.

Niles was weak and shaky when he came out of the bathroom. Garnet helped him lie down and bathed his face with cool water but it was clear he wasn't well enough for a pilgrimage to the Taj Mahal.

"I feel awful, Garnet. Tell me a story so I can sleep."

Garnet sighed. She was tired of making up stories. "How about the tale of a prince who journeys to a strange exotic land in search of a magic potion to heal his life?"

Niles nodded and she wove a princely fable of hardship, crowded trains, wizards and adventures. He shut his eyes, leaned back and remained motionless on the bed.

She thought he was asleep as she tiptoed to the door but he raised his head from the pillow and pleaded, "Don't leave me, Garnet. The Taj Mahal can wait until tomorrow. I need you."

She bent over and felt his forehead with her lips. "You don't have fever. It's probably a touch of *Delhi belly*, Indian *turista*, wretched but not serious. Ring up the manager if you need anything. Relax, and don't fret. I'll see you later."

Garnet explained the situation to the manager and asked him to look in on Niles while she was gone.

"Yes, yes, of course, Madame," he answered with a big smile, showing off his prized gold tooth, and nodding his head from side to side, a touch of sweaty sensuality revealed in his eagerness to please the pretty American.

He summoned a taxi for her, one of the ubiquitous yellow and black mini cabs mounted on three wheels like a toy car atop a tricycle, jolting cheap fares around the cities of India, but the manager opened the door with a flourish as if it were a Rolls and assisted her into the tiny car. She pressed a tip into his hand and his head-bobbing began again as if to say no, no, a man of his position was above gratuities. But he made no attempt to return the tip, simply folded his palms together and bowed his head as the taxi shuddered away.

She leaned back in the cab, a sigh of relief to be on her way to the Taj Mahal alone. She felt guilty but it was a stroke of luck, or the hand of God, that Niles was too ill to accompany her.

The driver helped her out of the tiny taxi and Garnet reminded herself not to be swept away by the Taj Mahal but to examine its reality, recalling Mark Twain's *Exaggerating the Taj*, satirizing tourists who mooned blindly over the tomb without really seeing it.

She understood that. It was easy for her to paint over reality, clinging to fantasy and clouding longed-for objects with old desires. *Beware of the opiate of beauty, God's honeyed wine for the spirit,* she warned herself, *or you'll end up drugged out by dreams. Addiction to illusion is the hardest habit to kick.*

But as she walked toward the Taj Mahal on the marble path where cypresses fringed the reflecting pool and the image of the Taj Mahal trembled in the water, the tomb seemed more of an illusion than ever. At a distance, with its domes and slender minarets shimmering in the sun and opalescent tints rippling over the white marble as light shifted in the sky it appeared a lovely toy, no more real than her childhood replica.

Yet, there was no denying the reality of its beauty as she neared the tomb and scrutinized the exquisite details, the arabesques carved into white marble, inlaid with precious stones, entwined with engraved Sanskrit passages from the Koran. *The most beautiful mausoleum in the world,* wrote Fergusson, the architectural authority of the 19th century.

Shah Jahan guarded his creation jealously. In 1632, when work began on the Taj Mahal, he ordered the construction of all other temples to cease until the tomb was completed. Twenty-two years later, in 1653, the emperor christened his creation the *Taj Mahal, Crown of the Palace*. Legend claimed Shah Jahan was so overwhelmed by the beauty of the Taj that he had the architect decapitated, the calligraphers blinded and the hands of the master builders chopped off to prevent their creating another tomb to rival his masterpiece.

Garnet rested on a marble bench close to the Taj where the colorful saris of Hindu women fluttered like silken banners of scarlet, indigo, tangerine and turquoise across the white marble as they strolled to and fro around the monument amid barefoot hippies and tourists.

From there she could see the arched portal Kipling called *The Ivory Gate through which all good dreams pass*. Again she reveled in the joy of *answered prayers* - absorbing the astonishing radiance of the Taj Mahal, exquisite beyond belief, that far exceeded her childhood imaginings.

She decided to save the interior of the Taj Mahal for last and spent the afternoon roaming around the outside, trying to shield her eyes smarting from the Agra sun glaring knife-white off the marble, then poked around the mosques surrounding the tomb, lingering at Shah Jahan's *Pearl Mosque*, his pearlescent *Moti Masjid*, a seven-year creation, and wandered through the flowering gardens of *Anguri Bagh*, the harem palace where courtesans devoted their lives to pleasuring their emperor. But despite the shelter of the red sandstone walls there was no escape from a feverish sun blazing with fire as it ascended.

When she was too dizzied from heat to continue, Garnet made her way back to the Taj Mahal, removing her sandals on the marble steps and paying two rupees to a ragged old man selling paper slippers for entrance into the sacred tomb where shoes were forbidden, and slipped into the cool semi-darkness of the tomb. In the domed upper hall, marble walls were inlaid with precious gems shaped into flowers and colored by rubies and emeralds. Alabaster screens of pierced tracery, carved delicate as lace, protected the two carved marble cenotaphs but the crypt containing the actual burial vaults entombing Shah Jahan and Mumtaz Mahal were a floor below where visitors were forbidden. Garnet gazed down at the sepulchers with an uneasy feeling as if the research she planned, digging up their secrets to reveal them to the light was an invasion of privacy, perhaps a trespass not taken lightly even from the grave.

Despite the hours spent in the coolness of the tomb Garnet felt lightheaded when she stepped out into the heat of Agra at the end of the day and realized she'd spent too many hours in the sun. She'd prepared herself mentally for the heat of India but her body was rebelling. The long New England winters of her past had accustomed her to the feeling of chill in her veins and it was difficult to reconcile her cool blood with the sweltering Indian landscape no matter how she willed indifference to its unreasonable temperatures.

There were no taxis outside the Great Ivory Arch when she emerged from the site. She was tired, her stomach was queasy and she was worried about finding her way back to the hotel, and depressed by the thought of facing Niles and his problems.

Ancient Hindus warned seekers to stay away from negative vibrations, that merely being in a room with a person emanating such vibrations was as dangerous as exposing yourself to an infectious disease. Bringing Niles was a disastrous mistake, but for now there was no way to avoid the problem.

She decided her only hope for finding a way back to the hotel was to begin walking and perhaps come upon a passing taxi. The road stretched out before her, a flat and dry expanse as far as the eye could see. A slight breeze swirled up a cloud of dust choking her throat as she walked, her lips were parched and her cheeks burnt by the hours in the sun. She wondered how far she'd have to walk before catching up with a cab. There were few people about, mostly vendors closing up their tables of souvenirs and shutting down makeshift stoves where they cooked samosas and hot breads for passing customers.

After about fifteen minutes she came upon a tiny food shop

that was open, and poked in her head. A boy of eight or nine years was behind the counter but he took her order for a *lassi*, and quickly served it up in a tall glass. She rested on the stool, sipping the cold yogurt drink and marveling at the child's efficiency as he cleaned up the small shop before closing for the night.

The sun had nearly set and the air was cooling as she began walking again. Suddenly, she was no longer tired and a feeling of great elation came over her. She had seen what she had come to India for and the Taj was even more beautiful than she'd imagined. She hugged the memory to herself, feeling unreasonably happy, stepping lightly, skipping along the dusty road, thrilled to feel a sense of lightness and freedom. Her past had been painful, but for the moment a curious sensation of joy streamed through her body.

The trip to India felt magical, although she'd been rhapsodizing about *the fantastic land of the East* for a long time, even more so when hordes of hippies made their way there. She was working as an editor for a small poetry magazine when the publisher suggested she could get to India if she put her mind to it.

Laurens Devereaux was the no-nonsense scion of a Boston Brahmin family, a rebel who disclaimed interest in his blue-blood lines, using his inheritance for the unprofitable venture of poetry but who saw no dichotomy in keeping up his prestigious club memberships at The Racquet & Tennis and the Union League. A sturdy Yankee, he had little patience for those without gumption to go after what they wanted.

"You can trek the golden pilgrimage if you apply for a grant, for godsakes," Laurens scolded, shaking his pencil at her. "They've been handing out endowments like free passes to the Ed Sullivan show."

"Send them a copy of "Death Summer," he urged, referring to a slim volume published in her late adolescence - poems based on the near tragedy of her fifteenth summer. "I'll provide the brilliant recommendation."

She acted quickly on his advice, wondering why the idea hadn't occurred to her, and submitted a proposal to an Arts Endowment Committee to write a book of poetry on the life of Mumtaz Mahal, beloved wife of Emperor Shah Jahan, entombed in the Taj Mahal.

To Garnet's surprise, her project was accepted, the grant awarded sooner than expected, and after a hasty and drunken celebration replete with saffron paper streamers strung across the ceiling, posters of Hindu saints tacked to the walls, takeout Indian food in cardboard containers and a surfeit of cheap red wine, she was on her way to India.

* * *

She smiled to herself as she sauntered down the dusty road, unaware that across the path a young man garbed in an Indian kurtah was watching her. Thinking her smile an invitation he smiled back, a great broad grin, and hurriedly began to push his bicycle across the road. Garnet waved him back with her hand, mouthing *no, no, no!* then turned her head away and laughed to herself - *you're not the one, if there is a one!* The boy looked disappointed but didn't approach her.

Some minutes later a taxi stopped at the side of the road. She waved frantically at the driver, ran over to the cab and jumped in. She sank back in the seat gratefully, scarcely noticing the lumps and ruts of the road shaking the cab as it rattled along.

vi

She was still in a jubilant mood when she reached the hotel, smiling at the Manager who bowed, beaming with pleasure, and at the shabby clerk leaning on the desk, and waved to them from the elevator as the rickety grilled door clattered shut.

Garnet paused outside the room, then quietly opened the door a crack before entering, thinking Niles might be asleep. He was sitting up in bed reading but as she took a step into the room he looked up, and without a moment's hesitation hurled the book at her head. She ducked and the book missed, slamming into the door behind her.

"Where have you been?" he shouted. "I've been stuck here all day like a monkey in a cage."

Garnet bent down and picked up the book, glancing at the title, *Thus Spake Zarathustra*, before tossing it on the table. She poured herself a glass of water and sat down. *Nietzsche was right*, she thought, as joy drained out of her body and exhaustion returned; *Distrust all in whom the impulse to punish is powerful.* She dipped a tissue into the glass of water and mopped her forehead. "There were no taxis at the Taj Mahal and I had to walk a long way to find one. It's not easy getting around India."

He glowered at her. "Why didn't you call me?

"Call you?" Her nerves were on edge now. "This isn't London. There are no jolly red phone booths on street corners. It's a nightmare to make a phone call in India."

"But I was terrified," he cried, his lips trembling with rage. "India's a dangerous country and I had horrible visions of you lying in a ditch, raped and robbed, murdered for your money and passport."

"Don't exaggerate. It's still early," she replied, feeling the old sense of hopelessness welling up in her. "Besides, I was safer on the streets than in here. There were no muggers trying to put my eye out with a book."

His face contorted with anger and he glared at her, rolling his eyes and clenching his fists.

Garnet remained silent and motionless, drawing a blanket of calm over her skin. Niles needed to be placated to prevent an escalation of his mood. It could be dangerous to leave him in this state. There was always the chance he could lose control and injure himself or her.

It was best to say nothing. There was a bottle of wine in her suitcase and a drink might calm him down. She poured the wine into the water glasses and handed one to him.

He drank the wine and held out the glass for more. After the second glass, his face brightened and color came back to his cheeks. Clicking his glass against hers, he smiled as if nothing had happened. For the moment, he'd recovered and the incident was over but she dreaded the next to come.

She was still shaken when she went into the bathroom to run water for a bath. There were no tiny give-away packets of shampoo and lotion in this modest hotel but she'd brought along a jar of bubble bath in case she needed soothing. She placed her glass of wine on the ledge next to the tub, turned the hot water tap on as far as it would go and stretched out in the tub, resting her head back as the bubbles foamed up around her.

While the tub was filling she drank a little wine and focused on the air as it came in and out of her nostrils, meditating on *Vasudeva, Lord of the Living Breath*, trying to evoke the memory of the Taj Mahal, willing its radiance to fill her mind and erase the encounter with Niles.

It was too difficult. She gave up trying to force the Taj Mahal into consciousness and surrendered, letting her body sink into the hot bubbles, trying to empty her mind and concentrate on her breathing. But memories jumped around in her head like fireflies in Sailship Point on a hot summer night.

vii

It was an early spring in Sailship Point, just after her fifteenth birthday, when Imelda, a classmate at Highcroft Hall, invited her home for tea and Garnet caught a glimpse of Niles. Imelda dragged Garnet up to her bedroom where they listened to Sinatra records, tried on makeup and new hairdos and danced with each other to *Blues In The Night* . . . *My mama done tole me, when I was in pigtails* . . . , then rock-and-rolled, laughing hysterically as they gyrated around the room to Elvis' *Blue Suede Shoes.*

Later in the afternoon, Mrs. Preston poured tea from a silver pot in a cool drawing room where silken ivory drapes shaded Chinese rugs and paintings from the sun, and Garnet saw Niles for the first time. He was standing just outside the door observing them in silence, a white face staring as if in torment, beads of sweat plastering his dark hair to his brow and gaunt shoulders tensed as if fending off a blow.

Imelda had warned her earlier. "Pay no attention to my mad brother," she announced, with a short laugh. "Niles doesn't go to school, just slinks around the house. My mother dotes on him, says he's a *genius* - claims his I.Q. jumped over the chart, but my father rolls his eyes and calls him a freak!

Niles' haunted ghost face and stricken eyes peered around the room as he slithered behind the chairs to the French windows leading onto a terrace. Garnet pretended not to notice his eyes frantically searching her as he passed. She studied her teacup, her face hot with embarrassment. Yet she longed to stare, to pin the mad boy against the wall, scrutinize him, discover his secret, the anguish of his madness. But she was too aware of Mrs. Preston's pain to intrude and kept her head lowered.

The mother. Thin trembly fingers, short hair sculptured to her head, translucent skin which tightened briefly in pain as Niles passed. A fleeting moment, then bravery, an attempt to recover by turning her attention back to the girls, offering them cakes, hoping to distract them from her sadness. The deep, deep sadness of the mother, like the wings of a wounded bird fluttering in your hands. Garnet's stomach contracted in pity and she averted her eyes, her discomfort intensified by Mrs. Preston's gentleness and her own awkwardness trying to balance herself on the edge of a spindly gilt chair.

But when Niles slipped through the glass doors opening onto the terrace, Garnet lifted her head and followed the lank figure lurching a zigzag course down an emerald lawn sloping to the sea.

Imelda and Niles were a curious pair of siblings. She was fat and white-blonde with china-blue eyes and a full mouth, half-open and moist, and a kinky mass of hair tumbling over plump cheeks (a relic of an Irish grandfather) while Niles, dark and gaunt, was a photo-negative of his sister. Where he was sensitive, Imelda was brutish and where he was intellectual she was a bit dim-witted.

After tea, Imelda walked Garnet halfway home through the tree-shaded paths of Sailship Point and confided in her.

"Father hates Niles and wants to send him to a school for nut cases but my mother won't permit it. Father's an awful bully, roars like a lion knowing my mother hates scenes and loud noises. She comes from an old Bostonian family, very la-di-da, who barely speak above a whisper. My father shakes his fist but doesn't dare touch her. My grandparents would kill him, or worse, persuade my mother to divorce him and take her money away. But Niles *is* embarrassing. After my friends came here, the little bitches ran back to school whispering about my weird brother. I won't let them come again."

"What about me?" Garnet asked.

"You're different. You're not a stuck-up snob," Imelda said, kissing her on the cheek and waving goodbye as Garnet made her way home.

Garnet wasn't overly fond of Imelda but she was lonely, with few choices on the isolated peninsula. And she came to love the gentleness of the mother who reached out to her loneliness. Waiting for tea to be served she'd sit on the floor next to the mother's chair and rub her cheek against the silk of Mrs. Preston's dress, glancing up at her face from time to time as if to reassure herself that such a loving spirit existed.

After some weeks, Niles gave in to his mother's coaxing and

joined their tea parties. Garnet grew to cherish the peaceful, ghost-like existence his mother created; long silences with Niles staring moodily into space, Imelda sprawled across the Chinese rug chewing on a pencil, Mrs. Preston dreaming over their heads into the distance as Garnet drifted in an unfamiliar tide of tranquility.

When the servant arrived with the tea tray they roused themselves, Mrs. Preston smiling with pleasure at the brood gathered around her, insisting Garnet call her Enid as her children did and amusing them with funny stories while passing out cups of tea, her eyes brightening as they laughed and joked back, especially when Niles responded to their antics. Garnet soon realized how pleased Mrs. Preston was when attention was paid to Niles and made an effort on his behalf, wanting to please Enid, hoping to wipe away the sadness from the mother's eyes.

Enid urged the girls to take Niles for walks and when Imelda became impatient and ran off, Garnet rested with him in a shaded grove of willow trees. Niles suffered from migraine and when an attack overtook him, pain paled his skin to chalk and darkened his eyes to ebony, casting a melancholy beauty over his face.

viii

In the ensuing ten years, Garnet's life took a far different turn so she was startled one day to receive a phone call from Imelda. They hadn't met since she was fifteen but Imelda insisted they get together for *a reunion tryst at the Cafe Reggio on MacDougal Street*. Garnet was reluctant but a bit curious, and yielded to her pleading.

She could hardly believe her eyes when Imelda showed up

at the cafe. There was no sign of the chubby girl of her childhood. Wrapped in a blue satin, flower-embroidered Chinese jacket
with a gold-threaded chiffon scarf tied around her blonde hair,
straightened and cut short into a sleek cap, she was as elegant as
a 1920s Vogue cover. Garnet was impressed. Fat, dull-witted
Imelda had recast herself as a vampish expatriate in a Scott
Fitzgerald novel.

Thin to the point of emaciation, apparently anorexic as the
sight of food seemed to terrify her, Imelda mostly smoked pot
and poked at lettuce leaves.

"I'm mad about *Art Deco*," she said, articulating her words in
a strangely eccentric accent which seemed to have no roots except in her head, and draping herself around the cafe chair in
the pose of an *Erté* gouache as she waved a long cigarette holder
in the air. "The sixties have been utterly boring. Love-ins! Dirty
hippies! Folk singers! Who'd have believed it!"

The good news, Imelda claimed, was her discovery of *acid*.

"I've *tripped* my brains out in the last five years. But it made
me see my life and my sick family with horrible clarity - the
brutality of my father, the helplessness of my mother and my
ravaged brother."

With that, Imelda got down to the real business of the reunion even before the cappuccino arrived at the table. It was
clear she hadn't sought out Garnet for friendship's sake but to
ask a huge favor. Pretensions aside, Imelda had a tough streak of
practicality.

Imelda explained that Niles had stayed with her in Italy the
past year when her mother could no longer handle his moods
and rages. But her drug-dealing Italian lover, Roberto, despised
Niles and didn't want him around.

Roberto was a brute, Imelda told her, with a perverted touch
of pride in her voice, a drug addict who abused her and chased
after women.

"But he's *my* drug of choice, my obsession. Roberto needs
heroin, hashish, and jolts of cocaine to keep himself going, and

I need *him*. In my way, I'm as bad as he is but neither of us is about to go cold turkey."

"Roberto refuses to take Niles back to Italy with us. *Go rid of your pazzo fratello* - my crazy brother. I've pleaded with Roberto but he's adamant and Niles has nowhere to go."

The reason for the meeting was now quite clear. Garnet felt sick to her stomach. Imelda was planning to dispose of Niles by pushing him on her.

Imelda stared at her, narrowing her blue eyes into slits, the same way she bullied her father.

"For God's sake, Garnet, you *owe* Niles, and I can't do it anymore. Niles' life was ruined and you were involved. It's a miracle he's still alive."

Garnet felt a terrible despair sweep over her. She gripped the edge of the table with both hands and tried to control herself.

"What about the damage to my life?" Garnet asked, trying not to burst into tears.

"You're strong, Garnet, you got over it." Imelda leaned over the table and tried to kiss her on the mouth but Garnet yanked her head away. Imelda laughed.

"What choice do I have?" Imelda argued. "I can't dump him back on my mother and I won't give up Roberto. Please take him in, Garnet. It's just temporary, a stopgap, a week or two at most. As soon as I find a place to care for Niles I'll take him off your hands."

Garnet was appalled at the idea but felt too guilt-ridden for a flat refusal. It was true he'd nearly died and she was partially to blame.

"Let me think about it," she answered, playing for time.

Garnet was still undecided when she received a call from Enid Preston entreating her to care for Niles temporarily. Her mother, old Mrs. DeForest, was ill and infirm and Enid was bringing her to a famous specialist in Switzerland. "I beg you, Garnet, darling. It's only a matter of a few weeks. I'll arrange something as soon as I return."

She felt sorry for Enid but was nervous about having contact with Niles. At fifteen, she vowed never to see him again. But time and a twinge of guilt had softened her resolve and she thought she might be able to handle him for a brief period of time. But she wasn't sure.

In the end she had no choice. Before she could make up her mind, Mrs. Preston was gone and Imelda and Roberto had slipped away in the night while Niles slept, and pushed a note under Garnet's door.

> *Sorry, sorry, sorry! Roberto can't take it another minute*
> *so we're off, back to Italy. Get rid of the hotel room, Niles*
> *has the keys, etcetera, etcetera, etcetera. Please don't hate*
> *me for unloading him on you . . . love, Meldy.*

Garnet allowed Niles to move into her small Village flat, relying on the promises that his stay would be temporary and short. But when she tried to contact Imelda in Italy after receiving news of her grant there was no response to her letters or phone calls. Then Enid Preston called her from Geneva to say the treatment would take longer than expected. She sounded worn out and Garnet didn't have the heart to tell her about her grant. Instead, she dragged Niles along to India. He swore he'd be no trouble but Garnet promised herself when the trip was over she'd insist the family make other arrangements. Much as she loved Enid, Niles was a problem they'd have to take back.

ix

When morning came Garnet chose to ignore Niles' tantrums of the previous night and the false cheeriness of his '*Good morning, old girl*!' as she tidied up the room and laid out fresh clothes for him. It was early morning and she was still exhausted from the night's encounter.

She suggested Niles rest for another day at the hotel but he insisted he was well and refused to be left behind. She assented reluctantly, hoping he'd be agreeable, but he turned cranky and irritable, complaining bitterly as they jolted along the crooked streets in a mini-cab.

"What's this toy car you've stuffed me into - this bizarre three-wheeled piece of tin? Are you trying to kill us?"

Garnet held her breath as the driver swerved to avoid hitting a cow in the middle of the road, then sighed.

"Please, Niles, it's cheap and it gets us there. Every penny counts, the grant money wasn't meant for two."

"We wouldn't need to scrimp if Imelda released cash from the trust fund," Niles answered angrily. "She's squandering our funds to prop up her junky lover's habit. The bitch denies me money while that bazooka sucks coke up his big Italian nose! I hope it eats holes in his sinuses."

He peered out the taxi window at the crowds milling in the street, muttering nonstop under his breath about Imelda.

She listened for a moment, then glared at him with what Niles called her *Medusa* stare. He began to stammer, but when Garnet didn't flinch or withdraw he stopped talking and stuck his head out of the taxi into the breeze to cool himself off.

The taxi let them off at the Great Ivory Arch. Niles tucked his arm in Garnet's and they walked slowly on the long pathway to the Taj Mahal, designed by Shah Jahan to symbolize Mumtaz Mahal's entry into Heaven, her tomb a metaphor for Islamic paradise. Every day without fail, the emperor stood beneath the arch of the gateway and visualized his beloved Mumtaz gliding along on her path to God. *How he must have loved her*, Garnet thought, with a sting of envy.

The death of Mumtaz Mahal was considered *Shaheed,* the death of a martyr-saint as she died in childbirth (bearing her fourteenth infant.) The Muslims regard all women who die in childbirth as holy, their tombs are sacred and their graves *Urs*, places of pilgrimage, so that the Taj Mahal is a hallowed site with inscriptions on its marble largely texts from the Koran.

Halfway to the tomb, Niles stopped and leaned on the cane he used to rest his leg on long walks, motionless as he stared toward the white marble tomb with its gleaming, iridescent dome.

Garnet turned to Niles with tears in her eyes. *"When blissful dreams of long ago come true . . ."* He didn't answer but his cheeks were flushed with color and he was breathing deeply.

Niles can't resist the spell of the Taj either.

She suggested exploring the gardens before the feverish heat saturated the morning air. At the entrance to the *Charbagh or Paradise Gardens,* she ran her fingers across Shah Jahan's verses inscribed on a marble wall.

Enter thou My Paradise . . .
Prayers here are answered,
It is in fact, the very spot where worship
Meets with a favorable reception.

The roses of pardon bloom throughout the gardens,
The perfume of which intoxicates the brains of the pure . . .
Should a sinner enter this mansion,
He will be cleansed from his sins."

They slipped into the garden and strolled past eucalyptus trees dappled silver with sunlight, walking slowly along shaded stone walks fringed with hibiscus and scented by jasmine and frangipani until they reached the formal gardens patterned in Persian style, with rows of cypress and fruit trees symbolizing life and death in Mogul gardens.

Niles paused at a marble pool and bent over to inhale the fragrance of lotus blossoms and water-lilies floating on the water, then rested on a marble bench under the gnarled branches of a banyan tree, while Garnet read aloud softly from her notes. Niles drowsed with his eyes half shut and his head leaning against the trunk of the tree.

She watched as his face relaxed, color suffused his cheeks and his body sprawled in repose. Perhaps the Paradise Gardens could cleanse him of his pain and misery . . .

But Niles disdained help. "Forget about me, Garnet. I prefer to lie quietly, unmoving, silent as a ghost. Save yourself."

It was true. She was the one who needed deliverance. *Let Niles go, and ask for your wounds to be healed in the garden. Remember the warning Winslow read from the Bhaghavad Gita:*

It is better to do your own duty, however imperfectly, than to assume the duties of another person, however successfully. Prefer to die doing your own duty: the duty of another will bring you into great spiritual danger.'

She closed her eyes and began to doze off when she heard a sound behind her.

"Psst, psst."

A disheveled man in a ragged *dhoti*, crouching behind the fence, held open an apron filled with flowers and beckoned her. "Madame, madame," he hissed. "Come, take some garlands. Beautiful jasmine, fresh and fragrant. The lucky flower of India. Only five rupees."

The flower vendor nodded his head from side to side and grinned at her with an uneven row of blackened and missing teeth, "In India, luck is a necessity," he whispered. "Buy my flowers, and you and your friend will receive many blessings from Hindu goddess."

"Any particular goddess?" she asked, moving toward the fence to look at the flowers.

He bowed deeply with his palms together before his wizened face. "Many, many goddesses send holy blessings to you, Madame. Shiva guarantees it."

"Sounds too good to be true," Garnet said, rolling her eyes

and taking out her purse. "Give me two jasmine garlands and don't forget the blessings. I can use all you have."

He thrust his arm through an opening in the fence and pushed the garlands into her hands, then swiftly shoved in his other hand to reach for the money.

"Quickly, quickly, Madame, it is forbidden to sell here."

Garnet dug the rupees out of her purse and pushed them into his hands. He nodded his head in thanks and scurried away from the fence and across the field.

Does my bad luck show? she wondered, *or is every encounter in India accompanied by a spiritual fortune cookie to enlighten Western heathens? Are mystical messages their idea of small talk, or just a ploy for tourists - buy my trinkets and I'll connect you with the Great Beyond.*

She slipped the garland around her neck and pressed her nose into the flowers to breathe in the scent of jasmine, then tiptoed to the bench where Niles was stretched out. He was half-asleep, barely stirring as she lifted his head for the garland, but he gave a sigh of pleasure at the aroma of the flowers. She awakened him gradually, helped him up and they made their way back to the Taj Mahal, their nostrils permeated by the sweet aroma of dying jasmine petals crushed against the warm skin of their necks.

When they arrived at the tomb Niles objected to removing his shoes, afraid to trust them on the steps of the Taj. "These are special shoes, Garnet. I can't replace them here."

"No one else could use your shoes," Garnet replied, trying not to lose patience. "The old man sitting on the step is paid to watch them. Shoes aren't allowed in the tomb - if you refuse you'll have to remain outside."

Niles made a face but complied, tucking his shoes under Garnet's sandals.

"It's so hot," Garnet said, wiping her dripping face with a tissue. "Let's go to the burial chambers where it's lovely and cool."

They examined the inscriptions on the cenotaphs and Garnet pointed out all she'd seen the day before, leading him through narrow passages twisting through the tomb until Niles was too tired to walk and begged to rest in the corner of a darkened room.

"I have to meet with the Director of the Museum about using the library," Garnet said. "Why don't you stay here and rest and I'll pick you up here or on the steps of the Taj in an hour."

Niles was terrified at the idea. "No, no, don't leave me alone, Garnet, let me come with you," he pleaded.

They stepped out of the Taj Mahal onto the marble promenade in the bright sun where the old man in charge of shoes was hovering about waiting to pick up more rupees. She pointed to their shoes still side by side against the marble wall, gave the man whatever change was in her pocket and knelt down to help Niles remove the paper slippers, pull on his shoes and tie the laces.

She was about to stand up when Niles poked her and pointed toward three men ascending the steps.

"The bearded man in the middle . . . He's the Sikh who helped me on the train."

"You must be mistaken," Garnet replied, shielding her eyes against the glare of the sun with the palm of her hand. "That man is wearing the robes of a holy man, a sadhu."

"I'm sure he's the *Wizard of O-h-h-m* who breathed life into me," Niles insisted.

She shaded her eyes and squinted to see more clearly. Niles was right. The Sikh on the train had shed the scarlet coat of Rajasthan for the saffròn robe of a holy man.

Two young men wearing white kurtahs, long tunics of thin cotton over tight, wrinkled pants, were climbing the steps with the saffron-robed Sikh. An odd accompaniment to flank the stately sadhu, this unmatched pair - one man small and scrawny, the other tall and sturdy.

As they approached, Garnet stretched out her hands to greet the Sikh. "I was so grateful for your help on the train."

The Sikh bowed his head and folded his hands before his face.

"Shanti, shanti," he murmured. "The darkness of disease is driven away by the light of God's perfect presence."

"But stopping my seizures without medication . . . American doctors would call it impossible," Niles declared.

The Sikh smiled. "The omnipotent *Paramatan*, Supreme Spirit, can heal anyone, doctor or no doctor. Attuned to God, our power is limitless."

"For me, it was a miracle," Niles said, with a look of gratitude that surprised Garnet.

"Any interruption in one's own orbit seems grave," the holy man replied, his voice tranquil as he looked kindly at Niles. "Yet many calamities are easy to repair."

"But only for one gifted with wisdom," Garnet queried shyly. The Sikh looked curiously at Garnet and nodded.

"Well, I guess we'll have to introduce ourselves," the larger man said cheerfully in an Anglo-Indian accent with a pleasing timbre. "I'm Ravi Singh, this is my cousin Vijay Singh and our guru, Sri Devanda, whom you apparently know."

Up close, Ravi Singh was attractive, even handsome, but in quite a different way from other men she'd known. His physique bore no resemblance to the hard-muscled tennis players and health club addicts who dominated the New York scene or to the poor broken body of Niles. Ravi resembled one of those fatted Arabian princes who yearly receive their weight in gold; bred like a calf force-fed for roasting with round stomach and fat cheeks, skin silky with ghee butter and spices, and fleshy-lidded eyes of sienna melting into gold. His full lips, sharply cut and turned up at the edges, looked soft and plump in the center, delectable as a chocolate truffle.

As Ravi laughed and joked with his cousin and the guru, Garnet realized he was flirting with her and felt a sudden, irrational craving to kiss his plump lips, lean her face into the roundness of his cheek and breathe in the scent of his soft neck.

You've really lost your mind, she chided herself. *This is madness. Or heat stroke. You're terrified of love, sex, intimacy, yet two minutes after meeting a stranger you're ready to leap over the precipice.*

She was embarrassed and tried to avoid his eyes, hoping he couldn't read her mind. Then he took her hand to say goodbye. Success-oriented American men looked women over with calculating, bone-chilling eyes but Ravi's gaze was placid when it rested on her.

"Where are you off to?" Ravi Singh asked, not letting go of her hand. "Why not come back to the Taj Mahal with us and we'll act as guides. Trust us, we're experts."

"Sorry," Garnet replied, pulling her hand away gently. "I'm on my way to the museum to confirm using their library for research. Hopefully, I can begin tomorrow."

"So, you've come to India for a purpose," Ravi asked, with a quizzical look.

"I'm here on a poetry grant," Garnet replied, feeling a bit ruffled and defenseless in his presence.

"We treasure artists and poets," Ravi beamed, eyeing her with a conspiratorial gaze as he folded his hands and bowed. "Namaste, India welcomes you!"

The guru moved away from the group toward the entrance.

"I'm afraid that's our signal to leave," Ravi said, smiling at her in a warm, intimate way as if they were already friends. "But I hope we'll meet again. Where are you staying?"

"Some funny little hotel. I'm not sure of the name," she answered evasively.

He looked at her for a moment as if realizing her reluctance, then shook her hand in a formal manner. He gave a quick goodbye to Niles and turned once more to Garnet.

"I hope things work out for you at the museum."

"Thanks. I'm counting on it," she replied, feeling awkward, like an adolescent hiding a crush on a teen-age boy.

She was almost relieved when he moved on with the Sikh to

enter the tomb. These disturbing sensations could shake up her life. The trip was difficult enough without adding complications she might not be able to control.

x

The curator of the library agreed Garnet could begin her research in the morning but when the sun squeezed its way through the slatted blinds of the hotel room painting hot streaks across her eyelids, she groaned and opened her eyes. A guru stared back from the wall, a cockeyed guru with one eye masked by a garland of fake marigolds flung across the glass. *It's too early for this*, she moaned, pulling the bedclothes up over her head to grab a few more minutes of sleep.

A sharp rapping roused her. She jumped up but before she could get the door fully opened, Ashish, a young waiter barely in his teens whose amber skin shone like polished fruit-wood, burst into the room, his energy as high as the breakfast tray he carried aloft his head.

Between smiles and bows, "Just as you ordered, Madame, exactly your wishes," and loudly humming a hit song from an Indian movie, he hurriedly set the table, laid out a pot of Assam tea steaming with boiled milk, sugar and spices, two bowls of yogurt and a mound of *nan*, thick puffy bread still hot from the oven, then held out his hand for the tip and rushed from the room, letting the door slam in his exuberance.

When Niles stirred at the noise, Garnet touched his arm to wake him but he pushed her away and crushed the pillow over his head to smother the sound of her entreaties to get up.

"Please, Niles, I can't be late today!"

His answer was to kick his legs out at her and bury his head further into the mattress.

In her anxiety to get to the museum on time, she prodded

him to hurry but Niles was in a rebellious mood, taking his time soaking in the bathtub, dressing and eating even more slowly than usual, staring at her in defiance as he chewed each mouthful, refusing to be rushed or allow her to leave the hotel without him. Finally, he conceded he was ready and permitted her to call down to the desk for a taxi, then complained and grumbled all the way to the Taj.

When they reached the museum library half an hour past the appointed time the doors were locked and there was no sign of anyone in the vicinity.

"I told you not to rush," he whined. "Now we have to stand around in this god-awful heat waiting for someone to show up."

She took a deep breath to control herself.

"Please, Niles," she implored, "you promised to behave!"

She pounded on the silver encrusted doors of the museum and yanked on a hanging bell. The chimes resounded across the garden but there was no response and she persisted beating at the door until she was close to tears with frustration.

A man's voice called out from the bottom of the steps. She whirled around, relieved the curator had finally arrived. Instead, two young men were waving and smiling up at her.

"Can you use some help?" the larger man shouted. "We're friends of Sri Devanda - we met yesterday."

In her impatience to get into the library and her irritability over the long wait, Garnet hadn't recognized Ravi Singh despite the wild attraction she'd felt the day before. Perhaps because they wore simple white kurtahs then. Now the young men were elegantly garbed in long fitted coats of brocaded silk.

"Do you know anything about the curator?" she called back. "My appointment was for an hour ago."

He laughed and cupped his hands to yell up to her, "I doubt the curator will show up before twelve. I know the fellow - he enjoys keeping impatient Americans waiting on the doorstep."

Niles poked her arm and hissed in her ear, "For god's sake, Garnet, don't get involved with those two characters."

But Ravi Singh ran up the steps of the museum, panting and laughing, his cousin following behind him. Garnet caught her breath as he approached. She'd forgotten how handsome he was. "We Indians are a lazy lot," he gasped, trying to regain his breath. "We're always late for appointments, an Oriental failing maddening to Western friends."

Garnet sighed. Promptness was a compulsion with her, waiting for latecomers a torment. But this was India and she'd better get used to it.

"Allow us to make it up to you," he said, smiling as he pressed his palms together in an Indian *salaam* and bowed his head in apology. "Join us at a cafe for some strong coffee to fortify you against that curator-beast who lives by Indian time. I assure you, he'll arrive at the museum at noon, sputtering excuses and huffing and puffing as if he's run all the way."

Garnet didn't reply as she scrutinized Ravi, searching for flaws to counteract the disturbing feelings he evoked. *Was he too slick*, she wondered, *with the slippery charm she disliked in European sophisticates? Or had he sensed her response to him the day before and sized her up as a gauche Americaine on the make, stalking passion in a foreign land.* A humiliating thought. It made her reluctant to accept his invitation but if the library didn't open until twelve there was no point waiting in the hot sun. The heat was exhausting and coffee might revive her.

She sighed again. "I resent the cavalier attitude of the curator - I guess I'm too American for *Indian time*. Coffee's a great idea but . . ."

"No, Garnet, no. Tell him no!" Niles whispered. "I don't want to go with them. We'll wait here until the curator comes."

"You'll have to wait by yourself then because I'm half dead and need coffee," she retorted under her breath, irritated by his constant objections.

The small wiry man smiled at Niles reassuringly. "Don't be afraid of us, we're good fellows."

He extended his hand in brisk British fashion. "Do take a

chance and come to the cafe. We'd like to extend a bit of Indian hospitality to friends of our guru."

They waited expectantly until Niles grudgingly assented and reassuring Garnet she'd be back by the time library opened, they linked arms and carried the two of them off to one of the narrow streets edging the Taj. A crooked lane, patchworked with tiny shops, glittered with wares spilling out onto the sidewalk. Garish jewelry, scarlet coats embroidered with gold and doors hung with brightly-hued silks and banners dazzled the dingy street with color while vendors shouted as they passed, "Come, have a look! Good bargains, cheap prices!"

Curls of incense drifted through the air mixing with the aroma of hot pastries and the smoke of harsh tobacco puffed out by wizened-faced men squatting silently in doorways as if in deep meditation. Skinny, undernourished cows wandered through the street and onto the sidewalks, bells clanging around their necks as they moved heavily through the crowds nudging hips of shoppers as they passed.

Ravi paused in front of a dingy coffee house, smoothed his hair back and straightened his collar. He hoped to make a good impression on the American. There was something fresh and spirited about her. He was tired of passive Indian girls who tried too hard to please. He waved his hand at the sign on the canopy. "Welcome to *Shubha Kamana, Café of Favorable Hopes.*"

So he's a bit vain, Garnet noted, watching him. *Probably knows he's totally gorgeous.*

She nodded her head, longing for coffee and anxious to sit down. "It's perfect - good omens and strong coffee."

The cafe was small and dark, crowded with Indian students and blonde-bearded hippies huddled over rickety tables, noisily competing to be heard.

Ravi motioned to the owner, "We'll sit outside, Chandni," and led them to a table on the sidewalk sheltered from the sun by a makeshift awning.

The cafe proprietor nodded and hurried over to inspect the

busboy setting the table, scolding him in a burst of Hindi and English.

"Bring fresh water, clean tablecloth. Make haste! Quickly, quickly. Lofty customers have no time to wait while you dawdle." Ravi discussed the order with the owner in Hindi, gesticulating as he explained while Chandni bowed and smiled, nodding his head back and forth to show respect while pointing to a tray of cakes. When Ravi nodded in agreement the proprietor backed away with still another bow.

A turbaned waiter arrived quickly with a pitcher of coffee, a jug of hot frothy milk and a tray of cakes. "Leave the tray on the table," Ravi ordered.

He motioned the boy away, and poured a small amount of thick black brew into each cup.

"South Indian coffee is an essence," he explained. "The taste is exquisite but it takes twenty-four hours to concentrate the liquid. A slow and backward process yet the flavor can't be duplicated by modern methods."

He filled their cups with steaming milk. "It's one of the pleasures fast disappearing in India in favor of instant coffee, DDT, and god help us, one day polyester instead of cotton as we absorb the rejects of Western society along with its technology. Take my advice and enjoy South Indian coffee while you have the chance."

Garnet watched him as he spoke, his cheeks flushed and his skin shining with energy. She felt a little shy but had an odd sense of comfort as if she were back in Sailship Point with her uncle, Ravi's enthusiasm and good humor a reminder of Winslow's endearing traits.

They sipped their coffee in silence and sampled small sweet cakes topped with sheets of silver. Garnet poked at the silver and looked askance.

"It's silver but edible," Ravi assured her. "Chandni takes pride in his cakes. *Real silver yet safe to eat,* he brags to tourists.

A palatable touch of Indian beauty! Chandni is sentimental about India. As for me, I pay homage to pleasure, Indian or not."

The coffee and pastries revived Garnet's spirits and she leaned back in the wooden chair with a ·sigh of relief. She glanced at Niles, relieved to see him occupied, eating cake and listening to Vijay whose face was bright with the discovery of a new listener for old stories.

Ravi Singh laughed. "Admit this is better than collapsing in the hot sun waiting for an ill-mannered lout. You look a different person, transformed by a Hindu adage - *pleasuring the body feeds the soul*. Don't you agree, Vijay?"

His mouth stuffed with cake, Vijay could not speak but nodded his assent.

Ravi leaned across the table and touched a wisp of her hair, gazing into her eyes as he spoke. "Still, it must be more than South Indian coffee and silver cakes bringing a numinous glow to your face. A *sadhu* would call it luminosity, the spirit by which one shines with light."

Garnet looked at him in astonishment and with a muffled gasp began to laugh. The heat, her fatigue, the humor of the situation made her laughter uncontrollable. She threw back her head and roared, hanging onto the arms of the rickety chair to steady herself as tears ran down her cheeks. Her shoulders shook and she was gasping for breath, dimly aware her laughter had turned into hysteria but unable to stop herself.

Vijay looked startled, Niles threw up his hands in delight, and the cafe patrons on the sidewalk turned in their chairs to stare at her. Ravi offered her a glass of water but she was shaking too much to hold it.

Finally, her laughter subsided. Ravi handed her a napkin and she mopped the tears and perspiration from her face.

"I'm sorry," she apologized, still trying to catch her breath, "It just tickled me."

Ravi looked rueful. Embarrassed by his scrutiny she tried to explain.

"I'm not used to extravagant compliments," she said in apology, dismayed at her outburst. "It sounded like a *pickup line* but the most literate and elegant I've ever heard. Forgive me for making a scene but to tell you the truth it felt fantastic. Maybe it was heat stroke. I haven't laughed like that in a very long time."

She bent toward Ravi and whispered so Niles and Vijay couldn't overhear. "What struck me funny was being flattered as if I were *a rich, lonely tourist seeking romance* when I'm only a broke writer living a raggedy life, scraping up pennies for my India journey."

Ravi showed no trace of irritation at her outlandish behavior, his face calm and amused as he listened. He enjoyed Garnet's spunky spirit but perceived a sensitivity under the sassiness that touched him.

"Just one point," he demurred. "This was no pickup - we met through a spiritual master, a holy man."

"I know. Forgive me for being rude," she said, in a barely audible voice.

"I'm a great admirer of American candor and refuse to accept your laughter as an insult," Ravi said cheerfully, smiling at her in the most disconcerting way. "Instead, I extend an olive branch. Pax vobiscum."

Garnet nodded ruefully. "I wish peace existed somewhere," she replied. "Between East and West, or men and women."

"Perhaps rejuvenation at the Shubha Kamana Cafe is enough to preserve peace between us," Ravi cajoled, pouring more coffee into her cup with an affectionate glance."

"Who can resist South Indian coffee and silver cakes?" she replied. Now she was in a good mood and teased him back. "But we Americans worry about over-stimulation, fear danger in too much indulgence."

"A sensible American idea," Ravi laughed. "Control and discipline, the path of hard work leading to material success. As for us, we're either addicted to extravagance and excess or asceticism and total denial of self. No middle ground in India. If we're not in control, we act out."

Garnet looked askance.

"Don't scoff," Ravi said, pointing across the street.

"Observe the drama being played out over there. Three women are quarreling over a piece of cloth as if their lives depended on it. Do they need the cloth? Probably not. More likely, they enjoy scream-fights and use shopping as an excuse to berate the shopkeeper instead of the husbands who deserve it. Such quarrels relieve their nerves and do little harm as the shopkeeper is a clever fellow who understands the game and gladly engages in any encounter as long as he makes a sale. It's an Indian paradox. We cling to an ancient, spiritually based culture but manipulate daily living like a chess match and turn business into *performance art*."

It was the kind of playful repartée relished by her poet friends in Village cafes, his high spirits another reminder of Winslow, but as Ravi bantered with her she grew tense, unable to concentrate on what he was saying. Despite an effort to distract herself the emotions experienced on meeting him the previous day flooded back like a relapse of the flu, leaving her lightheaded and weak, pulled toward him like the lovesick women she despised.

She tried to shake herself back to reality, fighting a crazy urge to leap into Ravi's life, merge with him and abandon herself. A feminist would sneer: *oppressed female gives it all away for a man*! And they'd be right. But it was impossible to stifle the craving to taste his plump lips with her tongue.

Strange how she'd assumed desire had been crushed and killed in her. A shock to meet old stirrings re-awakened on a teeming sidewalk in the shadow of the Taj. Ironic, in view of her caution at being swept up in illusion by the tomb. This was a far more dangerous *chimera*, a *Maya* who danced in her head with sexual intent, trying to lure her into obsession with a stranger.

xi

Such troubling, lustful thoughts made her blush until beads of perspiration dotted her forehead and cheeks. She bent her head to hide from Ravi and blotted her face with a tissue.

"It's a bit warm on the sidewalk," Ravi assured her, with a concerned glance.

"India's temperatures take getting used to," Garnet replied. "My blood thrives in a cold climate."

"It gets beastly hot here," he said, rubbing the sweat off his forehead with the back of his hand.

There was a moment's pause as Vijay stopped talking to take a breath. Niles glanced toward Ravi and Garnet and when he saw their heads bent close together he scowled and rose from his chair as if about to leave. He looked enraged and it was clear he might erupt in a tantrum if he thought she was flirting with Ravi.

Alert to the sudden tension and sensing its cause, Ravi realized a distraction was needed and came to the rescue.

"*Mes amis,*" he declared, tapping his water glass with a spoon to get their attention, "Time to present *la pièce de résistance* of the Auspicious Wishes Cafe, Chandni's white cake palace afloat on a blue-sauce lake."

"Bring on *le gateau!*" he called out, snapping his fingers at the turbaned waiter who stood behind the table, stiff as a statue, staring at them while they ate. This curious form of *attentive service* was prevalent in India but Garnet found it uncomfortable, hating to be watched while she chewed. She was used to New York where waiters ignored you.

There was no response to the finger snapping. Although his eyes were riveted on the table the waiter was lost in a dream. Ravi clapped his hands sharply, shouting "*Yahan ao tez!*" and aside to Garnet, "Chop-chop in India," then rattled off a string of Hindi at the speed of light as he pointed to a glass case behind the door. The waiter leaped out of his trance and rushed off to fetch the cake.

"Still clapping your hands at waiters?" Garnet remarked, pretending to be shocked. "I thought that was outlawed in the fifties along with princely states."

"*Touché*," Ravi conceded, with a *salaam* to her. "Scandalous behavior but the best way to get a waiter's attention. They take it in their stride as the masses of India haven't noticed our country is now a democracy. After the British were booted out, those of us with a few pennies in our pockets were still *pukka sahib*, whether we liked it or not."

Ravi sliced the cake himself and handed around the plates, making sure the first wedge went to Niles who shook his head.

"You dare not refuse me," Ravi said, with a smile. "At least you owe me a taste." Niles hesitated, still scowling, but took the plate and sat down in his chair. *Clever of Ravi to smooth over an awkward situation. And kind.* Niles was still watchful but for the moment calm, and she was relieved at the change of focus.

"Let me tell you the story of le gateau. The *cake-palace* began as the whim of a five-year old Crown Prince," Ravi explained. "A spoiled *tika raja* who pounded his small fist on the table and ordered the chef to create a cake modeled after the maharaja's summer lake palace: *My gateau must float in sauce like my father's palace floats on the lake. And make sure the water is blue*, the imperious brat demanded, *or I'll throw it on the floor!*"

Garnet glanced at Niles now raptly attentive, mollified by his love of fairy tales.

"The little monster should have been spanked for his rudeness but as the prince was heir to the throne the Court doted on him and forgave his wicked ways. The maharaja gave his nod of approval and the chef rushed away to bake the cake in time to present it to the little wretch at dinner, a spectacular cake castle afloat in blue sauce dyed with berries and ablaze with sparklers flashing from its turrets."

Garnet laughed to herself. *Perfect! A cake invented by a spoiled prince, eaten by Niles who behaved like one.*

"Was the brat prince pleased with his cake?" Garnet asked.

"Actually, he was," Ravi answered, "and for once had the grace to thank the chef. The cake became a tradition in Rajasthan and Chandni duplicated it for the cafe."

Vijay clapped his hands in appreciation. "A delightful story. Why haven't I heard it before?"

Ravi wagged his finger at his cousin. "If you'd come to Agra with me sooner you'd be sated with palace cakes and bored with my story by now. *Shubha Kamana* is an old haunt of mine."

"It's a pity to destroy a lovely palace by eating it," Garnet said, as she pricked the edge of a turret with her fork. "As a child I couldn't bear to see the tide flood in and dissolve my sand castles. I'd shut my eyes and refuse to watch. Now I'm a glutton, gorging on palaces."

"Enjoy it while you can," Ravi urged. "Indian pundits say life is ephemeral. Suffering results when we cling to what should be let go. If we saved the cake it would molder, become inedible and hideous."

"It's true," she conceded. "Hanging on is a trap. Better to risk all . . . *Safe upon the solid rock the ugly houses stand, come and see my shining palace built upon the sand.*"

"*D'accord,*" Ravi said, leaning toward her with a look she could only construe as tender.

Garnet changed gears. Sentimentality had its dangers.

"You talked me into it," she said lightly. "No guilt. I'll gobble up the palace and relish every mouthful!"

Ravi narrowed his eyes at her for a moment, as if studying her. "You hate the heat yet are willing to suffer our wretched climate for a journey of serious purpose," he reflected. "Shall I divine your future by psychic powers? The British claimed such gifts flowed in our dark blood, another excuse for despising us." He leaned his head back against the chair breathing deeply as he acted out the role of fortuneteller. "Ahhh, vibrations are emanating from the incarnation . . . sensitive, mysterious, literary, quotes Edna St. Vincent Millay . . . The incarnate is a *Vaisya*, a creative being of great accomplishment!

"Oh, she accomplishes all right," Niles said with a snicker. "Just don't get in her way while she does it."

Ravi ignored Niles, moaning like a clairvoyant emerging from a trance. "The crystal ball reveals all . . . the poet's light shall e'er shine bright."

Garnet mulled over his performance for a few minutes before speaking. Ravi was sweet and amusing but it could be risky to encourage him.

She lifted her coffee cup to him and smiled. "A clever act," she said. "But Americans are too materialistic for mysticism. Most of us aren't hippies hungering after the occult, or easily taken in."

Ravi rolled his eyes in mock astonishment.

"Take in a woman of your intelligence? Only a madman would attempt such folly."

She laughed. "Spare me." But she was grateful for Ravi's playfulness. Teasing was a protection, a barricade against emotion, a way to maintain a foothold of reality. She used banter herself to keep men at a distance but there was a seductive undertone to Ravi's teasing. She'd resented such tactics by other men, rebelled at being cast as their fantasy icon, a mix of *femme fatale* and genius depending how clever they were at flattery, or *girl-child* in need of their enlightenment. Ignoring those men was easy but Ravi was subtler, or more appealing, holding out *her* fantasy icon mingling comforting father with soul-mate lover.

"Is fortunetelling your chosen profession?" she teased, trying to keep the conversation light.

"In-house guru at the Good Luck Cafe?" Ravi made a face. "Wise men say exchange of money threatens divine gifts. But enough about magic. Tell us about your passage to India."

"I'd say your divine gift is for comedy." Garnet laughed and took a deep breath. "My uncle filled my head with tales of his exotic travels when I was a child and I became haunted by India. When hippies claimed the *Age of Aquarius* was approaching and fled here in hordes I resolved to see the enchanted land for myself."

Ravi snapped his fingers at Vijay. "And a New Age poet sprang like magic onto the dusts of India!"

"Not exactly," Garnet replied, wiping her steamy face with a handkerchief. "I needed money for my journey and managed to wangle a poetry grant. Then I wrote to the tardy curator at the museum for permission to use the library - and snoop around the dusty monarchs entombed in the Taj Mahal where happily they're too dead to criticize what I write."

She raised her coffee cup again. "Here's to the land of *Oz* brimming with soul seekers, hippies and rock stars. But I intend to immerse myself in 17th century India, focus my *prana* - you know what prana is - and hopefully create *l'histoire de Mumtaz.*"

"Why Mumtaz Mahal?" Ravi asked, curiously.

Garnet thought for a moment before answering. "I was interested in the concept of love, having seen little of it myself. Mumtaz Mahal and Shah Jahan's love was fabled. *Immortal ardor.* An enviable love, a mix of passion and friendship. I decided to explore the legend. Was it a royal fairy tale or did undying love exist in India's Moghul Camelot?"

"Ask my cousin, Vijay," Ravi said, patting his cousin on the shoulder. "He's an historian who enjoys digging up royal skeletons and their nasty secrets."

Vijay's face brightened with pleasure. Despite his preoccupation with Niles, Ravi's attentions to Garnet made him feel neglected. He feared exclusion from conversations as if being ignored diminished him in size, shrinking him until he disappeared into a speck on the table. Although an accomplished scholar, his self-esteem depended on the approbation of others and Ravi, sensitive to his need, made it a point to affirm him.

As soon as his cousin gave the go-ahead Vijay began to speak, excitedly, eagerly, as though time were short and words needed to be squeezed together to get them out. Quickly, quickly, breathless from trying to keep pace with his thoughts, he raced on, hardly pausing for breath.

"Theirs was a great passion," Vijay asserted, shaking his finger for emphasis. "Shah Jahan was a handsome prince, son of Emperor Jahangir, when he met Mumtaz. At fifteen, he was a talented poet with a famed lyrical singing voice, a student of architecture and Koranic calligraphy, and had fought in a war."

Vijay paused to take a gulp of air and hurried on. "Mumtaz was the aristocratic daughter of the Prime Minister, born in his harem. A self-assured beauty of fourteen and a brilliant scholar of Muslim holy books and the *Koran* - most unusual as such studies were ordinarily denied to women - she captivated the prince by her intellect and independent spirit."

At fifteen I met Niles, Garnet thought ruefully, *but he was neither handsome nor healthy, and I, though gifted, was far from self-assured.*

"Dazed by the impact of instantaneous love," Vijay continued, abandoning all constraint in his enthusiasm, "Shah Jahan, then Prince Khurram, hurried to his father for permission to marry. The emperor raised his right hand to indicate his assent but astrologers delayed the prince's plans. Signs were not auspicious and the wedding was postponed."

"Shah Jahan was forced to take other brides for political reasons, but Mumtaz was his *only* love," Ravi added.

"I'm sick of this love bullshit," Niles snapped, his face flushed and angry as he pushed his chair away from the table. "Boring, boring, boring! Let's go, Garnet. I'm hot and tired."

Garnet flushed in embarrassment, and looked at her watch. "It *is* getting late. I should try the library again."

"We'll all be leaving in a minute," Ravi said. "Let me get the check and we'll walk you back to the museum."

The check was slow in coming and Niles drummed his fingers on the table in irritation.

"Don't kid yourself," Niles asserted bitterly. "Mumtaz Mahal was a monster, an archenemy of Christianity who goaded Shah

Jahan to wage a war against a city of Portuguese Christians with the words, *Lord, defend us from the tribe of unbelievers*."

"So much for poor Mumtaz and her wicked ways," Ravi said with a smile as he took the check from the waiter."

"Yes, forget the empress. What do *you* seek in India, Niles?" Vijay asked, unable to hide the eagerness in his voice.

"Who cares what I want?" Niles answered, his face flushed and perspiring. "I'm nuisance value, a thorn in the rose, a flaw in the garnet, a pathetic creature chanting a mantra, *pity me, pity me!*"

Vijay put his arm around Niles' shoulder in sympathy while Ravi paid the robust proprietor of the cafe, tucking a handful of rupees in the white jacket bulging over his stomach.

"The cafe is flourishing, Chandni, and with good reason. Your coffee and cakes are the finest in India."

Chandni bowed and *salaamed* to Ravi. "*Namaskar*, Your Highness. Many thanks for your generous patronage. But don't stay away so long next time. A journey to the Taj brings good fortune."

Ravi glanced toward Garnet and laughed. "A wise saying, my friend."

xii

As they picked their way back to the Taj Mahal, pushing through crowds pressing along the pathway, Garnet was curious.

"Why did Chandni address you as *Your Highness*?"

"Chandni is an old tease," Ravi answered with a smile.

She looked toward Vijay who shook his head.

"My cousin is too modest. He brushes off his title of Crown Prince - acts like it's a disgrace rather than an honor."

"It's ridiculous, a phantasm," Ravi retorted.

"Not so," Vijay continued eagerly, "In fact, Ravi would be

salaamed to by all if he claimed the throne as maharaja."

"I'm confused," Garnet laughed, making a face and poking Ravi in the back. "Who *is* this Ravi Singh?"

"A bedraggled prince with holes in his socks," Ravi answered irritably, dismissing Vijay. "India's princely states were dissolved in the 1950's so the question of royalty is purely academic. Yet my poor cousin in his blind loyalty insists I could take on a meaningless title if I chose. Which I do not."

"Ah, so *you* were the naughty prince who stamped and screamed to get his way," Garnet giggled, wagging her finger at him.

"Bossy and full of himself at five," Vijay added. "Ravi led everyone around by the nose, including me. I'm still following in his footsteps."

The two cousins exchanged glances as Ravi held Garnet's arm firmly and changed the subject, pointing out various sights on the way to the tomb.

Vijay engaged Niles in conversation, walking slowly behind Ravi and Garnet, Niles exaggerating his limp for Vijay's benefit. Ravi turned back to Vijay and pointed, "Look at the Taj Mahal now. From this spot, it appears to float on air."

"Like a fairy castle in the sky!" Vijay exclaimed, gazing in wonder.

"Take a few steps forward," Ravi said, reaching out for Garnet's hand. "Then step back slowly and watch the Taj Mahal glide toward us."

They followed his lead and Garnet's face glowed with pleasure. "Too exquisite to be real," she murmured.

"Your face shines like a winter sun, a Lippi madonna," Ravi whispered.

Garnet laughed. "I wouldn't go down that road if I were you."

Ravi prudently changed the subject. "It's a clever optical illusion designed by Shah Jahan to depict the rising of the Taj Mahal to the heavens where Mumtaz dwelled."

"I hate to leave this fairy castle," Garnet sighed, as she

glanced at her watch. "But I must get to the library."

Ravi took Garnet by the arm and quickened the pace, leaving Niles and Vijay behind.

"I hope you're not bored with us because my auntie is giving a *soirée* at her villa on Saturday," Ravi announced. "Shushila's evenings are spectacular with musicians, sitars and tambas, dancers, singers, a sumptuous buffet, and her notorious salon of writers and artists."

"Dare we trust you?" Garnet asked, teasing.

Secretly, she was delighted at a chance to observe upper-class Indian life, along with a gathering of intellectuals and artists. The invitation was perfect but she went on with the game. It was fun to joke around. She hadn't felt carefree and frivolous since her uncle died.

"You two may be dangerous characters out to rob my jewels," she protested. "Unlucky for you, my only jewel is my name, a poor semi-precious garnet, worthless in the marketplace."

"My piercing eye tells me the jewel is not *semi-precious* but a rare gem," Ravi quipped. "I've looked for flaws and can find none."

Garnet laughed. "Too bad you can't see the hidden ones."

Ravi scribbled on a piece of paper and handed it to her.

"Next to a flawless gem, I like a flawed one. You *must* come to Auntie's party. If you have any doubts ring her up and she'll persuade you. We'll pick you up at your hotel at seven and promise to return you safely."

"Hmm. Indian ragas, a surfeit of slick charm, even possible jeopardy," Garnet replied. "Sounds like an offer I can't refuse."

"Mafioso talk?" Ravi asked, pretending shock. "You may be a dangerous character yourself."

"Oh, I am, I am." She tore out a page of a notebook and wrote down the address of her hotel. "Okay. We'll expect you on Saturday but I abhor Indian-time so don't be late."

Ravi gave a brisk British salute. "*Ours but to do and*

die . . . The troops will not be late, Memsahib, or disappoint you and your brother."

"Why do you say brother?" Garnet asked, feeling a little embarrassed.

"Well, I assumed . . ."

"What . . . Do we look alike?" she retorted, oddly annoyed.

"Not at all, as a matter of fact. Sorry if I was rude. Niles is. . . ?

"He's the brother of a friend," Garnet said apologetically, regretting her curtness. "Does that answer your question?"

"Not entirely. But it will do for now."

When they arrived back at the museum the doors to the library were unlocked.

"Thanks for reviving us at the cafe," Garnet said, extending her hand to Ravi.

"It's you who deserves the thanks for giving two wicked fellows the pleasure of your company," Ravi said, taking her hand and pressing it lightly to his lips.

She eased her hand away and tapped Niles on his arm. "We'd better get going. I have a lot of work to do."

Niles scowled.

"Am I supposed to sit around the library for hours watching you work?" he asked peevishly.

"If you'd rather go back to the hotel I'll put you in a taxi," Garnet answered, trying to hang on to her patience.

"I have a better idea," Ravi said. "Why not let us take Niles around for a bit, show him a few sights and drop him off at the hotel at the end of the day."

"Oh, I couldn't ask that of you," she replied, only wishing it could happen.

"We'd enjoy it," Vijay answered, putting his arm around Niles' shoulder. "Niles and I had a most interesting talk at the cafe."

"Niles?" she asked, praying he'd accept.

"It's better than twiddling my thumbs while you thumb through a pile of dusty books," he snarled, secretly pleased at the idea but not wanting Garnet to have the satisfaction of getting rid of him.

"Well, if you're sure it won't be too much trouble . . ."

"Not at all," Ravi said.

"Our pleasure," Vijay said, taking Niles by the arm to help him down the steps. "Don't worry, we'll take good care of Niles."

"Shall we pick you up for lunch?" Ravi asked.

"No, I'll be too busy to stop," Garnet said quickly. "Just drop Niles off at the hotel when you're ready and I'll get back by taxi at the end of the day. It's good of you to amuse him while I'm working. I'm afraid it's rather dull for him."

She stepped away quickly. Lunch was out of the question. No use putting herself in the way of temptation. Ravi was charming and endearing but she had to go slowly.

Ravi looked disappointed but waved, "*Namaskar!*" as he started down the steps.

Niles turned a sullen face in her direction as they left, a guilt-bomb of *you're abandoning-me-again*, but she pretended not to notice and watched as Vijay put an arm around his shoulder to help him down the steps, observing Niles relax his back and tilt his head until it rested against Vijay's neck.

A weight lifted off her shoulders as Niles moved away, the boulder pressing her neck bones into her throat fell off her back and she felt light and free, as exhilarated as in the days of her childhood when she escaped from her mother and sister to the solitude of woods and stables.

With a sigh of relief, she pushed open the door to the library. Bliss! A few hours of grace. The gift of peace to be alone and do her work. *Shakti*, Divine Mother of Creation, was shining on her.

xiii

She worked at the library until closing time, soothed by silence and solitude, relieved to immerse herself in an earlier century.

By the time she closed the last book and made her way back to the hotel she was exhausted. Anticipating a breath of cool air on entering the Rajmahal it was disheartening to find the lobby hot and steamy.

The skinny clerk at the front desk nodded his head back and forth sympathetically. "Sorry, Madame, the electricity has expired. Perhaps it will make its return in a few hours. We can only wait and hope."

The good news - Niles wasn't back yet and she could soak in the tub without being disturbed. Near darkness would be soothing after the heat and exhaustion of the day, and long hours spent lugging heavy books in the library and straining her eyes to read the yellowed pages.

When she finished bathing she wrapped herself in towels, flopped down on the bed and fell into a heavy sleep. She was still dozing an hour or so later when the door opened and she heard the sound of footsteps coming toward her. She opened her eyes to find Niles standing over the bed staring down at her naked body, the towels kicked off in her sleep. She tried to shake herself awake as she pulled the sheet up over her.

"I must have dropped off," she whispered, her voice hoarse with sleep. "I didn't hear you come in. Did you have a good time?"

"Skip the chitchat," he snarled, slamming the door violently behind him. "You're communing with a man in despair, a soul in the depths of hell."

"Now what's wrong, Niles?" she groaned, only half awake as she stared at his angry face.

"This is what's wrong," he said, yanking the sheet off her. "The *Naked Maja* is a filthy slut."

She yanked the sheet back and wrapped it around her.

"Are you crazy?" she cried. "What do you think you're doing?

She grabbed at her chemise on the chair, twisted around so she could slip it on under the sheet and sat up in bed. She was shaking but tried to control herself.

He leaned over and breathed in her face.

"You must have thought I was blind," Niles sneered, "throwing yourself at the ersatz prince like a teenage bimbo, tossing your hair, panting in his face with breathless sultry looks. But when you lowered your eyes and gazed down at your plate as if overcome by modesty it was a stroke of genius - Virgin Mary, saint and slut. Too bad he doesn't know what a cold, unfeeling bitch you are."

Garnet pushed him and tried to get up. "Whatever you imagined took place in your overheated dreams," she retorted.

"Don't push me away, you fucking Lorelei," Niles snarled. He pushed his face close to hers and held her arms. "Look, Jane, see Dick! See the dead man before your eyes!"

Take care, she cautioned herself, aware violence was often the aftermath of severe head injuries. *So far, there'd only been verbal tantrums.*

She spoke in a quiet voice, hoping to subdue him. "That's enough, Niles. Now calm down and let go of me."

"No, it's not enough," Niles shouted. "It will never be enough."

With a quick movement she thrust his arms back and jumped out of the bed.

Niles grabbed her and twisted her around. "You're not fooling me. I read your journal."

Garnet paled. "You what?"

"Yes, yes, I read the forbidden journal, so what? *Niles has become impossible. I can't bear it but don't know to extricate myself,* he mocked. "You can't, my dear. Don't even try."

"How dare you read my journal!" A wave of nausea shuddered through Garnet's body and she felt her head reel with rage.

"Why not?" Niles smirked. "*Yesterday I met Ravi Singh.*

Drawn to him against my will. And against mine, don't forget that!"

Niles stared at her, his eyes black with hatred.

"You fucking cunt, my life is nothing, I dread waking up every day but you don't give a damn."

"Let go of my arm," Garnet cried, trying to push him away. Niles gripped her arm tighter and with his other hand pulled a pocket knife out of his pocket and switched it open.

"Do you want me to call the police?" she hissed, trying to keep her voice down to avoid being overheard. "I don't think you'd enjoy getting thrown into an Indian jail."

"Don't worry, I'm going to stab my bloody, fucking self to death." he screamed, pointing the knife at his chest. "Then you can explain to the police why a poor lame boy took his life. Better still, I'll make it look like murder and they'll fucking hang you and write it up in *The Hindustani Times*! *MAD AMERICAN GOES BERSERK! Memsahib couldn't endure burden of demented cripple so she stabbed him to death.* Or *HOT PANTS FOR INDIAN PRINCE drives American slut to slay innocent victim.*"

"Stop this, Niles, stop it right now."

"Don't order me around," he shouted, his face flushing scarlet.

She pushed her free hand against the knife and jammed her knee up sharply into his groin. He cried out in pain and fell back against the bed sobbing.

She grabbed his arms and pulled them up over his head, pressed him against the bed and kneeled on the floor before him.

"I've had enough," she cried. "I'm packing your bags and putting you on a plane back to New York."

Niles crumpled to the floor still sobbing, his fingers clutching the hem of her chemise as he beseeched her.

"Please, Garnet, I'm an emotional wreck, a rotten cripple with no life. I'll be a dead man if you send me back to New York. I'm sorry, but it broke my heart to see the desire in your face when you looked at Ravi. I've loved you forever but you can't respond to me."

Niles wept quietly, burying his face in his hands. "If you only knew how I despise myself. Forgive me, Garnet, I'll destroy myself before I let this happen again."

Garnet turned away and stood at the window, staring out at the crowded street below. She'd heard his promises before. Niles' repentance was as hard to take as his acting-out. Sworn oaths, pledges on bended knees, best intentions were meaningless. His so-called remorse was only manipulation, false contrition to deflect her anger.

The explosive encounter with Niles left her shaken and it was impossible to get back to sleep. She picked up the *I Ching* and tiptoed out of the bedroom hoping Niles would stay asleep for the rest of the night. She crouched on the floor of the small bathroom, tossed the coins and found the page for her *Reading . . .*

The image of Exhaustion. There is no water in the lake.
It is empty, dried up,
The symbol of oppression and exhaustion."

One sits oppressed under a bare tree
And strays into a gloomy valley.

She *was* exhausted, at the end of her strength, stuck in a dark place.

How did her life get so screwed up? If only she could unravel the past and find out. *Go back to the beginning, back to Sailship Point*, a voice murmured . . . *like Macbeth who entreated . . .*

Pluck from memory a rooted sorrow,
Raze out the troubles of the brain . . .
Which weigh upon the heart.

II

SAILSHIP POINT

*I must go down to the sea again, to the lonely sea
and the sky . . .*

John Masefield

i

She could never get Sailship Point out of her bones and blood.
It was as much a part of her as the beating of her heart. Impossible to forget the painful beauty of the once affluent peninsula
which sprawled like a beached whale into the seacoast. Here the
harshness of bluffs was gentled by green lawns meandering up
from the sea where great maples, elms and silvery birches sheltered ruined mansions ravaged by neglect and the severity of the
Depression. Along high stonewalls erected to keep out intruders, weeping willows, flowering dogwood and magnolia trees
drooped their shade over dirt footpaths.

The air was balmy, the winter chill ameliorated by the warmth
of salt waters swirling below cliffs which served as bulwarks
against intrusion by sea, and the quiet of night tempered only by
the low moaning of a foghorn from a distant lighthouse and the
soft swell of waves against the shore.

Sailship Point had been a bastion of the privileged, providing the privacy and silence so treasured by the rich which as her

Uncle Winslow quipped, *would too soon be supplied by the grave*!
He chuckled about the road leading to the Point where a city
dump at the edge of town emitted an acrid smell of garbage,
*Sailship Point is a paradise - except when the wind blows the other
way.*

Her father, Edward, and his brother, Winslow, were raised in
colonial South Africa where their father fought in the Boer War.
Afterwards, her grandfather headed a company in Cape Town
but sent his sons back to England for a Public School education.

Winslow owned a decaying mansion perched on the edge of
a bluff, a rambling house surrounded by wrecked apple orchards
and overgrown fields. Built in prosperous years before the stock
market crashed, the property had been carelessly purchased after maneuvering a sharp financial deal in India with a Hindu
magnate. It tickled Winslow's sardonic sense to honor the Hindu
by naming the estate Khushi Keddah, *khushi* Hindi for sumptuous or *cushy,* and *keddah* an enclosure used to entrap wild
elephants. *Perfect for a mad beast such as I,* he answered drily
when asked to translate, with a sly glance at the questioner for
the name was deliberately provocative, intended to pique his
New England neighbors.

Garnet reveled in the natural beauty of Sailship Point and
the escape from her family. Early mornings before school, she
rode her bicycle on the road curving along the sea where scruffy
bushes edged a trail twisting down to the beach. A lonely beach,
desolate in winter and yet its very bleakness was a comfort; rough
tide beating on rocks, black wooden pier, splintered and broken, stone steps crumbling in disrepair.

Silence and tranquility. The gifts of growing up on a seacoast
where the loudest noise is the ocean pulsating against the shore,
the fanning of bird wings arcing into the blue as they headed
south, the sharp cries of sea gulls swooping down to pluck fish
from the sea, or the days of winter when blizzards muffled all
sound except for the crunch of footsteps on snowdrifts.

The Lawlers lived in a gardener's cottage on an abandoned

estate not far from Winslow's property. His estate was badly run-down but upkeep didn't concern him as he rarely lived there, using it mainly as a base to work out business deals and a drop-off for baggage between expeditions. On the infrequent occasions when he was back from remote corners of the world, drawn by business or his penchant for adventure, Winslow welcomed Garnet with affection. He accepted her adoration with the assurance of a charismatic man accustomed to adulation from the opposite sex and responded to her in kind.

"You're my only bearable relative, nothing like the rest of the Lawler clowns. You must have been raised in a jungle by kindly apes," he joked, as he lifted her up in his brawny arms and twirled her around, laughing as she clasped his neck and breathed in the delectable smells clinging to him, Yardley's lavender cologne mingled with smoky pipe tobacco, leather and wool, and the hint of a more primitive male scent.

A robust man with the expansive personality and good looks of a film star, perpetually tanned from travels in the sun, Winslow's natural good humor, creamy baritone voice and broad smile under a touch of dark moustache accenting strong white teeth, was irresistible to women. It was as if God accidentally sated him with an excess of male hormones leaving other men sadly lacking and this sensuality of presence contrasted by an immaculate wardrobe of white linen suits and pale silk ties, made even a glimpse of him unforgettable.

Unlike his younger brother, Edward, Winslow had an instinct for making money even in the worst of times, relying on inspiration and gut feeling for his risky speculations. Conservative investors threw up their hands at his daring, surprised when deals turned out to be profitable. But win or lose, Winslow emerged with a smile or tossed off disaster with a shrug.

Just before her twelfth birthday, Garnet dropped by to visit her uncle at *Khushi Keddah*, eager for one of Winslow's bear hugs, cherishing the blissful moments when he wrapped his arms around her and squeezed her tight. No one else in her family hugged or called her sweet names, not even the housekeeper, Graciela, who loved her but was too gruff to do more than pat her on the head. Winslow surprised her with an illustrated book on the Taj Mahal and a silk sari in peacock blue, her favorite color.

"It's *Garnet-blue* to me," he said, kissing the top of her head. "A paradox, but definitely *you*!"

Winslow draped the blue satin sari over her shoulders like a royal cape. "It's a little early for your birthday but tomorrow I'm off on another jaunt. We'll celebrate the day by giving my darling niece her first taste of champagne."

Garnet's eyes widened as Winslow deftly opened the bottle cooling in a bucket of ice and poured the golden wine into thin goblets.

Francesca would have a fit if she knew, Garnet said to herself gleefully as the sting of champagne exploded in her mouth. Not that her mother cared if her daughter drank wine but she'd be jealous, furious at Winslow's attentions.

She sipped at the icy bubbles, sucking the wine around the rim of the glass with delight as her uncle showed her pictures of the Taj Mahal and talked of the emperor who built the tomb.

"Shah Jahan was inconsolable at the death of his beloved empress, burning his royal robes and refusing to don regal raiment. For the rest of his life he rejected all but the simple white garments of mourning. *Kalim*, the Court Poet, described his brokenhearted emperor . . ."

The King of Kings cried out with grief,
Like an ocean raging with storm.

Joy no longer appeared on his face,
His lips would not part in smile.

The flower's bond with fragrance is not so enduring
As was the King's love for her."

"Despite his grief, the emperor vowed to build a tomb for Mumtaz Mahal so exquisite it would surpass any palace in the world," Winslow told her, pointing out the miniature paintings of Shah Jahan and Mumtaz Mahal.

"Mystics claim poor mortals can know no greater bliss than a love that rises from the soul," Winslow said, pouring a little more champagne in her glass. "Ignore the cynics, Garnet, and search for a mate to your soul."

There was a sad undertone to Winslow's voice and Garnet thought of the death of the young woman flier her uncle planned to marry. Many women were infatuated with Winslow and shameless in their pursuit, but the elusive playboy was captured by a spirited English girl in South Africa, the daughter of close friends who raised her on their coffee plantation in Cape Town not far from Winslow's farm. Shortly before the wedding she joined an expedition for a brief trip to the Antarctic but on a routine reconnaissance flight a sudden *white-out* caused her plane to crash.

Garnet was saddened by his loss but Winslow consoled her.

"Sibley has passed on and I must release her. Don't grieve when my time comes but celebrate my spirit, remembering my adventurous, pleasure-loving life as I tango toward the light."

"I wish I had Sibley's courage," she yearned.

Winslow gave her a hug. "You have a brave spirit of your own, Garnet. Trust it."

A few days after Garnet's visit, Winslow cut short his business deals and left the States for a series of expeditions and safaris in an attempt to distract himself from his loss - big game hunts in Kenya, searches for sacred relics in Peru, through jungles, deserts and impassable mountains, making only rare and brief stopovers back in Sailship Point. Occasionally, a postcard or curio would arrive for Garnet from an exotic port - an African mask, ivory carving or a small pre-Columbian statue of some value. She missed Winslow but hoped he was finding comfort in the exotic world she could only imagine.

Just before Garnet's thirteenth birthday the news of Winslow's sudden death was cabled to the Lawler family. The inveterate adventurer of nine lives died mysteriously on an exploration in the jungles of the Amazon searching for a cache of stolen gold reputedly hidden by Spanish pirates. He was following a treasure map purchased from an unsavory fellow encountered in a London pub who sized him up as a romantic soldier of fortune and easy mark, charging him accordingly before handing over a faded, barely legible paper.

Mystery veiled the manner of Winslow's death with various rumors circulating through his clubs; he'd located the cache and was murdered before he could remove the gold; he'd drunkenly missed his footing in the dark and fallen into the river where he was gobbled up by piranhas; brushed his teeth with river water and died of typhoid, or least believable fable; the notorious lover of women and reformed rake, was strangled in the act of sex with a native boy who wanted his gold watch.

But the enigma was never unraveled, and remained one more perplexing myth in a family where reality could not always be separated from fiction.

ii

Garnet was devastated by the loss of her uncle but grateful his will had made her father heir to *Khushi Keddah*, the crumbling mansion and the fields she loved. Winslow's bequests also provided a trust fund for Garnet's education along with the legacy of his study in Khushi Keddah, which he '*bequeathed with contents intact to my beloved niece, Garnet, for her exclusive use. Nothing is to be disturbed or changed except by her wish.*'

The suite Winslow called his *atelier* became Garnet's sanctuary. As soon as her parents took possession of the house Garnet moved in, abandoning the bedroom she shared with her sister, Valerie, taking only her clothes and the small gifts and tokens of

Winslow's travels. She stubbornly refused to allow her old bed to be installed, insisting she preferred to sleep on Winslow's sprawling couch spread with exotic shawls and rugs. The studio was a conglomeration of curios, furniture and objects picked up on his travels; teak and brass chests filled with treasures, a crude wooden cross carved by an Amazon Indian and a great golden lion of a rug, his eyes gentle brown, his jaw gaping and fierce. A friendly beast who seemed to wait for Garnet to pat his head when she came into the room.

She was comforted to be in Winslow's old house with its dazzling array of rooms, halls and secret passageways, and she sidled along the halls, running her fingers across the smooth wood until the hands of the house seemed to reach out and caress her. *Uncle's love is still here*, she thought, *trickling under the eaves and along the passageways. I love you, old house, and promise never to hurt you,* she whispered, leaning her cheek against the cool wall.

But with the hostility and endless bickering of Francesca and Edward, Garnet feared Khushi Keddah would retreat from their bitterness and become a silent ghostly house. *The old house feels it*, she thought, *knows love left when Winslow died.* She murmured reassurances to the drafty halls, *poor old thing, I miss the uncle, too.* But on nights when sharp salt winds howled up from the sea the house creaked and groaned with despair.

She kept a few of Winslow's jackets hanging in the closet and when she felt sad wrapped the arms around her and rubbed her face along the shoulders and lapels to breathe in the smoky scent of pipe tobacco permeating the wool. She slept in his Indian shirts and *khurtas* or wore them while studying, soothed by the garments as if his spirit lingered in them.

Surrounded by Winslow's treasures she discovered the first stirrings of happiness she'd known living with her family. But she kept the door securely locked, refusing to admit anyone but the old Spanish housekeeper, and began to spend her hours at home in the study, emerging only for meals or to sit with Graciela in the kitchen.

She begged Graciela not to disturb anything when she cleaned or allow her mother to go in and snoop around. The old woman nodded gruffly, and when Francesca tried to intrude Graciela shouted insults and pushed her from the door.

iii

It was clear her mother was obsessed with Valerie and that *she* was Francesca's scapegoat, a receptacle for her rage against Edward. But for years Garnet couldn't help yearning after her, enticed by Francesca's beauty despite her cruelty and neglect, and the shame she felt for secretly loving a mother who had no love for her. She tried to pretend indifference when Francesca's attentions were directed toward her sister, but longed for her touch and the fragrance wafting through the rooms wherever Francesca walked, a musky scent exuded by her flesh which emanated not from the artifice of perfume but from the natural pores of her skin.

Hindu mystics perceive the world as a dream, and speak of *maya*, the dancing spirit who spins veils of illusions to block out reality. They warn that fleshly beauty is the most dangerous illusion of all as outer perfection may appear to mirror inner purity. As in the case of the flawless Francesca.

The pansy-purple of Francesca's eyes, poisonously dark, should have mirrored the shadows in her soul but did not. A deceptively clear light shining from her pupils produced an innocence of gaze and her sorceress charm blotted out all but the senses at the pleasures of translucent skin, arched neck and sculptured cheekbones. Despite evidence to the contrary, even Garnet questioned whether a beauty so delectable and unblemished could mask evil.

One night when Garnet was thirteen, drifting off to sleep fantasizing about lovers and touching herself in secret places, she heard a noise downstairs. It was dark but the radio was playing softly as she tiptoed down the carpeted stairs. She heard a man's voice, low and seductive, coming from the speaker. *Let yourself go,*" he murmured, *experience the pleasure of your senses. Dance to the music and you won't be lonely.*

Garnet began swaying to the haunting rhythm when a shadowy woman appeared out of the darkness. She was bare shouldered, her body gleaming in a white satin gown as she glided to the music.

"Will you dance with me?" Garnet whispered. As the figure drew closer, she realized the woman was Francesca but in the dimness and shadows of the room, she appeared softer and more yielding.

Garnet put her hand around the slender waist. "I'll lead," she whispered.

"I prefer to tango," Francesca murmured. "Follow me," she commanded imperiously, leaning her head back as she whirled Garnet around the room.

Francesca danced lightly and expertly but so quickly that Garnet found it difficult to keep up with her especially as Francesca kept a distance between them.

"Don't you ever dance close?" Garnet yearned. "I'd like to put my head on your shoulder."

Francesca didn't answer but whirled her deftly in a series of circles, then executed two backbend dips, movie star style, as if performing in a film.

Garnet was admiring. "You do dip back beautifully."

Francesca smiled to herself as if in a dream and broke away from Garnet. "I like best to dance alone," she caroled, singing softly to the music as she danced around the room in beautiful swirls and dips, her face lit with pleasure. After awhile, she drifted up the stairway while Garnet lingered in the darkened room, unable to stop swaying to the music. Then she, too, slipped upstairs.

When Garnet woke in the middle of the night she was unsure

if she'd been dreaming or if the incident had actually taken place. She could still feel the softness of Francesca's skin against her cheek but in the morning Francesca was cold and distant, and Garnet realized sadly that her only moment of intimacy with her mother was a dream.

She was wounded and mystified by Francesca's obsession with Valerie, unaware of her mother's dark secret and motive for pampering and protecting her elder daughter. Along with the secret of paternity, there were other reasons. Fat, crude, and ill-mannered, Valerie was not blessed by any of the social graces with which Francesca adorned herself and she pitied the vulnerability of her daughter, sensing that her own sensual passions had been bestowed on a girl born unlucky, without the weaponry of beauty to satisfy her desires.

Spoiled by her mother's possessive love and seething over her father's indifference and Winslow's preference for Garnet, Valerie vented her frustrations and rage on her younger sister.

Francesca chose to ignore Valerie's violence when at the age of twelve she pushed seven-year-old Garnet off stone walls, tried to suffocate her by squeezing her nose and clamping a hand over her mouth and tipped over the canoe when they were alone on the sea. Francesca made no attempt to restrain her daughter and Garnet was left on her own.

But Garnet was determined to survive. She learned to swim under water like an eel, slipping and sliding out of Valerie's grasp to avoid being bashed with a canoe paddle or shoved under the waves. With a few sharp pinches on the inside of Valerie's fat thighs she would dive down and glide away, skimming the stony sea bottom back to shore, her sister chasing her with the canoe in vain pursuit.

Graciela hobbled to Francesca muttering under her breath about the rude-mouthed monster. But her complaints about Valerie were answered with a dreamy smile and a pat on the hand.

"Rub my neck, Graciela, I feel a headache coming on. And

stop fretting. You mustn't take their childish play seriously. Valerie is just high-spirited, she can't harm the little wretch."

"Why you so foolish? She hurts the child, and she takes her alone in boat. She could drown the little one in the sea."

"You cluck like an old hen," Francesca answered impatiently, waving off Graciela's anxieties. "Stop fussing at me with your old woman worries."

"An ounce of mother is worth a pound of priest," Graciela muttered as she limped away.

One day, Valerie tried to smash the miniature Taj Mahal Winslow had given Garnet. Helpless to stop her or ward off her blows Garnet screamed to her mother sitting at the window but Francesca ignored her as she howled out her despair. She was busy examining her long red nails for chips in the lacquer, proud of her arched fingernails which Edward derided as *the scarlet claws of Fu Manchu.*

"Make Valerie stop hurting me and breaking my things!"

Francesca looked up from her ruby red fingertips and gazed through the window at the crystals of snow weaving ice-lace along the branches of the fir trees. Without turning her head, she yawned and spoke in a low voice, "You're boring, Garnet. Extremely boring. You know how I despise whining. Run off and amuse yourself and stop annoying me before your nonsense gives me an attack of migraine."

Garnet bit her lip to stop her tears and left the room. It was time to stop chasing after her mother's love. Later, Imelda warned, *"The beauty-monster will never change. She'll drown in her own reflection. Give up on the bitch before she takes you down with her."*

Valerie continued her abuse and after Winslow's death Francesca, resentful of the favoritism shown by Winslow's legacy and her withdrawal from the family, began to pick on her.

"You look awful," she shuddered. "You're a bag of bones. Put on a little weight. You could scare a ghost."

"What about you?" Garnet retorted. "You're thin and everyone says you're beautiful."

"There's a big difference, my dear," Francesca yawned. "You're skinny, and I'm *slim*! My bones are tiny and don't need much flesh but you look like a skeleton and it's not a pretty sight."

Valerie taunted her yelling, *stringbean! scarecrow!* and singsonging *Skinny Melink, the barber . . .*

One night, nearly asleep on her couch, Garnet felt Winslow's spirit hovering over her. She thought she saw his broad shoulders emerging from the shadows flickering on the ceiling, his teeth gleaming in an endless, eternal smile. She waited nightly for his spirit to emerge, aware of his presence when suffused by a warm glow.

She wondered how it was possible for his ghost to emerge, then remembered what he told her after his fiancée died. He'd come across a half-naked *sadhu* meditating in a mountain cave in Nepal. The sadhu, a great sage who'd taken a vow of silence, answered his question by writing in Sanskrit on a scrap of paper . . .

> *Only a thin curtain separates the spiritual from the incarnate. By the power of love one can draw a spirit through the veil onto this plane of existence.*

One night, Winslow's spirit filled the room with his presence. "All guardian angels aren't garbed in white dresses with wings," his voice whispered. She heard his familiar laugh. "This ghost is wearing riding pants and a tweed jacket."

"I've come back to help you," he said, "to let you know of the infinite love and power here. Claim your strength, fight for your life, and don't allow yourself to be abused. Be strong, Garnet."

The shadows moved away from the ceiling, the whispering stopped and Garnet fell into a tranquil sleep. But Winslow's voice floated into her dreams . . . and his words echoed in her head all day.

"As much as possible live your life as you please. Learn to defeat your enemies, develop your strength and will to survive."

Winslow's advice took seed, impressing on Garnet that she had to conquer her weaknesses. She read books on physical fitness, practiced exercises in the study and invented a stringent regime for herself; running through fields, riding her bike, climbing trees and taking part in school sports. She played tennis, learned to play hockey and rode the old horse tethered in a nearby field. Once pale and delicate, she turned brown and rosy in the sun as the muscles in her legs and arms developed and grew strong.

One day, after a bitter battle in the kitchen where Valerie banged her head against the iron stove, Garnet threatened to kill her sister if she struck her again.

Valerie ran from the room screaming hysterically to her mother. When Edward came home, Francesca insisted he chastise Garnet.

"What's the meaning of this, Garnet?" asked Edward from the depths of his leather chair in the study. "You can't threaten your sister."

Garnet walked to his chair and leaned over him, her hands resting on the leather arms as she stuck her face into his.

"Tell her to stay off me or I *will* kill her. She has no right to keep hurting me. If you were any kind of a father you'd have stopped her long ago but you don't want to see what goes on in this house. Your head's always stuck in a book, even when your daughter is attacked."

Garnet glared at him, then turned and walked out of the room. Edward watched her leave, her back tense, angry as an irate lion. She reminded him of Winslow - another indomitable force. She was too much for him, Francesca would have to handle her.

It was *all* too much for him, the unhappy marriage, burden of family and erosion of hope. Edward gazed through the leaded windows of the study built as a chapel. Snow was drifting silently from the skies whitewashing the lawns, and ice had crystallized the branches of the great oak tree. Stillness and peace, another reminder of his British schooldays at St. Andrews, studying in the hush of a Gothic stone library. He sighed, smoked an *English Oval* and resumed reading his book.

Later, Francesca warned Valerie. "Stay away from Garnet. She might go berserk and kill you."

After that, Valerie was fearful enough to keep a safe distance, and on rare occasions when she came too close Garnet would give her what she hoped was a murderous look until her sister backed off.

iv

The summer she was fifteen Sailship Point was warmer than usual and Garnet spent a good deal of time at Imelda's house, drawn to the cool surroundings, shady groves of trees, and the comforting presence of Mrs. Preston. Her loneliness had intensified in the two years since her uncle's death. Somehow, with Winslow gone forever she could see her family more clearly, Francesca's hatred, Edward's indifference, and as always, Valerie's desire to annihilate her. Despite her reluctance toward Imelda, a hunger for the loving mother, Enid, drew her back to the Preston home.

"Where's Garnet?" Edward asked idly one evening, with no particular interest, as the Lawlers sat down to an early dinner.

"Probably at the Prestons as usual. I can't imagine what the fascination is over there - a fat little *albino* girl and a mad brother who looks like a killer."

"I'm here," Garnet said, slipping into her chair at the dining table. "Being blonde doesn't make her an albino. We can't all be dark goddesses."

"She's more than blonde, my dear," Francesca said scornfully. "She's a blob of white lard. And I'd be careful around the crazy boy if I were you - that type is unpredictable. As for you, Garnet, you're a mystery to me. Who knows what you're capable of?"

Garnet stared up at the ceiling. "Worried about your genetic legacy?"

"Sarcasm? Edward, do something. For once, reprimand your daughter."

"Don't involve me in your quarrels. I've no time for nonsense," he answered, turning his attention back to his dinner.

"I refuse to put up with rudeness, Garnet," Francesca said, tapping the wine goblet angrily with her long nails.

"*D'accord*," Garnet replied, nodding her head. "Rudeness and crudeness are the domain of your precious daughter, Valerie, princess of vulgarity."

"She's always got something nasty to say about me," Valerie whined.

Francesca stubbed her cigarette out in the tiny silver ashtray and glared at Garnet but decided it was a no-win situation and turned away.

* * *

Summer mornings were spent at the Prestons' private beach secluded by stone walls where Imelda persuaded Garnet to slip out of her bathing suit and swim nude in the sea. The sensation of waves surging over their naked skin was exhilarating and they played like children released from bondage, diving between each other's legs, somersaulting backwards into the sea.

Imelda liked to push Garnet's head under the water but as Garnet could hold her breath for a very long time, she'd frighten Imelda by sinking down to the bottom and staying there as if she'd drowned.

Imelda would pull at her and yank her up to the surface.

"Up, up, come back up! I hate when you scare me to death. I don't want anything to happen to you." Once, while struggling and laughing under the water, Imelda pulled her close and touched her breasts. Unsure if the touch was accidental, Garnet twisted away and swam out over the waves to the raft.

The Preston siblings were opposite sides of the family coin. Imelda was blessed with a dogged stubbornness which came to her rescue when her alcoholic father threatened to strike her. Unlike Niles who was defenseless before his father, Imelda stood her ground like a little bull, her white skin flushed to crimson. "Touch me, and I'll call the police! There's a law against beating children."

Her father would stare back at her, his cheeks reddened with whiskey and rage, then turn and stride away. It was easy to intimidate Niles whose weakness he despised, more difficult to deal with Imelda, so like himself in willfulness and crudeness of manner.

At first, Garnet befriended Niles for Mrs. Preston's sake. He didn't seem crazy then, only bitter and unhappy, hating his life and despising the values of a society he was born into for which he felt no affinity, with particular disdain for the imposing estates and snobbish attitudes of Sailship Point.

But Garnet had spent much of her childhood wandering alone around Sailship Point exploring the pleasures of the peninsula. No one questioned her absence, the *up* side of parental neglect being the freedom to come and go as she pleased. The only restriction was to show up for dinner on time, punctuality being one of Edward's British compulsions.

Garnet tried to show Niles the joys of the peninsula. She walked him along the tarred road leading to the beach and down to the boulders at the bottom of the cliff now worn and rounded by the sea, comfortable to sit on, and pointed up to the edge of a cliff where a life-size, painted-wood Sea Captain stood guard over a mansion's boat house.

She warned him to tread carefully on the jagged rocks, to

step around barnacles glued to rocks which could tear the tender flesh of feet. She showed him masses of yellow daffodils swarming down the long hill to the beach, their tall necks swaying in the sea breezes and whispered, *I wandered lonely as a cloud . . . when all at once I saw a crowd, a host, of golden daffodils . . .* She told him how in cold months she walked on the frozen edges of the wintry sea where the sun glinted sparks on ice-frosted waves.

But nothing convinced Niles. "I hate Sailship Point. This privileged peninsula, so envied by the impoverished, *is a beached whale* - a nearly dead cetacean bloated by excess but sucking up all the oxygen to prevent the little fish from taking a gulp."

Fearing people, Niles craved solitude and read avidly. Poetry was his obsession and Baudelaire and Rimbaud his idols. He could quote long passages from memory and was a skillful critic, pointing out flaws in Auden, and the genius of T.S. Eliot, observing bitterly, "Eliot understood men like my father - He's an archetype of The Waste Land, *the hollow men, the stuffed men . . . leaning together, headpiece filled with straw.*"

His knowledge was surprising considering he'd been unable to attend school for years, and when he felt more secure with Garnet he shared his enthusiasm for poetry. He brought his books into the woods and sitting under the weeping willow tree read aloud from his beloved poets. Lazing under lacy branches patched with blue by the summer sky, Garnet found herself drawn to passions expressed by poets which she sensed were locked inside her.

Niles encouraged her to write, correcting scraps of poems and urging her on, "Pablo Neruda says *we must pass through solitude and difficulty . . . to reach the enchanted place where we can dance our clumsy dance and sing our sorrowful song . . .*"

"*You* should write poetry, Niles," Garnet urged, impressed by his knowledge. "You know so much."

"No, no, no, it's impossible for me," he answered, visibly agitated. "Creation looms before me like a rickety bridge sway-

ing across a deep canyon, a chasm too hazardous to be crossed."
iv

For the sake of the gentle mother whom she loved, Garnet persuaded Imelda to take Niles for walks in the woods. Imelda would run away out of boredom but Garnet stayed to soothe the poor mad boy, and Mrs. Preston would smile and kiss her cheek on their return.

Some days Niles refused to speak, only sobbed, cries which shook his body and left him trembling. Garnet begged Niles to tell her what was wrong but he was unable to speak or explain, burying his face in her shoulder until the weeping subsided.

On his blackest days he threatened her with his despair, "When I spin off this wretched planet no one will be able to summon my soul back from the abyss . . ."

Murmuring gloomy lines from *Remords Postume* he insisted he was not long for this world.

"My dark and lovely thing, when I at length lie dead,
And sleep beneath a slab of marble black as pitch . . .
And have, for perfumed alcove and seductive bed,
Only a rainy cavern and a hollow ditch . . ."

She shivered, but answered cheerfully, "You'll outlive us all, Niles. You're too wicked and spoiled to die young." But she, too, feared for his survival.

Often he suffered attacks of migraine in the woods. He'd crawl in her arms in pain, stiffening up like marble, or curl on the grass in a fetal position. Garnet would rub her hands up and down his back massaging his protruding, bony spine until he relaxed.

"No one understands how much suffering every day holds for me," he cried in her arms. "My mother's experts claim my torture is self-inflicted and maybe it's true . . . like Baudelaire . . .

I am the wound, and the knife that inflicts the cut!

I am the blow, and the cheek!
I am the limbs, and the rack,
The victim, and the executioner!'

"But I can't stop tormenting myself," he wept, closing his eyes in anguish as he guided her hands over his face and throat, kissed her fingers in gratitude and buried his head in her palms.

v

As summer drifted on Niles grew bolder and tried to touch her, at first clinging to her hand as if innocently, but refusing to let go when she tried to withdraw it. One day, he stroked her legs and ran his hands up and down her arms. She was repulsed by his touch, his fingers felt like wet eels crawling over her skin and she pulled away.

But seeing the stricken look on his face she rebuked herself. *Niles is a poor wounded creature*, she thought guiltily. *How can you be so squeamish not to endure the graze of his fingertips. Such a lack of charity can't be pleasing to God - not even lepers nauseated Jesus.*

She tried not to damage his fragile psyche by rejection, unaware he'd embarked on a strategy of seduction. From day to day he encroached further, slyly pressing his body against hers when she rubbed his temples, sliding his hand down her back, kissing her neck and trying to hold her breasts. She protested and pushed back his hands but he sobbed and moaned, his suffering seemed so acute she was overcome with pity and in her desire to end his pain she allowed more and more liberties. During these episodes she stiffened herself and remained mute hoping her coldness would discourage him but Niles didn't seem to notice.

One day, he pushed up her skirt and forced her panties down far enough to rest his head against her pubic hair. He made no attempt to go further, simply lay there without moving, breathing deeply as if asleep.

For days after that he appeared content, lighthearted, laughing and joking with Imelda and Garnet for the first time since she met him.

"What's going on with Niles?" Imelda asked later. "He seems almost human. Is this your miracle cure or did God pee on his face?"

She was taken aback, distressed that Imelda was implying Niles' well-being rested in her hands.

The interludes in the woods with Niles continued and she accepted them as a fate over which she had no control. In spite of her repugnance she sympathized with his longings. Her own child-need for affection had been ignored by parents who never touched or embraced her. She hated being touched by him but sensed there could be joy in caresses from someone she loved.

Niles kept pushing her to go further. Garnet shook her head and got up from the grass. "It's wrong, Niles, and you know it. Keep this up and I'll stay away for good."

"Don't abandon me, Garnet," he wept. "I promise to behave." But promises meant little to Niles and after a few days respite he tried again. She allowed him to stroke her arm but when he put his hand on her breast she slapped him hard.

"I'm leaving, Niles, and you won't be seeing me for awhile. In the meantime, chill out."

He wept and pleaded, his face contorted from sobbing but she was adamant and stayed away from the Preston house for over a week until Imelda called her on the phone, hysterical.

"Niles has gone berserk," Imelda cried. "He paces the floor all night groaning and he's making us crazy. Please, Garnet, my mother begs you to come over and see him."

Garnet couldn't refuse Mrs. Preston and her arrival at the house was greeted warmly by Enid who kissed her on both cheeks.

"My dear child, how good of you to help my poor boy."

For a few days Niles was grateful for her presence and be-haved himself without pressing her for sex or touching her beyond the point she'd tolerate. But a week later he lay beside her with his head on her breast and ran his hand up her leg along her tanned thigh. She tried to pull away but he held her fast.

"Doctors say my chance of surviving is slim," he pleaded. "All I ask is a taste of pleasure while I'm alive. Is that too much to hope for?"

She shook her head and moved away but he caught her hands, covered his eyes with them and wept, soaking her palms with tears.

He finally evoked enough pity in her so that when he reached inside her panties to touch her she no longer resisted but shut her eyes and allowed him to mount and penetrate her. But when it was over and the groans and spasms of Niles subsided she felt sick and despoiled, like a ruined virgin in a nineteenth century novel, archaic words biting into her flesh, unclean, defiled, sul-lied forever.

She had difficulty sleeping, her nights interrupted by night-mares of cold and slimy hands crawling over her, covering her nose and mouth so she couldn't breathe while her body was at the mercy of hundreds of disembodied hands.

She tried to scream out, "Help me, get them off me, take them away!" but her voice strangled in her throat and no sound emerged. In the dream she saw Niles sitting on a brick step star-ing at her, his face cold and expressionless. She pleaded for help but there was no response.

She woke from the nightmares gasping for breath, afraid to go back to sleep, trying to get the dream out of her system to avoid another nightmare even more terrifying. To comfort her-self, she took out the box of letters from her uncle and reread the tales of adventures he'd written to her through the years. She prayed for the Winslow-angel to return but it was over a year since his last appearance. Then she remembered the *sadhu* in Nepal who also wrote, *But do not pull back a spirit who is on the path of infinite bliss*, and Garnet decided it would be selfish to disrupt his spiritual journey.

She saw Imelda again but avoided Niles. Imelda sensed what had gone on and as if to reassure Garnet, confided with a note of pride that she and Niles had played sex games in the woods for years.

Garnet was horrified.

"For God's sake, Garnet, what century are you living in? There's nothing abnormal about straight sex. Remember Dana, the clunky girl in dance class? She taught her dog to go down on her when she was eleven. That's what I call weird shit."

"But you're talking about incest," Garnet stammered.

"Cleopatra married her brother," Imelda yawned, lighting a cigarette and puffing out the smoke at Garnet. "Besides, Niles is useless, a weirdo. But when it comes to sex he's hot - oversexed and over-excitable. He trembles and shakes and the slightest touch sends him off to Planet Nine."

"I can't believe you're telling me this," Garnet said, feeling sick to her stomach.

"Don't get me wrong," Imelda, added quickly, noting the expression on Garnet's face. "We don't *go all the way*."

"Come on, Imelda, who are you kidding?" Garnet asked indignantly, fanning her face to get rid of the smoke. "You must think I'm an idiot." It was clear these siblings had no interest in limiting themselves.

"Don't look so shocked," Imelda laughed. "Sexual knowhow is a woman's greatest asset. Why shouldn't I practice on my brother?"

Garnet dropped the discussion, sickened by Imelda's disclosure. After that, while she occasionally spent time with Imelda, she avoided Niles. She no longer let him read her poems and refused to go alone with him into the woods. Summer was nearing its end and she made up her mind there would be not be another episode no matter what the consequence.

But one day by chance, she ran into Niles coming out of the

woods. He blocked her way, caught her by the arm and got down on his knees, pleading and threatening, trying to make her feel guilty for refusing to satisfy him.

"I can't do it, Niles," she said, trying to be tactful but firm.

Niles sobbed and clung to her, shaking and shuddering as if he were about to have a convulsion. She was frightened and stroked his head.

"Calm down, Niles. I care about you, but this is all wrong and has to stop."

"No, no, it can't stop," Niles shrieked, as he pushed her down on the ground and straddled her. Garnet put both hands on his hips and pushed upwards with all her might, lifting her knees at the same time and thrusting them into his stomach. But Niles shoved her back with a maniacal strength, pressing her down on the earth with his chest while ripping off her skirt and panties. She cried out but he put his hand over her mouth and then forced himself into her.

She held herself rigid as he molested her, shutting her eyes and freezing herself into a statue, feeling unreal as if she were floating above her body and the act was happening to someone else.

Afterwards, Niles rolled off and lay on the ground with his eyes shut. Garnet pulled herself up and sat on the grass. There was a bump on the back of her head, her face was bruised and bleeding, her shirt torn and stained with grass and dirt. She yanked on her clothes and tried not to cry, digging her nails into her palms to stop the tears.

Niles opened his eyes and watched as she tried to pull herself together. "I'm sorry, Garnet," he muttered, "but I couldn't help myself."

She stared back at him, feeling as if she were about to shake apart. "You must be crazy, Niles, to think you could rape me. Touch me again and I'll kill you."

Niles began to sob but she turned her back and slowly stood up. She ached all over but managed to get herself home and up to her room without anyone seeing her. She showered for a long time, trying to wash off the ugliness of the assault, then fell on the couch and tried to sleep.

She felt a deep sense of shame and revulsion for allowing Niles to dupe her, realizing that he'd tricked her into sex by playing the helpless victim while hiding the snag-toothed predator. He'd taken advantage of her compassion, her naïveté at his duplicity without a twinge of conscience. But she hated herself most for not seeing through his game, for succumbing like a sacrificial lamb.

She wished there was someone to confide in but knew she was alone in this. The only solution was to cut the tie with the Prestons. School was beginning and she'd find excuses to avoid Imelda and Niles, even poor Enid whom she'd miss.

She stayed away, absorbed herself in books and poetry hoping to ameliorate her disgust and suffering, and found some peace reading in the solitude of Winslow's study or in the woods. Sometimes she bicycled down to the end of the Point and sat on the sea wall staring across the waves, letting the autumn sun warm her face.

When the school term began she threw herself into sports, joining the hockey team where she was much valued for she played as if her life depended on it, running like a demon and smacking the ball with all her strength. She only wished she could smash in Niles' face with the same force and end a wretched chapter of her life. But the nightmare continued, with an even more disturbing ordeal to follow.

vi

In late September, not long after school opened, Garnet felt ill, dizzy and queasy as if a lead weight were sitting on her chest. She thought it was a stomach virus and attributed it to the outbreak of flu spreading throughout the school. But remembering her mother's revulsion at illness, she nursed herself, secretly dosing herself with Francesca's remedies in the medicine chest until nausea overwhelmed her and she ran into the bathroom to throw up. Once it began, she couldn't stop and spent the rest of the night vomiting and fainting from weakness. She sponged her face with a cloth dipped in cold water and held onto her head when she vomited, like the good mother of her dreams, and changed her nightgown when soaked with perspiration.

She passed out in school the next day and was sent home with a note, collapsing just as dinner was served. Francesca finally noticed.

"You look like death warmed over, Garnet. What's the matter with you?"

"I think it's the flu that's going around school but I can't seem to shake it."

Francesca sighed. She hated the nuisance of a trip to the doctor's office but they didn't make house calls any more and Edward couldn't be bothered. It crossed her mind that Garnet might have inherited a family disease. Francesca's grandfather, the infamous Spanish general who led the army in the Spanish-American War, died of Cooley's anemia, a genetic blood disease prevalent in the Mediterranean which was passed on to her father in a less severe but painful form of the disease. If Garnet was a carrier of their genetic curse Francesca wanted to nip it in the bud. She had no patience with illness and was confident modern medicine had a new and efficacious cure unknown to past generations.

Francesca explained all this to the doctor and he listened patiently, nodding his head while he observed the daughter's face, checking out her skin color and looking for telltale signs of the disorder. He took blood samples and ordered his lab assistant to examine them immediately.

Garnet had been delicate as a child, often ill with strep throats and flu so the doctor was concerned. But when the lab technician returned with a preliminary report that he found nothing wrong, the doctor took Garnet into his office for a private talk.

"Unhappiness and emotional turmoil can break down the body's defenses and cause illness," he said gently, seating her on the other side of his desk. "Persistent nausea can be psychological - something in your life you can't stomach."

Aware of her mother's antagonism to Garnet, the doctor questioned her relationship with Francesca. But Garnet could not speak. Loyalty, betrayal, fear? Her voice strangled in her throat and she turned her head away from his kindly eyes without answering. Nor did she dare mention Niles and the suffering she was experiencing because of him.

Francesca was irritable when they left the doctor's office. "What did the old fool say to you?"

"Nothing much. He gave me some medicine and said I'd be all right."

"Another day shot to hell over nothing," Francesca grumbled, hurrying her out of the office.

Garnet dragged herself back to school though she was weak, had no appetite and constantly nauseated. Maybe the doctor was right and the illness was in her mind. There was certainly plenty in her life she couldn't stomach.

But she couldn't shake off the malaise and Francesca hauled her back to the doctor to recheck her blood. The doctor demurred, insisting blood work could wait until after a general examination and led Francesca to the outer waiting room over protestations she had the right to stay with her daughter.

He returned alone a half hour later, leaving Garnet in the examining room. He sat Francesca down in the chair opposite his desk, his voice subdued as he explained there was no evidence of the genetic blood disease she feared - Garnet was pregnant.

Francesca turned white and gripped the arms of the chair. "It's impossible," she said. "Garnet isn't interested in boys."

"I can only tell you an internal examination revealed pregnancy," he replied. "Perhaps you'd like to talk to her in private. I'll send her in when she's dressed."

"Wait," Francesca said, as she mulled over the possibilities in her mind. Garnet showed no interest in boys or dating, unlike Valerie who was in a constant state of agitation over schoolgirl crushes.

Who could it be? It was impossible. But, but . . . She dismissed the thought. Imelda's brother, Niles, the mad boy? Too crazy to attend school? Yes, perhaps he raped Garnet and she was too afraid to tell. No matter. She'd take care of it. The doctor's office was a private clinic where in the past he'd performed two abortions on Francesca.

"Don't let Garnet get dressed. I want to talk to you," Francesca demanded.

In the examining room, Garnet could hear the sounds of her mother quarreling with the doctor and from the gist of the conversation realized what was wrong. The possibility of pregnancy never occurred to her. Her periods came irregularly, often skipping months at a time and menstruation began late for her, nearly fifteen. Doctors blamed it on her slenderness and sports activities, "A common problem in athletic girls or dancers. Nothing to worry about."

She had skipped a month or so but was sure the flu was hanging on when she felt sick in the morning or nauseous from the smell of frying bacon, never connecting it with Niles or sex.

Francesca's voice soared from the doctor's office like the screech of a wounded sea gull. "I expect you to take care of this, do you understand?"

The doctor's voice rose in response. He sounded angry and upset. "I can't do it. She's too young. If anything went wrong I'd be ruined, end up in prison."

"See that nothing goes wrong," Francesca hissed, a metallic edge to her voice. "Your so-called clinic could be in big trouble unless you fix her little problem. Illegal abortions, etcetera, etcetera?" she threatened. "Don't force me to bring you down."

Francesca was adamant and the doctor, fearing her wrath and its consequences, acquiesced even to her insistence the procedure be performed immediately.

"I want the pregnancy terminated before she realizes what happened. She's a willful little bitch and I've no intention of raising the bastard of a crazy boy."

The doctor and his assistant moved Garnet to a small operating room flooded with lights and strapped her onto the table. "Why are you doing this?" she cried, but they held her down and proceeded without response.

She relived the abortion over and over in her dreams. The nightmare began with a struggle to free herself from the bonds of the table, pain erupting as the doctor inserted cold instruments, agony ascending in pitch with her screams. In her dream, she could see the sweat on the doctor's brow, a kindly country doctor leaning over her slight form, his face wrinkled in apprehension, fearful for the fifteen-year-old girl stretched out before him on the surgical table.

"Be brave," he whispered. "I'm afraid to give you too much anesthesia."

When the procedure was over, Francesca drove home in silence. She was furious but refrained from attacking Garnet in her weakened condition. Instead, she drove recklessly, speeding up the gravel drive to the doorstep where she honked the horn and dumped her daughter into the hands of Graciela before racing off again. The old housekeeper shook her head in disbelief but helped Garnet up to bed and tried to make her comfortable, bathing her forehead and urging her to sip soups and juices.

But the aftermath of abortion was an infection that rampaged through Garnet's reproductive organs, its spread barely contained by antibiotics. The old doctor seemed upset as he explained to Francesca the scarring effect such infections had on the ability to procreate. "There's little chance she'll conceive again."

"It's just as well," Francesca answered sharply. "God knows

what monster brats she'd bring into the world."

Enraged by the problems complicating her life and unable to berate Garnet in her precarious state of health, Francesca telephoned Niles' father, Gil Preston. She attacked him in a fury, blaming him for his son's *rape* of Garnet, the abortion, and resultant infection damaging her prospects of bearing children.

"You should have kept that crazy boy locked up in a cage!" she snarled into the receiver.

Gil was furious. He'd always disliked Francesca, considered her a social-climbing bitch who put on airs (ignoring the irony of his own position). He listened to her ravings for a few minutes, then slammed down the phone, poured himself a double vodka and proceeded to finish the bottle.

A few days later, Garnet got a call from Imelda. She was still confined to her bed by the doctor, struggling to recover from the infection, and although the antibiotics were beginning to kick in she couldn't shake the fever or persistent pain. She felt too dizzy and weak to talk but Imelda sounded frantic.

"I've got to see you. Something terrible has happened. I'll come over - be there in ten minutes."

"You can't come here. My mother would kill you."

"Then meet me at the sea wall."

"Are you crazy? I'm not allowed to leave my bed, much less the house."

"Please, Niles is dying."

She felt a chill quiver through her body. "What happened?

"I can't explain over the phone. It's too horrible. I'll tell you everything when I see you. Sneak out of the house, for god's sake. Choose the place."

She felt too sick to get up but too frightened to refuse. "All right, meet me in the old stable behind the fields. No one goes there so we can sit inside and talk. I just hope I can get there without passing out on the way."

Luckily, Francesca was gone for the afternoon and Graciela was in the kitchen cooking up Spanish delicacies for dinner.

She could smell the aroma of *saffron* and *chorizo* rising from Francesca's favorite *Paella Valencia* as she slipped down the back stairs and shut the door quietly after her. She felt dizzy but by walking slowly and stopping to rest she made it to the barn.

Imelda was waiting for her inside the stable, trying to hide but peering out anxiously from behind the barn door. Her face was flushed and splotchy, her eyes swollen as if she'd been crying. Garnet had never seen Imelda weep or show a sign of vulnerability. She was always in control, rarely expressing any emotion except anger and sarcasm.

When she saw Garnet she threw her arms around her neck and sobbed.

"Thank God, you're here!"

Garnet stumbled and landed heavily on a bale of hay. The barn smelled musty from old hay decomposing in piles scattered around the stable. It was years since Winslow stabled horses there but a faint aroma and happier memories lingered in the earthen floor. She felt weak and shaky but was determined not to faint and cause a big scene with Francesca if she had to be carried from the barn. She took a deep breath and dug her nails into her hands to give her strength.

"How is Niles?"

"He's alive, but just barely."

"What happened? Was he in an accident?"

"It all began with a phone call from your mother," Imelda said, blowing her nose and wiping away her tears as she spoke.

When Imelda arrived home from school that afternoon her father was in the library. She could see he was drunk and in a rage, making faces and grunting as he cursed out Francesca, so she slipped by the door unnoticed and tiptoed up the stairs to her room.

When Gil's footsteps pounded up the stairs Imelda feared he was coming after her and hid in the closet hoping he wouldn't realize she was home. But he walked past her room and banged on Niles door. Then she heard the sound of blows and Niles' screams. She stepped quietly down the hall to his room, the door was open and she peered in. Gil was roaring at Niles in a drunken fury.

"Slimy little bastard, you couldn't control yourself, you had to fuck the skinny bitch. That Spanish slut screamed her lungs out at *me*, claimed you raped her virgin daughter and blames me. You bloody idiot, I'll show you what fucking is."

"I watched as he straddled Niles and pulled off his trousers and his underpants. Then he turned him over and I saw Niles' white butt shining in the light, and realized what he was about to do. I was terrified but I couldn't let him attack Niles like that so I cried out and ran into the room. I pleaded with my father but it was as if he couldn't stop himself, like a steamroller set on automatic with no shut-off switch. I grabbed the back of his shirt and tried to pull him away. "Let him go!"

"He lifted up his arm and slammed me against the wall. "Shut up, bitch. This is none of your business."

"Niles was screaming and screaming but I couldn't do anything. I stood there frozen as my father held him down and raped him, pounding himself into his body. I put my hands over my eyes but wasn't able to shut out the sound of Niles' shrieks as he begged him to stop."

"It was horrible, horrible. And I was helpless. All I could do was cower in the corner and pray for it to end. But when my father finally pulled himself off Niles he shouted, *I wanted a real son, not a fucking weakling, a sick piece of shit with no balls. You should have died the day you were born!*"

Imelda stopped for a moment and took a deep breath before she could go on. "He grabbed Niles by the hair and smashed him in the face. Niles' skin was ashen, he seemed barely conscious but that didn't stop my father, he punched him in the stomach with his fist and kicked his legs and back. Niles no longer cried out but hung from my father's hands like a rag doll."

"I couldn't breathe. I began to retch and ran out of the room down to the floor below. I'd just stepped away from the landing when I saw my father fling Niles down the stairs. There was a terrible crash as Niles tumbled over and over hitting the steps until he landed on the marble floor in the center hall. I ran back to pick him up but my father slapped me in the head and pushed me away. He screamed at me, *leave him alone or I'll beat the shit out of you, too.* He blamed me, said it was my fault for bringing home *that cunt Garnet!*"

"Luckily, my mother arrived a few minutes later or Niles wouldn't be alive. My father claimed Niles attacked him, threatened to kill him and he only defended himself. But I confronted him, said I'd seen it all and told my mother the truth while he stood there. She nearly fainted but had the presence of mind to call an ambulance and arrange for Niles to be taken to a private hospital. She wanted to notify the police but when she phoned my grandparents in Newport they insisted she say nothing for the moment, avoid a scandal, and they'd fly down to Sailship in the morning."

"My grandfather summoned a famous brain surgeon in New York to come up and operate that night, but it was touch and go whether Niles would live. His skull was fractured in several places and his left hip and thigh were shattered. During the operation his brain swelled and they had to insert a shunt to drain the fluid. The doctors say he's still critical and may not live. Even if he recovers it's doubtful he'll walk normally."

A wave of dizziness washed over Garnet. She felt herself losing consciousness as if she were blacking out. She wanted to put her hands over her ears to block out the image of this monstrous act but clutched at the bale of hay to steady herself and asked in a faint voice, "What did they do about your father?"

Imelda put her arm around Garnet to comfort her.

"The family lawyers threatened to have my father arrested but my grandfather had no intention of carrying that out," she said, her voice shaking. "I don't blame him, the scandal would be horrible. Anyway, by taking a tough line *Grandadda* softened him up to accept his offer. If he gives my mother a divorce, leaves the country and settles overseas, my grandfather will arrange a financial settlement."

"The bank will send him money on a regular basis - monthly payola for the brute - as long as he stays away. But if he shows his face in the U.S. of A. all funds will be cut off and Grandadda swears he'll turn him over to the police. He's so outraged I believe he would. Everyone is sick over it. Not that I was close to Niles, he was such a pain, but he didn't deserve this. Even if he lives, how can he forget? My father is despicable and I hope I never see his ugly face again."

vii

A few days later, Imelda begged Garnet to visit Niles in the sanitarium. "I don't blame you for hating us after all you suffered from this crazy family," she pleaded, "but Niles is in a bad way. He's begging to see you.'

Garnet shook her head. She dreaded going. She was still ill, in pain from the infection and terrified to see what his father had done to him. But Imelda persisted and she felt obligated.

One morning, on a day Francesca planned to be away until dinnertime Garnet slipped out. She took a bus to town, then boarded another for the long ride into the countryside to the sanitarium. The jolting of the bus aggravated her pain and cramps but she tried to will herself not to faint or collapse.

The sanitarium, a rambling wooden structure in a secluded woods, was in disrepair but their clientele overlooked that for the specialty of the institution was privacy. Disturbed family members of the rich, their black sheep offspring, or elderly parents whose heirs conspired to control their assets could be tucked away and protected from intrusion or escape by high metal fences circling the grounds.

Here the Prestons were able to demand a conspiracy of silence, with a cover story that Niles' injuries were accidental or self-inflicted. The Head Psychiatrist, owner of the facility, knew the truth but carried out the charade. A good deal of money was involved, not only for Niles' care which went on for months but for the huge donation promised by the DeForests, several million, Imelda claimed, which would substantially increase the facilities of the sanitarium and put cash into his pocket.

The chief nurse refused to admit Garnet in to visit Niles so she waited outside on the grounds for an hour and slipped back in through another entrance. Imelda had given her the room number and while the nurses were serving lunch she hid behind his door until the coast was clear.

Niles' head was encased in bandages, tubes were sticking out all over him, his left arm was in a sling, his leg trussed up by a steel contraption suspended from the ceiling. She wanted to run out of the room but forced herself to walk over to the gauze-bound *Frankenstein*. She wasn't sure he was conscious but came close and tapped him on his right arm. He looked up at her as if he had no idea who she was.

"The poet is like the prince of clouds," Garnet whispered. *"His giant wings prevent him from walking."*

"Baudelaire," he murmured, staring at her as tears ran down his cheeks.

She tried to comfort him, speaking softly so as not to be overheard in the hall, grazing the un-bandaged portion of his face with her fingers.

"Oh, Garnet," he said, in a voice husky with pain. "Why didn't they let me die?"

She leaned over and laid her hand on his forehead, trying not to retch from the medicinal and putrid smells emanating from him. But Niles was beyond comfort although his damaged body still clung to life.

viii

Garnet felt ill on the bus back to Sailship Point but her mind whirled with images of Niles lying broken in the sanitarium, Imelda's recounting of his father's brutality and the lies promoted by the doctor.

She got off the bus at the last stop in Sailship Point but still had a walk to Khushi Kheddah. She felt dizzy and feverish as she sneaked into the house, tiptoeing up the stairs past Graciela in the kitchen. She tore off her clothes, tossed them in the back of the closet and fell onto Winslow's couch before calling Graciela to come up.

The old housekeeper felt her forehead. Garnet was burning up and Graciela ran to the phone to call the doctor. He was surprised by the call, expecting his patient would be well on the way to recovery by now. But the infection had reoccurred, escalating at a galloping pace. Within hours Garnet's temperature reached a perilous high despite Graciela's efforts to keep her soaked with ice water.

The doctor came quickly. Infection was his greatest fear posing a serious risk not only to the patient but to his professional life. Physicians paid severe penalties for performing abortions, licenses lost, doctors sentenced to prison. A hospital was out of the question.

He ordered more antibiotics, massive doses this time but the infection resisted and spread from her female organs into the blood stream and glands throughout her body. The pain was intense, her uterus cramping from the assault, her chest aching from infection and as the fever rose she drifted in and out of delirium.

She tried to distract herself during conscious moments by reading a book Winslow left in the drawer of the night table, a novel about India during the monsoon. In her fevered state the tale invaded her delirium and she was plunged into India where torrential rains were pounding villages into mud, rivers overflowing, drenching waters dousing her burning skin as the infection erupted and her temperature rose, her heart pounding as fevered blood pulsated through her veins.

The doctor stayed at her side until she came through the crisis, leaning over her day and night with the same anxious face she remembered from the abortion. As the antibiotics took hold she came out of the delirium and woke one morning to find the doctor sitting at the edge of her bed. He held her hand and gently explained the seriousness of the infection.

Half asleep, Garnet rallied herself to ask, "Will I be able to have children?"

The doctor shook his head sadly. "I'm sorry. I don't see any possibility of your conceiving again."

The doctor disappeared, and Graciela was in his place, sitting under the lamp watching her. Garnet had awakened but she was still in the dream. Reality seemed far away as she slowly came back to life.

Garnet could only grieve. Innocence, and misplaced compassion for Niles had deceived her, ending with an infant soul who came to the planet too soon and her loss of hope that she'd ever bear another. She wept and could not stop. She lay motionless in her bed, tears streaming down her face like the Ophelia of Burne-Jones, bereft dead maiden with the leaves of autumn scattered over her face, drowned in the waters of her grief.

She refused to speak to her parents and sister or permit them to enter her room. Graciela hobbled up the stairs with her meals on a tray and sat in the corner of the room in silence, staring sadly at Garnet as she ate her dinner. The old woman hardly spoke but once, looking away from Garnet as if talking to herself, blurted out in a sudden loud voice,

"*God stays near to the brokenhearted and saves the crushed in spirit.*" When she left with the tray she paused at the door to rasp out a Spanish blessing in an even gruffer tone, as if trying to keep her compassion under control, "*Dios te tenga en su santa mano.*"

Garnet wept, breathing the words to herself in English, *May God keep you in his holy hand.*

She tried to stop the memories reverberating in her head but slept intermittently pursued by nightmares and days of bleakness where she could only weep, unable to pull herself out of the pain.

When she reached the lowest point, where it seemed only death could put an end to her suffering and she began planning an exit, it occurred to her it might be possible to renew herself and remake her life.

She found Winslow's adventure books and explored ideas of rescue and survival, tales of prisoners who stayed sane in dungeons and prisons by computing mathematical problems in their heads, sailors adrift in life rafts enduring weeks before rescue, who sang songs or recited school ditties and poems to each other. She put away her clothes and dressed herself again in Winslow's garments hoping to be consoled by them. She wore his Egyptian cotton shirts in the daytime, slept in his silk *kurtah* tunics from India, lounged in a paisley silk dressing gown and stumbled around in his oversize leather mules, dabbing herself with *Russian Leather* Eau de Cologne and rubbing scented pomade into the ends of her hair so she could inhale the nostalgia of his aroma. She used his white *djellabah* from Morocco as a housecoat and when the room grew chilly wrapped herself in Winslow's hooded black *burnoose*. When feeling forlorn, she sat in front of the fire elegantly attired in his red *moiré* smoking-jacket with black satin lapels, puffing on a pipe she dug out of his desk, soothed by the scent of his smoky tobacco circling the room.

She rummaged through his letters and scented *billet-doux* from ladies professing undying love, read his books, poring over notes scribbled in margins, the sight of his writing like a touch of his hand. She took the framed photos out of the chest and placed them around the room; Winslow as a boy in Cape Town holding a spear, arm in arm with his friend, a young *Kaffir*, Winslow with his foot resting on a dead tiger, Winslow smiling at her from exotic corners of the world, all the images of his life, and she clung to her uncle's remembrances as if she could evoke his presence through them. Sometimes she played backgammon sitting opposite his empty chair, pretending he was there and giving him all the winning moves.

As soon as she regained some strength she clambered down the cliffs to the sea and sat for hours on the stone seawall at the end of the Point staring out across the waves. The ripples of the Sound glinted blue in the sun, waves churned grey on stormy days and sea breezes curled into her heart as if she were a Chekhov heroine convalescing on the Black Sea.

She watched sea gulls swooping down beneath the whitecaps to catch fish and robins arching over her head into the trees. Some days she walked along the rocks at the edge of the sea or drowsed in the sun stretched across a large boulder. She waded in waves lapping at the shore, snapped bubbles in the yellowish seaweed floating between the rocks and rummaged through the beach picking up stones burnished by the sea.

Out there alone, the salty winds grazing her cheeks, the natural beauty and tranquility of the peninsula made the world seem flawless. God did a good job of creation. Mortals ruined the *garden* and despoiled His work.

ix

Garnet's sixteenth birthday came and went in the early Spring. She insisted there be no celebration, refusing presents or visits except for Graciela, allowing her to carry up a home-baked birthday cake ablaze with candles and sparklers. The old woman brought along a bottle of Porto and a handful of scented Spanish occult candles, one to be lit each night for a week to bring a year of luck and happiness. They stuffed themselves with cake and drank most of the bottle of wine. Garnet got a little drunk and collapsed onto the couch, woozy but happy as she drifted into a long, dreamless sleep.

She took out her journal and began to write again, scribbling about the summer of loss and death ending her girlhood and innocence of spirit, mourning the infant soul who tried to come to earth before a place was ready. Reading it over she decided she had to write *fini* on the anguish of that summer, and planned a funeral in the woods for her lost baby.

To symbolize her baby's death she selected her most beautiful doll, bought in Paris by Winslow and christened Consuela, or *consolation*. The morning of the funeral she bundled up the rest of her dolls for Graciela to donate to a Spanish orphanage, and went out to the shed where she created a casket for the burial, pasting baby gift paper, decorated with toy rattles, teddy bears and cherub faces, on the outside of a box and lined the inside with a soft doll blanket and pillow.

She couldn't bear to disfigure Consuela's sweet porcelain face, her thick-lashed eyes that opened and closed, scarlet lips curved in a smile revealing tiny pearl teeth, curls of honey hair nearly matching her own, so she spared the head but pounded the rest of the doll with a hammer, sobbing as the body broke apart. Suddenly, with the last smash of the hammer, the doll's eyes flew open and stared at Garnet, as if pleading with her. Garnet's tears streamed over Consuela's face as she kissed the cupid-bow lips and murmured, *I'll never forget my baby, never.* Then she entwined a wreath of flowers around the hair and wrapped the broken doll and the torn remnants of her silk organdy frock in a white shawl.

She chose a spot under the weeping willow and prayed for God to keep the soul of her unborn baby in his arms, then dug a hole in the earth and made a cross to mark the grave by wrapping twine around two twigs, pressing it into the ground against a rock to hold it steady. She put the cover on the box, placed it in the grave and sang a few measures of Brahms, 'How lovely is thy dwelling place, O Lord . . . blessed are they that dwell in Thy house . . . She piled earth onto the grave and stared down at the little mound on the ground, wiping the tears from her face, then sat down and leaned against the weeping willow tree.

She thought about her life. Conrad said In art, we shed our sickness. Niles had admired the fragments of poems she'd shown him, insisting they revealed a precocious talent but she hadn't taken him seriously. Now poetry seemed a solution, and remembering her journal she saw its potential for creation and healing. She realized that unlike Niles she wanted to shed her sickness, to make the effort and devote herself to whatever bit of talent she possessed.

She shut out everything and withdrew to Winslow's study, isolated from all but brief contacts with nature, the shaded paths, birds, trees, and sea of Sailship Point. In the morning before sitting down to write, she lit a candle on the desk under Winslow's portrait hoping to evoke his spirit to give herself confidence. She prayed, concentrated, and absorbed herself in the task of writing, poring over her journal and extracting the painful events of that summer. Death and loss. She took out a notebook to use for drafting her poems and printed Death Summer on the cover.

Memories evoked by the journal whirled in her head like dervishes but she allowed them to settle at will, trying not to control what bubbled up from the cauldron of her unconscious, letting herself be swept away scrawling random thoughts and recklessly spilling her pain onto the pages. Writing down the unspeakable soothed her grief and helped her detach from the past.

She was drawn to the fragmented images of poetry and its brevity of expression. Poems could mask and reveal with perceptions shaped in a few lines, a life delineated in ten. She began to live in words, crafting sounds and shapes into poems, feeling the power of creation. In the beginning was the Word and the Word was with God. And the Word was God. She was sure her salvation depended on developing herself as an artist, and vowed never to marry.

She heard Niles was recovering but refused to see him or Imelda, and continued to avoid her family, remaining sequestered in her room, informing her parents through Graciela she wouldn't be well enough to return to school until the fall semester.

* * *

Toward the end of the school year she made an appointment to meet with Winslow's executors, his lawyers and the Trust Officer of the bank and requested money from her educational trust to finish high school at a boarding school and continue on to college.

The executors arranged everything, including her admission to an excellent school and carried out her uncle's wishes sanctioning the payment of all bills for Garnet's tuition and expenses. Edward and Francesca objected but the executors, forewarned about the family situation, carried out Winslow's directives and disregarded their attempts to interfere.

Garnet continued writing in the months remaining and the work grew quickly. She accumulated a pile of poems and when she felt she'd explored the theme to her satisfaction and written herself out, she rewrote and edited the poems. When the task was finished she fastened the manuscript into a binder and placed it in Winslow's leather briefcase.

She wanted to see Enid once more before leaving for boarding school and was invited for tea at the summer's end while Niles and Imelda were visiting their grandparents in Newport. She brought along a copy of the manuscript as a gift, needing to share that terrible summer with Enid.

Enid kissed her and wept. A few months later she showed the poems to an old friend who headed a small publishing company. He thought the work moving and impressive and wrote to

Garnet for permission to publish them in book form. She was taken aback by the idea of publication but Enid was persuasive.

Garnet dedicated the book to Enid and Winslow. A year later, *Death Summer* was published to surprisingly good reviews. '*An auspicious debut by a talented young poet* . . . '

The publication of her poetry and the approbation she received gave her confidence for a new life, and forged the link bringing her to India.

III

AGRA, Sushila's Villa

> *O, my Luve is like the melodie,*
> *That's sweetly played in tune."*

Robert Burns

i

Raj Mahal Hotel, Agra

Satisfied to be in the land of her child-dreams Garnet embraced India, even the dingy, rundown Raj Mahal Hotel. But there were difficulties.

After the harrowing struggle with Niles earlier in the evening she'd fallen asleep on the bathroom floor and stumbled to bed in the middle of the night. But once in bed she found it impossible to sleep. The episode evoked a terrible hatred for Niles, and the revulsion she felt at fifteen re-emerged. She tried not to despise him but rage was choking her throat. Niles had robbed her of a normal life and now, though wildly attracted to Ravi she could foresee no future with him.

She was unable to get back to sleep and spent a wretched night staring up at the ceiling, soaked with perspiration, tossing and turning trying to figure a way out. She thought she'd distanced herself from the damage Niles had inflicted on her when she moved to New York and made a new life for herself. In time, she was even aware of a bright spirit rising up in her, as Winslow promised.

But with the return of Niles in her life, dumping his frenzied moods and hostility on her, the gains she'd made in creating a new existence began to crumble like an ancient document that disintegrates when exposed to air. She felt at risk of collapse, engulfed by old feelings of vulnerability and helplessness. *Save yourself, save yourself*, a voice urged.

Toward morning she came to a decision. She heard Niles groaning in his sleep and gave him a sedative, hoping he wouldn't stir when the desk clerk rang with her early wake-up call. At six a.m, she picked up the phone on the first ring, dressed quietly and slipped out of the room without waking him. On the way out, she left a message for Niles with the manager that she'd be back later, and asked him to send up his breakfast in a couple of hours.

She went first to the Air India office and reserved a ticket for Niles for a flight to New York the following week. She didn't want to deny him Ravi's gala, but after that she'd see that he returned to the States. He was sure to resist, throw fits and pull out his bag of tricks but she was determined. If need be she'd get help from Ravi and Vijay or even the police if necessary.

After reserving the flight she used the public phones at the post-office and made a call to New York. She spoke to the desk clerk at a small, somewhat rundown, but affordable hotel in the Village, and the clerk agreed to take Niles on a weekly basis until his mother returned from Switzerland. Everything was arranged but she decided not to tell Niles until the last possible moment. At worst, if he protested too much she'd slip him a sedative to get him on the plane.

She tried to behave normally in the days following but Niles sensed something was amiss and tried to be on his best behavior. He always worried after a violent attack that he'd gone too far. But it was too late for repentance.

* * *

At precisely seven o'clock on the evening of the gala while Niles was still at the mirror fussing with his hair, his shirt not yet buttoned, the clerk at the Front Desk rang up to say two gentlemen were waiting in the lobby.

"Shall I send them up, Madame?"

"Of course not," Garnet answered sharply. "What are you thinking of?" *The desk clerk must be an idiot.* "Tell them to wait. I'll come down."

"Finish quickly, Niles," she said, firmly. "Meet me downstairs and don't be long. I've no patience left for nonsense."

The elevator creaked dangerously as it approached the first floor, then shuddered to a stop with a sharp cracking noise, reminding her of the ancient Hindu adage: *With every breath one draws, death can strike seventeen times.*

As she stepped out of the elevator she found Ravi standing at the door waiting to greet her.

"Thank you for coming, memsahib," he said, kissing her hand. "Please observe two wayward Indians who followed your orders and arrived on time!"

Garnet glanced at her watch and smiled. *"La ponctualité est la politesse des rois - Louis XVIII."*

Ravi laughed, and kissed her hand again. "Did you hear that, Vijay? This American princess may change our ways."

"Yes, yes," Vijay said impatiently, waiting for a chance to thrust a huge bouquet of flowers into her hands.

"What's this?" Garnet asked, holding the massive array of blooms in her arms. "You shouldn't be giving me flowers. Escorting me to the gala is quite enough."

"Shhh," Vijay said, looking uneasily toward Ravi. "My cousin selected these flowers himself," he whispered breathlessly, pointing to the various blossoms. "He's very exacting so it took awhile to concoct this mix of jasmine, hibiscus, poppies, lilies, roses, amaryllis, tiger orchids and frangipani blossoms. But it's the best India has to offer."

"This is a jungle of rare blooms - and I love them all," Garnet said, bending her head to inhale the varied fragrances. She looked up at Ravi and smiled at him. "Such an unexpected treat."

"It's nothing," Ravi answered, looking a little embarrassed as he glanced furtively around the lobby, at the stained wall paper, shabby rugs and scratched, chipped chairs. "You deserve far more."

Garnet noticed his dismay at the dilapidated state of the hotel but there was nothing she could do about her lack of funds. Poets were meant to disregard poverty and take consolation in their art.

She could see Niles was making an attempt to act cheerful when he came downstairs. Vijay greeted him enthusiastically, plucked a rose from Garnet's bouquet and slipped the flower in the lapel of his white linen suit.

"Now you look a true gentleman, a proper sahib of the Raj," Vijay said, with an admiring glance as he tucked his arm into Niles' to escort him out the door.

"We should leave," Ravi said. "We're taking you in auntie's car, an old relic and a bit temperamental if made to stand idle too long."

Garnet slipped into her cape and handed the flowers to the manager, and asked to have them put in a vase in her room.

"Of course, memsahib. These exquisite blooms will receive my personal attention," Mr. Chaturvedi replied, looking at Garnet with new respect. Clearly, her friends were upper-class Indians. He bowed to Ravi and Vijay in an obsequious fashion and rushed out to open the doors of the car, standing at attention as they seated themselves. Ravi tipped him and the manager's face lit up at the amount. "Most gracious of you, Sir. My humble thanks."

Garnet paused and ran her hand over the ivory door before

getting in. "This is no relic. A 1928 *Hispana-Suisa* is a treasure!"

"You sound like an expert," Ravi exclaimed in admiration.

"Far from it," Garnet laughed, waving off the compliment. "My uncle taught me a bit - antique cars were his hobby."

"Auntie's gala is a rare treat," Vijay said, shaking her hands happily as she stepped into the car. "Shushu's version of Hindu heaven is a lavish spectacle, nearly vanishing in India now that maharajas are forced into tourism to survive, as Ravi says."

Ravi smiled at her. "One small warning, her sumptuous buffet. Auntie Sushila takes pleasure in stuffing her friends. She believes excess is barely enough and since only gluttony pleases her we starve ourselves before facing her groaning table."

"Ravi's right," Vijay interjected. "Dinner at the villa is known as Auntie's onslaught."

They sped off, Ravi negotiating the car through traffic narrowly avoiding three-wheeled taxis, trucks, oxen drawn carts, rickshaws, bicycles and pedestrians recklessly weaving between cars, yet managed not to collide with the stream of moving objects.

Garnet held her breath and shut her eyes when a crash seemed inevitable but he avoided them all and she had to admit his driving was superb although she decided not to encourage his madness by complimenting him. She was relieved when the car screeched to a halt at the gateway to his auntie's villa.

ii

Auntie Sushila's white villa was styled in Greek Revival; a 1920s version, long, low, marble-pillared, with a stone terrace fronting the gardens. Art deco Raj, built in 1928 by a worried young Englishman to placate his spoiled bride. Perfect for a jazzy debutante bored with India, homesick for British country week-ends and Mayfair cocktail parties. Twenty years later, Ravi's aunt, the *Kanwar Rani of Madhgaya*, bought the estate as a setting for her literary and musical salons.

Ravi and Vijay guided Garnet and Niles through grounds lush with trees - *banyans* with ancient twisted limbs, *golden-mohurs* cascading orange flowers, silvery-green *eucalyptus* and flowering *cork* trees - to gardens ablaze with tiny lights tracing *areccanut* leaves and the branches of white-blossomed *neem* trees. Streams of water gushing from fountains sent a mist of opalescence over the colored lights set in marble-sculptured pools, lotus blossoms floated in scented waters, weeping willows drooped overhead and sandalwood incense drenched the silky night air.

As they neared the villa strings of colored Chinese lanterns glowed and swayed over their heads. They reached the foot of the marble steps and began to climb toward a sweeping terrace when suddenly Ravi's Auntie Sushila, resplendent in a shimmering gold sari, emerged through the French doors. She leaned against an ornate balustrade to greet her guests but the moment her nephews came into view she waved excitedly and called out in a shrill voice.

"Come see me at once, you naughty fellows! It's been too long since you paid me a visit."

Ravi and Vijay bowed in respectful Indian fashion, palms pressed together, then waved back.

"She's not really our aunt, only a distant cousin of my father," Ravi explained, taking Garnet by the arm and walking ahead as Vijay and Niles lagged behind.

"Auntie Shushu," Ravi called out as he hurried Garnet up the steps to the glittering, rotund figure smiling happily at the edge of the terrace.

"Pretty boys! Come give Auntie a kiss," her pudgy cheeks flushed and beaming as she enfolded them in her fat, planting a perfunctory smack on Vijay's cheek, and a long lingering kiss on Ravi's mouth.

Garnet turned her head away in embarrassment to avoid what

appeared to be an unseemly sexual advance but Ravi took it good-naturedly, amused by the passion of her embrace. "Ah, Auntie, you haven't forgotten how to entice a man," he laughed, giving her plump sari-clad bottom a pat and skillfully disengaging himself.

"Do meet Garnet Lawler, a lovely new gem I brought for your collection," Ravi beamed as he put his arm around Garnet's shoulder. "You see before you a poet, frighteningly intelligent, mad for our backward country, and writing a book on Mumtaz Mahal. You may take pleasure in fattening up this slender nymph."

"Pay no attention to this rude, naughty boy." Sushila smiled fondly, unable to mask how she doted on him. "You look a bit peaked yourself, Ravi, a good feed will do you no harm. Come along to the buffet, the musicians are already setting up."

"And don't forget my friend, Niles Preston," Vijay said, pushing him forward. "He's a blighted genius."

Sushila reached out her hand to Niles. "Vijay's a funny boy, but a dear one."

On the side of the terrace facing the formal gardens elaborate serving tables were set with lace cloths, garlands of flowers and scented candles burning in silver candelabra. Huge silver tureens brimming with spicy delicacies and platters piled high with hot baked breads emitted a pungent steam into the warm evening air. Turbaned waiters in princely Rajput garb, fitted wine coats over white leggings, eagerly served guests clumped around the table; a brilliant assortment of Asian jewels gleaming in ruby and emerald satin, gold-threaded silk saris or slim-coated kurtahs slit at the sides to reveal tight silk pants. Europeans in black-tie, their wives glittering in spangled evening gowns, chatted around the table with Indian politicians in buttoned-down Nehru coats and mingled casually with Indian poets, artists, and musicians, unworldly souls in white cotton *kurtahs* and *dhotis* making a political statement by their simplicity of dress.

"Take good care of Niles," Ravi told Vijay as he took Garnet's elbow firmly and guided her over to the serving tables, winking at Sushila as he assured her, "Don't worry, Auntie, I'll make sure this undernourished American is properly fed."

Ravi picked up a blue and gold porcelain plate and pointed out the embossed crown and regal. 'N.' "Auntie's a *Francophile*, adores Napoleon and takes his words to heart - *an army travels on its stomach*! We're no army but that doesn't faze Auntie Shushu. She stuffs us, anyway."

He filled her plate with Indian delicacies, heaping on fresh shrimp, briny and sweet, sauced with tamarind, coriander, and coconut cream, crisp-skinned chicken fragrant with saffron and fenugreek leaves, roast potatoes spiced with black mustard seeds and red chilies, saffron rice and thick dhal, crisp fried samosas stuffed with meat, a rich duck vindaloo, and a creamy stew of peas and cubes of curd redolent with ginger and mint.

"Have a taste of Indian bread," he said, dropping a puffed chupattie, a crispy spiced pappadum and a tandoor-baked paratha on top of the food piled on her plate."

She bent over and inhaled the melange of spicy aromas. "It smells delicious but I can't possibly eat all this," she protested.

Ravi kissed the nape of her neck. Garnet shivered at his touch but moved quickly out of his reach, rubbing the back of her neck.

Ravi didn't seem to notice. "Never argue with a prince, my dear," he teased. "We always know what's best for everyone, even if we're not so clever about ourselves. Be a dear little princess and allow me to take care of you."

"How lovely to be a little princess - untroubled by problems," Garnet sighed, glancing up at Ravi with a rueful look. Then, seeing his round cheeks shining under the Chinese lanterns the desire suddenly came over her again to cling to him, to enfold herself in his arms and press her lips against his soft neck. But embarrassed by such dangerous yearnings, she turned her head away.

"What is it, Garnet? Is anything wrong," he asked, his face full of concern.

If only she *could* talk to him. She had no one to confide in and she'd been impressed by his kindness and concern for Niles, for his cousin, even the cafe owner in Agra. But involving him in her problems was forcing an intimacy that might boomerang. Nor could she recount the hideous story of her past with Niles.

She shook her head. "Tonight I want to forget about unpleasant things and devote myself to pleasure."

"Ah, now you speak of my favorite pastime," Ravi beamed, patting her on the shoulder.

She was glad he didn't probe further and gave him a grateful smile as they moved away from the serving board.

"Auntie Shushu expects us at her table," Ravi said, handing their plates to a waiter and beckoning to Vijay and Niles to follow as he guided her in the direction of the garden.

"*Auntie* is a term of respect for an older woman, not necessarily a blood tie," Ravi whispered. "Perhaps I should call you auntie instead of memsahib," he teased.

Garnet made a face. "Don't be rude to foreigners, or aliens from Venus. You may need a friend."

Ravi took her hand and pressed the ends of her fingers to his lips. "You seem more than a friend already - strangely familiar, as if I knew you in a previous life. Don't you recognize me?"

"Oh, yes," Garnet teased back. "You're the cruel teacher in the 1800s who beat my fingers when I didn't know my lessons, the father who forced me into a nunnery in the twelfth Century and the wicked lover who betrayed me during the Renaissance. I wonder why fate gave you another chance to exert your evil power!"

"I hope you're listening, Vijay, and benefiting from my experience," Ravi said, turning back to his cousin. "Don't try to best an American, they're born to win. Retreat gracefully as we did with the British. Miz Garnet is far too clever for me. Auntie Shushu, a woman born to wiles and cunning will have more success with this jewel of the West. Yes, dear Garnet, I'm no match for you but Auntie will be pleased so come along."

Garnet felt comfortable bantering with Ravi. He had an ability to make repartée pleasurable. Unlike the men she'd met in New York whose fragile egos experienced wit as a hostile putdown by the new breed of feminist barracudas and viciously attacked back, teasing was a playful game to Ravi, meant for enjoyment.

Nor did he have the painful sensitivity and paranoia of Niles, evoking fears of either wounding him by a wrong word or setting off a terrifying tide of violence. Caring for Niles was a balancing act on a precipice, one slip and a death crash. It was comforting to be with a man like Ravi who could take care of himself.

iii

Sushila, seated at a table overlooking the gardens, waved for them to join her. As they approached she observed Garnet carefully and scrutinized Ravi, pleased at his exuberance. Despite his sense of fun and good humor Sushila was aware of his loneliness. Her matchmaking attempts had achieved little success and she yearned to enfold him in her fat and comfort him, but motherly love wasn't what was needed.

Perhaps this American, with the look and graceful manners of an English girl, would achieve what she hoped for. Had Divine Wisdom in its mysterious knowing come up with a solution? Sushila cautioned herself against romantic foolishness, pinning her hopes on an elusive traveler, even worse, a young poet absorbed by a calling. She sighed, reminding herself to let the *Divine Powers* exert its will without meddling.

Swept into the beauty of the night, Garnet tingled with pleasurable sensations. The rich fragrance of tropical trees and flowering gardens mingled with the scent of incense and spicy aromas of food intensified the charm of the setting; tables draped in pink damask with fresh rose petals twined in intricate patterns between the plates, crystal vases stuffed with jasmine. Delicate touches to rouse the senses, Garnet relaxing into pleasure as champagne shivered in cut-crystal glasses and young waiters, handsome in scarlet turbans and white ballooned trousers, darted from table to table anxious to please, smiling and bowing.

Yet remembering the poverty and squalor of the other India, twinges of guilt marred the pleasure of indulgence. She couldn't forget pushing her way along teeming streets through crowds of beggars, children with haunted eyes in thin faces, old men dying in gutters, young mothers in rags holding out infants and grabbing passersby pleading for a few rupees. An impoverished land with millions of needy in despair. But conscious of the little difference one person could make Garnet began to avert her eyes from the suffering. She still gave coins but could see there was no immediate solution, no quick American fix.

Then why not indulge herself for an evening without guilt? True, these were over-privileged people, easy to despise. In a lesser way, so was she. But her puritanism evoked guilt at extravagance while an ancient wisdom taught them to pleasure themselves, a culture honing the art of gratification for thousands of years. Perhaps it was less harmful than she'd been led to believe. As she looked around, the guests were like happy children at a birthday party with Sushila hovering in the background to pet and pamper them.

In the center of the garden eight musicians dressed in the white dhotis of peasants were seated cross-legged on a colorful Persian rug spread over a large platform. As they tuned their oddly shaped instruments a large golden moon rose in the sky, washing the gardens in moonlight.

Garnet caught her breath. "What luck to have a full moon tonight."

"Ah, you mustn't imagine the moonlight is an accident of fate," Ravi answered, pleased by her delight. "Shushu plans her musicales for the evenings when the moon lights up the garden like a stage set. This is no random universe, dear Garnet. Perfection is cleverly executed by Auntie, with only a little help from the heavens."

The raga began slowly, instruments joining in one by one until the garden reverberated with the pounding of *tablas* and high-pitched whine of *sitars* piercing the melancholy hum of the *tanpuras*.

Guests drifted over to the table to pay respects to their hostess and meet Sushila's *precious* nephews and the Americans. Garnet watched as Ravi joked and laughed with Shushu's friends. Impossible to resist his exuberant charm with his face shining in the candlelight, skin satin-sheened, eyes gleaming with amusement and mischief. Vitality flowed out of him, reminding her of a ruddy child bursting with health, the kind you long to squeeze and bite as if you could consume their plump glow the way you'd devour a ripe peach.

It was difficult to concentrate on the conversation. She felt shaken by her reaction to this stranger Ravi, lost in unfamiliar and dangerous territory. *Stop being a fool*, she scolded herself, wondering what the I Ching would reveal if she tossed the coins. The reading could be *Lu: The perseverance of a dark man brings good fortune*. Or its opposite, *K'un: Oppression at the hands of the man with the purple knee bands!* She chuckled to herself. *She'd have to check Ravi's knees . . .*

The group was joined by Rabrindra Sharma, an elderly poet. His thin limbs shivered in a cotton dhoti but he wore it proudly as a badge of poverty for a life consecrated to art. His face bore a shadow of sadness and the sensitivity of his glance hinted he carried the burden of suffering humanity in his soul. But he smiled serenely at the group and bowed to Auntie Sushila, brushing a kiss across her hand and raising his voice so all in the garden could hear.

"A toast to Sushila, revered friend, goddess, and beloved patron of the arts who created this tableau of beauty to spin our senses. Since we are poor mortals in pain and turmoil, these moments light up our existence and allow us to sink into a co-coon of pleasure, honored by your lavish spirit."

Laughter and applause, then Vijay lifted his glass. "A toast to Auntie Sushu, and to our distinguished poet! May he indulge us by reciting passages from his great works."

Rabindra shook his head. "I hesitate to glorify my modest verses and turn instead to the sacred Vedas; a hymn to *Ushas*, goddess of dawn, as homage to our dear Sushila."

He began to recite the ancient verses, his voice undulating in a rolling wave of sound, penetrating the insistent beat of the ragas.

Hail, golden goddess . . .
Thou comest like a lovely maiden . . .
To our admiring eyes;

Through years on years thou hast lived on, yet
Thou art ever young.

There was a hush, followed by a burst of applause which Rabindra acknowledged with a slight bow. Then raising his hand and pointing a finger to the sky, he admonished the audience,

"But heed the guidance of the *Bhagavad Gita*: caution must temper pleasure."

The wandering winds of the senses
Cast man's mind adrift
And turn his better judgment from its course.
When a man can still the senses
I call him illumined.

"My dear friend," Sushila smiled, raising her glass of champagne. "You tease my indulgences but are forgiven for you teach us the pleasures of mind and spirit. As for me, I follow the guidance of *Hatha Yoga*: *Do not struggle to rid yourself of the world.*

Pursue it to the end and the world will give you up. I'm still in my pursuing stage and enjoying it immensely. Let your tolerant shadow of compassion fall over the face of an elderly sinner unwilling to withdraw from the temptations of youth."

iv

The musicians moved to the edges of the Persian carpet covering the platform to make room for the dancers.

"The *woman* stepping onto the platform is a young man named Kumar," Ravi whispered to Garnet. "Female roles in sacred dances of the 13th century were performed by Brahmin males so Kumar will portray one of Lord Krishna's favorite wives, a violent character; angry, vain and jealous but immensely charming."

"Sounds like my mother," Garnet said, with a laugh.

"How strange. Mine is exactly the same," Ravi smiled.

Elaborately costumed, face pale and smooth with makeup, his full lips stung with red and eyes outlined black with kohl, Kumar whirled and spinned around the stage, swirling translucent colors of shimmering silk, his arms heavy with gold bangles, the bells on his thin sandals jangling as he stamped his feet in the intricate steps of the dance.

Accompanied by the dissonant music of harmonium, sitars, and tabla drums, the dancer created a tapestry of sinuous gestures portraying woman as a slithering serpent of evil, frenzied motions painting her a demon of rage and jealous harpy, then with hips swaying voluptuously he depicted sweet wiles of seduction.

"It's hard to believe he's a man," Garnet whispered.

"Feminine qualities are prized by Indian men," Ravi whispered back, taking her hand in his. "We venerate the female, worship more goddesses than any other culture. The feminine role is crucial in our scheme of things."

"For what purpose?" Garnet asked, not wanting to pull her hand away but embarrassed by the intimacy. "To rescue the dying in the streets of Calcutta or to coddle a spoiled prince?" she asked, gently removing her hand.

They were interrupted by Sushila and the old poet returning from the platform to join them. "*Brava*, Miss Lawler, I heard that," Sushila laughed.

"*Shiva*, god of the dance, will be performed by a young female dancer," she explained, a little out of breath as she seated herself heavily on the nearest chair. "She'll use her right side to show his male traits and express his female features with her left."

The poet, Rabindra, spoke quietly. "Shiva is the renewer of the cycle of life. He creates and then destroys but we say creation cannot exist without destruction any more than man can exist without woman. So, *creation* is symbolized by woman and *destruction* by *man*."

"Shiva teaches us not to abandon either our male or female attributes," Ravi added.

"Hmm," Garnet reflected, sipping her champagne. "But are women allowed to express their *macho* side?"

"India has some strong and wild women," Ravi chuckled. "My mother is a fearsome specimen."

"Ditto *ma mère*," Garnet replied.

"Strange that men who worshipped goddesses for thousands of years feared *real-life* women and veiled them in *purdah*," Sushila mused. "Ironically, it was the men who endowed the goddesses with powerful attributes - like *Durga*, the goddess with eighteen arms who could kill fifty demons at a time."

"Men must have scared themselves to death when they created Durga," Garnet commented.

"Her power scares me," Ravi said. "What about you?"

"Oh, I'm all for power," Garnet said, tweaking his ear. "Especially over men."

"I'm willing," Ravi whispered, leaning his soft cheek against her neck. "Enslave me."

"Do all Indian men clown around?" Garnet laughed, pushing his head away.

"Only if they want to captivate a lovely American."

A splendid array of fireworks ended conversation as blasts of light and color shaped into flowers and stars, burst over the darkened night. An enchanting sight. Garnet leaned back in her chair to savor this illumination of the sky.

As the evening ended and guests slowly drifted out of the garden, Ravi brought Garnet and Niles over to the gateway where Sushila was bidding her friends goodbye. Garnet offered her hand but Sushila brushed it aside to embrace her with both arms.

"How clever of my nephew to discover you," she said, kissing Garnet with gusto on both cheeks. "Promise you'll come back to see me."

"Don't worry, Auntie darling," Ravi said. "I'll be Garnet's guardian angel and bring her to you again."

"For an angel, you're quite a devilish fellow," Sushila said, beaming at him. "Now be off! If Miss Lawler must work tomorrow she should rise early before the heat begins. Drive her home but watch the roads carefully and be sure to see her safely into the hotel."

"Yes, yes, Auntie, stop worrying, we're not your baby nephews any longer, we've grown up."

Sushila shook her head. "Indian men never grow up."

"Oh, Auntie, you love to tease your boys," Ravi said, planting a kiss on her neck as he grasped her by the waist and whirled her around."

"That's enough," Sushila gasped, out of breath but her eyes glistened with excitement. "Stop teasing an old lady."

"*Yoosterday, loov was sooch an eezy gyme tuh plye . . .*" Ravi crooned in a garbled Paul McCartney accent.

"Off, off with you. I don't want you running around the streets of Agra all hours of the night," she said, trying to be stern as she shooed them out of the garden."

v

The morning after the gala Ravi and Vijay called at the Hotel Rajmahal laden with armfuls of flowers, bags of Indian sweets, cakes and candies.

"What's all this?" Garnet asked suspiciously, taken aback by the abundance of goodies piled on the table.

"Don't blame us," Ravi laughed. "Auntie Sushila pressed it on us with an urgent message. She expects you for dinner this evening."

"I'm not sure . . ." Garnet said doubtfully, though she found Sushila fascinating and hoped a friendship would evolve if they met again. But Niles' behavior was so unpredictable - perhaps it was best to wait until he left for New York.

"She begs you to come," Ravi pleaded. "Auntie is lonely. Vijay and I are such bores, we have no secrets left. Shushu needs stimulation, fresh blood to make her feel alive. You'll get a kick out of her tales of intrigue, royal gossip and sexual liaisons. Auntie enjoyed a sinful past and nothing gives her more pleasure than recounting the details. Even I relish her stories and I know them by heart."

"Please, Garnet," Vijay joined in. "Auntie's villa is a great place to relax."

"We're under strict orders from auntie," Ravi said, wagging his finger at her. "No excuses allowed when the Kanwar Rani of Madhagaya issues a command."

Garnet looked at Niles, he nodded a grudging assent, and she agreed, somewhat reluctantly.

Toward evening they drove up to the villa under a waning moon tipping into the darkening dusk. Sushila was waiting in the shadows of the portal to greet them with hugs and kisses. Garnet hoped Niles wouldn't be irritated by her effusiveness and turn moody and difficult but he seemed pleased by her attentions.

Before they had a chance to say a word, Sushila led them into the villa and thrust an assortment of caftans, pajamas, and dressing gowns at them. "Choose what you like but get rid of those cramped clothes and make yourselves comfortable. *Surtout les plaisirs*! is the motto of my chateau."

Niles sulked at the idea but joined in after a threatening look from Garnet who searched through the pile to find golden silk kurtah pajamas for herself and a turquoise kurtah for him.

After changing they lounged in the white-washed drawing room with its massive glassed windows, stone fireplace, white fur rugs and huge porcelain pots crammed with palm trees, drinking glasses of wine or milky *lassi*, Sushila urging them to stuff themselves as servants passed trays heaped high with hot Indian appetizers.

Garnet found the informality of semi-undress before the servants surprising but was reassured by Shushu.

"We Indians adore comfort and arrange our homes only to please ourselves. Am I right, Ravi?" she asked, reaching over to tickle his feet.

"Yes, Auntie, *toujours, toujours*," Ravi said, patting her hands as he pulled them off his feet.

Sushila beamed at Garnet. "We loathe spending evenings *en famille* stuffed in tight clothes like wax dummies and persuade our European friends to rip off their suits of armor and relax into idle, sensual creatures."

Ravi laughed and nodded in approval. "Listen to Auntie. She'll turn you into a devilish girl like herself, in love with pleasure."

Sushila's servants had served her for years and as their mistress didn't demand formality on casual evenings the elderly domestics made themselves comfortable, wearing their drab everyday coats and grumbling to each other, behaving more like querulous old uncles and aunties than employees. But Sushila overlooked their quirks in true Indian fashion, accepting her entourage as the flesh and blood of household and family.

Sushila led Garnet and Niles into the dining room with Ravi and Vijay trailing behind. The decor was Parisian *art deco* garnered from her hedonistic years on the Left Bank. *Art nouveau* Bugatti dining chairs hand-carved in teakwood with silver inlays, slanted backs and seats covered in white parchment, daringly modern in 1895 were oddly Egyptian, much like the child-throne of King Tut - although his tomb wasn't unearthed until 1928. The walls of the dining room were studded with surrealist and impressionist paintings - Dali, Magritte, Man Ray, Monet, a lone Picasso and a Brancusi sculpture, a curved gold abstraction of a bird perched on a marble pedestal overlooking the gardens.

Despite the elegance of the room the informality of slippers and nightclothes made Garnet feel at home, comforted as if she were a child again in New England eating in the kitchen with her old Spanish housekeeper.

Sushila's playfulness was contagious and after dinner Garnet, relaxed and sated with spiced curries and creamy desserts sprawled on the couch, slippers kicked off, wiggling her bare toes with the rest of them as she sipped sweetened tea and chewed chopped-up *betel* nuts and cumin seeds passed around in tiny silver bowls.

"Mmm, so soothing," Garnet sighed, sinking into the soft cushions as she stuffed an Indian sweet in her mouth. "Opulence and gratification. It would be tempting to get addicted, give up my Calvinist ideas of hard work and accomplishment and fall into a dissolute life of ease."

"A splendid idea," Ravi said, reaching for her hand across the couch. "We'll indulge your every whim."

"It's a enticing offer," Garnet said. She licked the last crumbs of spiced cake from her lips. "Alas, I've been sent to India for work, not play."

"Oh, my dear," Sushila said, gazing at her with compassion.

"You could use more pleasure and less hard work. Don't throw away your youth on effort and struggle. I had a wicked and thoroughly enjoyable youth and don't regret a moment of it."

Then Sushila regaled them with stories of her adventures, the past of a woman who lived without restraint, who'd sucked at life as eagerly as a bee inhaling the sweetness of flowers. Garnet watched her as she spoke. Sushila's fat seemed but a garment flung over her true self, hiding a slim, full-breasted sylph whose urgency to embrace life fired sienna eyes with an ardor men found irresistible.

"How did your freedom come about in such a male-dominated culture?" Garnet asked curiously, as Sushila paused in her exotic tales of sexual license.

"Freedom didn't come to me!" Sushila answered indignantly. "I seized it with my own hands, tore at life like a tiger who rips apart its kill and devours it. When I embraced the Hindu belief that life is only a game for the enjoyment of gods, I pursued the path of pleasure and became a *Leela* - Sanskrit for *Divine Amusement.*

Sushila closed her eyes and blotted her face with a lace handkerchief. She leaned back against the silk cushions and was silent, seeing her exuberant beauty in the mirror of the past, hearing the voices of beautiful young men whispering words of adoration as they caressed her. An enamored poet-philosopher once wrote a treatise on Sushila lauding '*the power of a primeval woman who delves into the archaic core of herself and showers her sexuality like dew on thirsty flowers.*'

Her lovers claimed it wasn't Sushila's beauty that made her extraordinary - although she was a luscious young woman, but that she was uniquely satisfying, as if the *archetypal woman,* craved by males, danced in her soul. Men asserted she excited their deepest urges and exhausted all the fervor and desire in herself to satisfy every hunger she awakened, but claimed her sensuality ruined sexual liaisons with other women who paled unendurably by comparison."

Sushila shook herself back to the present, lit a cigarette and blew rings of smoke over their heads. "So I surrendered to the teachings of Shiva Purana; '*Who goes through life without honoring the phallus is truly pitiful, guilty or damned.*'"

Ravi and Vijay were listening intently, shaking their heads at the turn the conversation had taken.

"I can't believe this sexist propaganda," Garnet protested. "Women's lib tells us not to worship the phallus."

"I didn't worship just any phallus," Sushila protested. "I chose only the best."

Niles stared at her in amazement while Ravi and Vijay could hardly contain their laughter. Garnet couldn't stop from laughing and spluttered, "But we're supposed to glorify the vagina!"

Sushila's chubby cheeks wrinkled up in merriment, her eyes narrowing into bright squints as she shook her head in disbelief and laughed till her plump body quivered with mirth. Garnet joined in and they howled until their eyes dripped with tears.

"No more, *ca suffit!*" Sushila cried, holding onto her body as she tried to stop laughing. "My stomach hurts. Let's get serious."

"Serious about sex, auntie?" Ravi asked. He poked Vijay and they burst into laughter.

Sushila wiped her eyes and fanned herself.

"Yes, why not? Sex doesn't enslave women when we use it for our pleasure," she asserted. "I didn't bow down to the phallus but venerated it as a symbol of the gratification I stole from men. As a young girl I stumbled across a passage from the sacred *Vedas* and jumped with joy when I realized my desires were sacred! *Who venerates the phallus, understanding it to be the source of consciousness, the substance of the Universe, is closer to me than any other being. If one weighs against it charity, fasting, pilgrimages, sacrifice and virtue, it is phallus worship which is preferred.*"

"*Voila!*" Sushila said, shaking her fan at Ravi and Vijay. "The *Puranas* and *Tantras* gave me license to do exactly as I pleased. Now, cozy in my fat and old age I sit back and amuse myself with memories, content as a cow to chew over the cud of my life. In retrospect, it tastes even more delicious as I spit out the unpleasant residue."

Ravi jumped up and gave Sushila a big bear hug, lifting her up and twirling her around. "What a woman you are, auntie, what a woman! There's never been another like you."

After the laughter subsided Garnet grew silent. It was fun to join in the merriment - a release- but the subject of sex was disturbing. *Get over it*! she told herself. *Ten years is long enough to suffer*. But it was no use trying to force herself. The damage was done. She'd been coerced into sex by someone she found repulsive, terrorized by rape, and left locked in by apprehension and dread.

She was crazily attracted to Ravi, felt herself falling in love but it was cruel to encourage him if she couldn't carry it through to the sexual act. *Nolo me tengere!* To fear the touch of the beloved had to be the most sadistic form of hell ever devised by Satan.

If only she could be like Sushila, sexually alive, fearless, taking pleasure in her sensuality. But wishing to be someone else was a negation of her life. One must hold onto one's own soul no matter how ragged and damaged.

Ravi and Sushila noticed her silence. "You look tired," Ravi said, his face full of concern. "Perhaps we should leave."

"Yes, my dear," Sushila added, padding over to her and gazing into her face. "Ravi's right, you look exhausted. You mustn't overdo. The heat in India is debilitating and if you're going to the library tomorrow you need to rest. Don't bother to change, grab your clothes and Ravi will drive you home."

"But, but . . ." Garnet stammered.

"No buts," Sushila said firmly. "Keep the Indian outfits and wear them. They're more suitable for our dreadful climate and I've plenty more piled up in closets."

Sushila bundled them off in the car waving and blowing kisses. Vijay helped Niles into the back and by the time Ravi got the engine going Niles was asleep, his head resting on the soft leather of the seat.

Garnet glanced back at Niles. She hesitated for a moment, running her hand over the gleaming dashboard studded with silver gauges before she leaned close to Ravi and whispered in his ear, asking if he'd come to see her the following day.

"Of course, gladly," Ravi answered, with an intense gaze of curiosity although reluctant to question her. She felt hot and embarrassed at having to appeal to him but she needed help. "Thanks," she murmured, and hesitated again, hating to ask for anything more. "Do you think Vijay would take Niles out for awhile while we talk?"

"Oh, I'm sure Vijay would be delighted to take care of Niles," he chuckled. "Late afternoon?"

"Perfect." She breathed a sigh of relief. "It's very good of you."

"My pleasure," Ravi said, taking his hand off the wheel for a moment to pat her hand before pulling the car in front of the hotel.

The following afternoon, Ravi drove to the Raj Mahal hotel. Vijay tried to engage him in casual conversation, not daring to question him about the meeting with Garnet, but Ravi remained silent, preoccupied with his thoughts. He puzzled over the passionate attraction he felt toward Garnet. Obsession? He wondered. Despite his encounters with many women he'd never been gripped by this fervor of emotion. It was true he'd felt a pervasive loneliness for a long time, not just for a woman - a myriad of high-born Indian girls chased after ex-princes - but for one who could touch his heart. Then Garnet appeared out of nowhere, unexpectedly, and gazing into her face as they met he was astonished by the emotion evoked in him.

He was aware that instantaneous attractions, *love at first sight,* or an overwhelming pull toward a stranger, was explained by Carl Jung as emerging from a kaleidoscope of earliest memories, sight, taste, smell, that evoked the primal love of a child's life.

The bonds of childhood, he thought. *Impossible to escape the forged links that bind us forever.*

He'd idolized his grandmother, a daring young English beauty who defied her Viceroy father to elope at seventeen with the Crown Prince of Gajpur. Rani Elizabeth lavished love on Ravi, her only grandchild, in sharp contrast to the indifference and coldness of his parents. Garnet resembled her fair-haired beauty. But there was more to it than that. He grew up admiring Granny Elizabeth's strong character and like her, Garnet was independent and strong-minded, with a bright intellect and a gritty determination. She was also kind. Ravi marveled at her patience with Niles who could be a difficult and irritating presence.

Don't fall too hard, he warned. *Loneliness and resemblance to a beloved person can pull Maya's veil of illusion over your eyes and obscure reality.*

Love-madness and obsession were a royal tradition in his family. His grandparents remained lovers forever. But sometimes mad infatuations crashed and burned, with a royal union ending up a bleak prison from which there was no escape. His maharaja father had sought beauty and discovered too late his ravishing treasure was a cold-hearted virago.

At four o'clock Garnet was waiting for them in the lobby. A few minutes later Ravi appeared with Vijay trailing behind him, loaded down with another mass of cellophane-wrapped flowers.

She took Vijay aside and suggested he phone Niles himself to invite him for sightseeing. "He can be temperamental and moody," she warned. "I hope you're up to it."

"I'm an eccentric fellow myself so it should work out," Vijay replied, smiling. He turned to the desk clerk and asked to be connected to the room.

Garnet squeezed his hand and murmured thanks. Vijay nodded and waved his hand in a gesture of reassurance. "Don't worry about a thing," he whispered. "I'll keep him busy for a few hours."

After the call, Vijay went to the elevator to wait for Niles and

Ravi turned to Garnet. "Why don't I arrange for coffee in the garden?" he suggested.

He turned to the manager who was near the desk rustling papers, pretending not to listen but taking in every word, and directed him to serve South Indian coffee and an assortment of sweet cakes out in the garden at once, with haste.

"Yes sir, naturally sir," the manager answered, ringing the bell on top of the counter until the clerk hurried out of the back room. He hoped to make a good impression on Mr. Singh. A gentleman like this could send him the right kind of guests and perhaps the hotel would begin to make money. He lived in such dreams, hoping a stroke of luck would hit him by accident. *The wrong kind of people frequented his hotel*, he told himself. *Raggedy tourists and penniless hippies filled up the space so there was no room for the right people who would make it a paying proposition*. This was his chance to impress aristocrats. If he handled things right business could pick up. It was time his luck changed.

He served them with pomp using his best china and silver and left them alone to sip their coffee in the tiny garden sheltered by wisteria, bushes of scarlet hibiscus climbing the brick walls, the air scented sweet with jasmine.

Ravi poured the coffee and offered her the plate of cakes. She took the coffee but shook her head at the sweets. She had no appetite for food, her throat was choked with anxiety.

"Perhaps later," she said. She was nervous, not knowing how to broach the subject wondering if she were expecting too much from someone she hardly knew.

Ravi took a sip of his coffee and relaxed back into the caned-wood lounge chair. He knitted his fingers together and smiled reassuringly at her. "Tell me," he urged.

Garnet took a deep breath before speaking, wondering how she could explain the situation without revealing too much.

Get on with it! Stop piddling around, she admonished herself. *There's no time to waste!*

"I'm sending Niles back to New York," Garnet said, looking

down at the plate of cakes on the table, hesitant to meet his eyes. "I made a reservation on Air India for the day after tomorrow but I'm afraid he'll resist leaving and thought you might help."

Ravi looked at her without speaking but she could see the compassion in his face.

"I can't go on with it anymore," she whispered, her voice breaking a little. "It was a mistake to bring him to India. A nightmare."

"Will he be safe in New York on his own?" Ravi queried softly.

She hesitated. "I don't know." *The question is, will I be safe if he stays?* "But his mother should be back from Europe in a few weeks," she added. "I've arranged for him to stay in a small hotel until then."

"I see," he said, nodding his head as he pondered the problem.

"I can't handle him any more," she blurted out, feeling anxious and tense.

Ravi patted her on the shoulder, his voice calm and soothing as he spoke. "Of course, I'll help you if you think it's necessary to send him back."

"I'm sure of it," she said, avoiding his eyes as she gathered herself together to speak in a rational voice. "I hadn't seen Niles since I was fifteen when my life was damaged by some terrible events. A couple of months ago, his sister showed up and begged me to take him in for a few days but she reneged on her promise to pick him up and fled to Italy with her lover, leaving no address and no way to reach her."

Garnet tried not to cry but tears ran down her cheeks. "I've been such a fool."

Ravi leaned over and blotted her tears with his fingers. "Don't cry," he entreated her. "I'll help any way I can."

He took a small cake and held it near her mouth. "Take a bite," he urged. "A little taste of sweetness will do you good."

Garnet gave a wan smile and bit into the cake.

"Do you think it's safe to send him back on his own?" Ravi asked. He paused to brush crumbs off the side of her mouth. "Perhaps there's another solution."

"I can't think of any," she replied, resisting his questioning a decision arrived at by such nerve-wracking deliberation.

"Vijay has fallen in love with Niles," he said, with a hint of a twinkle in his eyes. "He's bewitched by his intellect, relishes his idiosyncrasies while Niles seems pleased by his interest. Poor Vijay has been lonely for a very long time. Living in India is a ticklish situation for a man so inclined. *Verboten* in our society."

"A strange twist of fate," Garnet said, shaking her head dubiously. "But how does it change things?"

"Auntie Sushila grabbed me for a long talk this morning. She's crazy about you and insists you leave what she calls your *wretched little hovel* and stay with us at the villa. Vijay would be happy to take charge of Niles in a separate wing and we'd all protect you from him."

Garnet looked doubtful. She twisted her handkerchief between her fingers and turned her head to stare at the moss covered wall of the garden. *Think this one over very carefully.* She glanced back at Ravi for a moment, his skin shining in the afternoon light, his eyes clear and guileless as he gazed at her. *His intentions seemed good but men could promise anything. That didn't mean they were able to deliver. Niles was a smoking gun that could go off at any time and they might not be able to handle him? She'd end up taking care of him again. On the other hand, if she sent him to New York and something happened to him the guilt and anguish she'd suffered so long would return to plague her.*

Ravi reached over and covered her fingers with his hand. "We could try this, Garnet," he suggested. "If it doesn't work out I'll put him on a plane to New York myself. For the moment, leave everything to Sushila. She's a great fixer of people."

"I'd hate to impose on her," Garnet answered, running the

pros and cons and possible perils through her head as she spoke. "It's a big step to intrude into her home with these problems."

"No imposition for Auntie Shushu," Ravi protested. "Helping people is her pleasure. She swears it's my duty to persuade you or she'll have my head!"

She tried to resist but was tempted by the warmth of Sushila and the charm of the cool and pleasant villa, its whitewashed rooms and Spanish tiled floors, fringed with pools and shaded trees.

Niles objected when he heard the plan and badgered her with entreaties and threats, unaware of the alternative she had in mind for him. Finally, in disgust, she pulled out his flight reservation and waved it at him.

"Ravi and Vijay are trying to save you from exile but it's your choice. New York or Sushila's villa?"

Niles hung his head. He never dreamed Garnet would go this far.

"And you'd better be on your best behavior!" *If he starts up with me again, he's history*, Garnet vowed.

vi

Sushila arranged everything in her tactful fashion, assigning Vijay and Niles rooms in the far wing where they could be undisturbed, and undisturbing. Ravi occupied the family suite overlooking the pool and gardens, the same rooms he'd used from childhood like his father before him. And she selected the prettiest of rooms for Garnet, a sunny, pale blue bed-sitting room with French windows and a view of the fountains next to her own suite.

It was an opulence Garnet had never experienced. In the early morning a young servant boy padded silently into the room to awaken her with breakfast on a brass tray set with linens, freshly cut roses, puffed breads, curds, and a silver pot of the inky South Indian coffee, fast becoming an addiction with her.

Luxuriating against billowing pillows encased in daintily embroidered slips, she watched the morning birds rise against the amber rose of the sky and mixed steaming milk into the thick coffee essence. After breakfast she rose, reluctant to pull herself away from the soft bed, and slipped into a gauzy white kurtah and sandals provided by Sushila who insisted Western clothes were a monstrosity in the Indian climate. Then she walked slowly along a flower-scented path to the library where she spent the morning deep in 17th century India, enmeshed in the lives of Mumtaz Mahal and Shah Jahan.

She tried to thank Sushila for her generosity but was waved away.

"Of course, I'm generous," Sushila answered with a sly grin. "When you've seized every joy from life and squeezed it dry, you can afford to be generous. Indulging you happens to be my newest pleasure."

Afternoons, Garnet discussed the morning's research over tea and cakes. Sushila's indulgence and her freedom from Niles, thanks to Vijay's strict adherence to his pledge, made it easier for Garnet to drift back into the sixteenth century and immerse herself in the cloistered harem of Emperor Jahangir.

It was here, in Agra's massive Red Fort designed by the great Emperor Akbar on the banks of the Jumna River, that Mumtaz Mahal, the aristocratic daughter of the Minister of Finance, was born in 1593 as Arjumand Banu.

Garnet envisioned the dreamy, poetic girlhood of the young Mumtaz Mahal against an exotic backdrop where veiled women of the harem lived and frolicked in their own palace set in the *Anguri Bagh*, or grape garden. Here lush Persian carpets were spread over walkways, doorways were adorned with richly embroidered folds of silk, and a pool for swimming was scented with rosewater and strewn with rose petals . . .

Arjumand sat with the ladies of the harem gossiping beside the pool, cooled by fountains arching sprays of rose attar over the water, amusing herself by teasing the blue parrots and peacocks strutting in the garden or wandering through the Palace of Mirrors whose walls were covered with thousands of tiny glass reflectors.

She prayed in the privacy of the harem's mosque and spent hours studying the scriptures of the Koran. In the hottest days of summer, she escaped to the coolness of the sunken chambers below the garden where there were baths of hot and cold water, or slipped down the steps of the secluded stairway to swim in the open moat.

It was an idyllic and privileged setting and Mumtaz Mahal flourished, a princess-like child protected by the seclusion of the harem, the importance of her father, Asaf Khan, and the tutelage of her aunt, Nur Mahal, the most influential woman in India and the power behind the throne of Emperor Jahangir, all a prelude to the fateful day in the bazaar when she sold a glass jewel to the Crown Prince.

"A fairy tale existence," Sushila said, serving up the tea and cakes. "As for Nur Mahal, Emperor Jahangir married her for love, an unheard of act for a monarch, and was so enslaved by her dazzling beauty and political genius that he placed the threads of the empire in her hands. She became the most powerful woman in India, a source of immense pride to the emperor who struck the currency of the State in her name and boasted that his beloved was a crack shot, a markswoman who could kill four tigers with five bullets."

"Incredible," Garnet said, biting into an Indian sweet. "Its hard to believe a woman could achieve such power."

"And she knew how to use it," Sushila retorted. "Nur Mahal appointed her father Prime Minister, arranged for a daughter from an earlier marriage to wed Jahangir's youngest son, and decided that a marriage between her beauteous niece and Prince Khurram would preserve the political power of her brother, Asaf Khan. She had no idea it would turn out to be a love match."

"I'm sure Nur Mahal set up the fateful *accidental* meeting," Sushila added. "Mumtaz was selling glass beads for charity at the Royal Bazaar that day and Nur no doubt advised her niece not to acknowledge the prince, suggesting he'd be tempted by teasing and playing hard to get."

"Yes! Prince Khurram wanders in, catches sight of the young beauty and approaches her on the pretext of asking the price of a diamond-cut glass jewel," Garnet interjected. "And coached by Nur, the ravishing fourteen-year old treats the prince as a commoner who dares to flirt with her and must be punished. She snubs him, acts as if he can't afford the *faux* diamond and tries to embarrass him by demanding an outrageous price. *Ten thousand rupees!* she declares in a rude voice and snatches the stone out of his hand."

"But, just as Nur Mahal predicted, Prince Khurram was taken with the sassy beauty, " Sushila continued. "He's not insulted, only smitten. *'Wrap it up, I'll take it!'* he murmurs in Sanskrit, accenting his famed honeyed tones as he pulls out a wad of rupees, happy to pay for a phoney jewel to impress this beauty. Then he runs to his father for permission to wed her."

"What I find enviable," Garnet said, "is how Shah Jahan's devotion endured after marriage. They remained inseparable."

"Never more than a room apart," Sushila replied, shaking her head in amazement. "Even insisted she accompany him on his military campaigns.

"Shah Jahan valued Mumtaz as his most trusted confidante and political advisor," Garnet mused. "He consigned the State Seal to her, the priceless *Muhr Uzak*, a Seal which once imprinted on a document could not be revoked, even by the emperor."

"He was awed by her brilliance and loved her passionately to the end," Sushila said. "It's what I admire most about him."

She picked up a worn leather volume from a nearby table and showed it to Garnet. "Qazwini, the Royal Poet, wrote that Mumtaz was more precious to Shah Jahan than his own life." She leafed through the pages, translating the text from the Sanskrit as she read aloud . . .

'*The intimacy, deep affection and attention he had for Mumtaz, he did not have for any other. She was his intimate companion, colleague and close confidante in distress, joy and grief. She had the honor of his constant company, companionship, and in the closeness and intimacy with His Majesty there was a friendship and oneness between them not seen in husbands and wives from any classes. This was not out of carnal desire but the physical and spiritual compatibility on both sides was the cause of great love and affection.*"

Garnet looked away and bit her lip, holding back her tears. *My heart's desire,* she thought with a pang. *A companionable, affectionate soul mate. What I want and will never find.*

"Don't be sad," Sushila said, patting her hand. "Life has a way of surprising us." She lit a cigarette and blew smoke rings at the ceiling, thinking about the lovers in her past.

"Of course, Mumtaz Mahal was not as angelic as legend would have us believe," she asserted suddenly. "No, not naughty with sex like me. She was a virtuous wife and model queen who provided food to peasants and beggars. But she also had a penchant for murdering Christians and witnessing prisoners being tortured as entertainment."

"My passions were sexual in nature," Sushila confessed, looking pleased with herself. "My *sin* was mixing in other people's business, trying to fix up their lives whether they wanted it or not."

"No, no, Auntie, you mustn't run yourself down," Vijay objected, overhearing the discussion as he walked into the room. "You've helped so many people."

"And annoyed just as many with my interfering," she scoffed. "Perhaps even you. You mustn't overpraise me, I know my faults as well as my virtues. The truth is we're all a mixed bag, a witches' brew of good and evil, which makes it hard to point the finger even at an empress."

Garnet spent her days immersed in the legends and lore of

India, puzzled by the intense love she felt for the land. Sushila teased her, insisting Garnet had past lives in India.

"A swami would say India was a homecoming for you. Perhaps you were a princess in your last life."

"More likely a peasant wife, beaten down by a brute," Garnet quipped.

vii

One afternoon, while looking through a pile of photos of Ravi as a child Garnet came across an old snapshot of Sushila. Shushu snatched it out of her hands but not before Garnet studied the slim figure curved against a pillar, skin gleaming and eyes offering a seductive invitation.

"Forget that girl. She doesn't exist any more," Sushila said, tossing the picture into a drawer and slamming it shut. "Beauty had her day and now the fat goddess makes the best of what's left. Living in the past will break your heart."

The photo piqued Garnet's curiosity and she questioned Ravi about Sushila. He replied with unconcealed admiration.

"No man could resist her. Shushu was a goddess of sensuality."

Sushila wore the banner proudly. "There is potency for women in the sexual act," she insisted. "And that power is sacred. *Tantra* says, *Approach the sex act as if entering a holy temple and the world and the Divine will merge as one*. Tantra considers all sex holy, even a fleeting hour between strangers."

"I wish I could feel that way," Garnet responded, in a barely audible voice."

Sushila reached out a hand to ruffle Garnet's hair. "Sex is sacred," she asserted. "Including sex for cash. And sex for cash became an integral part of Indian culture, mostly to protect the purity of brides. The elite of whores were called *Ganikas*, beautiful young women educated to consort with kings. They were taught to sing and dance exquisitely, learned to be adept in social graces and clever conversation and acquired expertise in politics, giving counsel to kings who showered them with extravagant gifts and gold. A Ganika was said to be *the jewel of the city* in which she resided and many amassed fortunes. Ganikas reigned for hundreds of years until eradicated by pressure from the British."

"Mmm, leave it to the Brits to take away pleasure," Garnet said, sleepily. She leaned back on the couch with a soft pillow under her head and shut her eyes, listening to Sushila in a half dream, finding pleasure in the sweet tones of her voice and accent.

"Our finest literature focused on Ganikas and prostitutes," Sushila continued, as she got up to put another silk pillow under Garnet's head. "*Kshemendra*, a witty and cynical genius of the 11th century, authored *The Harlot's Breviary*, a literary masterpiece compared by critics to Voltaire's *Candide*. He wrote of '*a courtesan in the sensuous court of Kama, the fortunate house of games and laughter, the place of the waves of the lascivious sea which women rule.*' The young heroine is trained by a wealthy old Ganika who exhorts, '*When love is a business, the first lesson a courtesan must learn is to be hardhearted; no mercy can be shown to men. A lover who loses his riches must be discarded, spit out like a chunk of sugarcane after it is chewed and juiceless.*'"

Garnet laughed, her eyes still shut as she snuggled into the pillows. "Reminds me of my mother, the beauteous Francesca."

Shushila raised her eyebrows and smiled. "Lower caste prostitutes were ruthless and tough, even dangerous. In the 8th century, Damodaragupta's "*Lessons of a Bawd*," describes an old whore with rotted teeth, a disappearing chin, sunken bleary eyes, flattened breasts and a bloated belly who teaches young prostitutes to ply their trade. She admonishes them to cultivate honeyed lips and a heart of stone, to pretend passion for her customers while insisting on cold cash and swindling them out of their jeweled rings and gold ornaments. The author gave warning to men who foolishly frequented harlots - *such women have as much pity for a man as a panther has for a snake. Like bees they coax open their victims, then suck them dry.*"

* * *

After dinner, they sat around Shushu's living room smoking *bidis* and drinking *lassi.* Ravi, who was stretched out on the couch, turned his head to Garnet and asked idly, "What fascinating Indian lore did you two discuss today?"

"India's age-old penchant for cash love, from ganikas to broken-down hag whores," Garnet retorted.

"Hmm," Ravi said, pretending to be shocked. "Nice topic for well-bred ladies."

Actually, all the talk about sex with Sushila had been rather disturbing. She'd been chaste since Niles' assault and brutal invasion of her body, but her celibacy was not by choice for she was aware of sexual desires and longed to fulfill them.

When she moved to New York she tried to overcome her reluctance but found she could not bear a man's touch, so haunted was she by revulsion and memory. Occasionally, she invited someone into her Village apartment and allowed him to kiss her but as soon as he tried to caress her body she'd push him away with *No, no, I can't!* enduring the angry response of men who called her names and slammed the door behind them.

A few times she even attempted a sexual experience, gone beyond the kissing stage, naked in a stranger's bed. But when she felt hands moving over her bare skin they became the clammy hands of Niles crawling over her body, his sweaty face panting against her cheek, and she'd jump out of bed and cry, *"No, no, enough, enough! I don't want it!"*

Once or twice she narrowly escaped being raped but her childhood battles with Valerie came to her rescue and she fought like a tiger, scratching and clawing, astonishing the man with her strength and rage.

She became disheartened by these experiences and resentful for she knew the seeds of passion and delight were there before her disastrous involvement with Niles, recalling how she loved to jump in her uncle's arms and hug him. Although it wasn't sexual, the bliss she experienced was the childish stirrings of attraction to a male figure. Niles destroyed her innocent pleasure which should have ripened into a warm and loving sexuality.

viii

A few nights later Garnet cried out in her sleep. She was submerged in a nightmare, an old dreaded dream - her body tied down with ropes, stretched out on a white table while above her head a man held a butcher knife poised to plunge in her. She was struggling to get free, gasping for breath and calling out for help when Sushila heard her cries and came to the room.

Sushila held her in her arms, stroking her hair as Garnet, shaken and disoriented, tried to pull herself out of the dream.

"It seemed so real. I touched the man's white coat, felt the rough skin of his hand as he pointed the knife at me."

Sushila insisted on taking her back to her room. "It's important to distract yourself after a nightmare. If you go back to sleep fiendish dreams will be in hot pursuit."

She led Garnet into her room, helped her lie down on a chaise longue spread with velvet throws, draped an embroidered silk shawl over her, lit candles and incense, poured two glasses of *Lafite bordeaux* and played a tape of a slow Indian raga, the tone low and muted.

"Rest, Garnet, you're safe here," Sushila soothed, handing her a glass of wine. "Take a few sips of wine, listen to the music, and empty your mind of the past and future. Surrender to the moment where all is well."

Garnet nodded and tried to relax.

"Just rest," Sushila whispered. "Perhaps later you'll share your pain with me in the assurance your secrets and sufferings are sacrosanct here."

"It's difficult to speak of these things . . ." Garnet murmured.

"Shhh," Sushila said softly. "Not now. Drowse a little, if you can."

Later, resting with Sushila on the terrace watching the sunrise cast a tawny blush across the white pillars of the villa, Garnet garnered her courage to speak of Niles and that summer.

Hesitating, stumbling over the graphic details, she poured out the ordeal she suffered ten years earlier, then paused. "There may be more but I'm exhausted," she apologized.

Sushila urged her to lie quietly. "Rest, my darling. You bared your buried secrets, the wounds you can't shake off. We Hindus say *the Self is the Savior. Befriend the self and the self will save you.*"

"I wish I *could* save myself," Garnet cried. "But I'm all messed up. Damaged goods."

"Don't even think that," Sushila replied, kissing her on the forehead.

Garnet shook her head. "I'm terrified of sexual intimacy. What man could deal with that?"

"Intimacy is more than sex," Sushila said softly, brushing her hand over Garnet's hair. "It's caring for another's life and well-being, wanting to give pleasure and comfort. It has nothing to do with forcing sex."

Sushila adjusted the pillows behind Garnet's head on the lounge chair. "Niles' coercing you was also rape," she said. "You didn't want sex, you said *no* but he ignored your refusal, pushed your qualms aside and forced himself on you, robbing you of the innocence rightfully yours at fifteen. Nor were you responsible for the rape assault - you were the victim. Niles would have been in serious trouble had your parents pressed for his arrest."

"But I'd have had to testify," Garnet protested, "I couldn't face the ordeal and Niles was near death."

Sushila stroked her hair. "I understand. But don't lose yourself in pity. True, Niles was sick to impose himself on you but he's the one who must be held accountable, not you."

"It was all so awful," Garnet said. "Niles spent months in the sanitarium. His leg was a mess and to save it doctors fused the knee - turning him into a *semi-gimp*, he says. But they couldn't control the seizures from his head injuries."

Sushila shook her head in dismay. "Impossible to fathom a man who inflicts such atrocities on his own son. We say such men are like *pisachas*, mythical demons created by man's vices who haunt the earth after death - the ghosts of liars, drunkards, criminals, murderers."

ix

The following night Sushila surprised Garnet by coming to her room after midnight.

"Don't be afraid. I'd just like to lie next to you for awhile," she whispered, as she heaved herself onto the bed and stretched out beside Garnet. She was quiet for awhile, then began chattering and for hours they gossiped and joked like schoolgirls at a pajama party. Before leaving Sushila planted a chaste kiss on her forehead.

For the next three nights Sushila came to her room bringing sweets, crumbly squares of cakes with ground almonds, slivered pistachios and sweetened with honey, insisting she taste them.

"No, no, Shushu," Garnet protested. "You've already stuffed me like a Alsatian goose. I can't eat another thing."

"Of course you can. Sweet cakes aren't for hunger, they're for pleasure," she said, breaking off a piece and placing it in Garnet's mouth with her fingers.

Then she rested on the side of the bed and regaled Garnet with anecdotes of her life. She made no overt motion but Garnet sensed Sushila's desire for her. Afterwards, she put it out of her mind, lulled by Sushila's warmth and hospitality, the excess of luscious food and comfort, and by Vijay who kept Niles out of her way.

But indulgence had an unexpected effect. As she relaxed, her head swarmed with Shushu's stories of lust, prostitution and sexual pleasures. Sushila had left a book of erotic paintings and sculptures on a table next to the chaise longue, but Garnet found the Khajurao statues disturbing, at once repulsed by the blatant sexual poses and drawn to them. When she discovered a 17th century miniature of a Rajasthan prince who resembled Ravi, engaged in sex with a courtesan, she was dismayed at the surge of feeling evoked by the sight of the prince's lips pressed against the throat of the ganika, his hands cupping her naked breasts.

Garnet slammed the book shut and turned away. But erotic images disrupted her sleep, intruded into her dreams and pursued her during days at the library. She felt inundated with sensuality. Voluptuous sensations and strange longings swept over her like the onset of an illness, as if she were afflicted with a lethal virus. She fought off the perilous idea of Ravi but Sushila's lust permeated her mind and she ruminated about being touched by her. *Why not?* she chided herself. *Maybe I should give it a try it,* Garnet thought, weakening. *You're too frightened and shutoff to have sex with a man. Risk a woman if you have the impulse. Sushila isn't rough or harsh, and there's no danger of falling in love.*

A few days later Sushila came to the room again and ran her fingers over Garnet's arm. "I couldn't stop thinking about you. How desirable you are - how sexy."

"That's ridiculous," Garnet protested. "I'm too skinny to be sexy."

Sushila laughed. "Your skinniness is the sexiest part of you - those beautiful bones, the angles and arch of them. So delicate, like a line drawing, *une peinture Japonaise.*"

She didn't feel threatened by Sushila yet the idea of sex with a woman was distasteful. Sushila sensed her reluctance, and began by rubbing Garnet's head, comforting her, holding her like a child. She was the mother of Garnet's longings, a madonna with a soft touchable body and a nurturing embrace. Sushila caressed her, then slid her lips over her skin while Garnet held Sushila's great breasts in her hands. She was surprised to find she didn't mind being touched by Sushila. She felt protected by Shushu's tenderness. Nor was she repulsed although she couldn't bring herself to do more than respond politely to kisses pressed on her mouth and run her hands over Shushu's body, feeling the fat, satiny skin under her fingers, fondling the large breasts which spilled out over her hands, relishing the lushness of Sushila, the pleasure of her soft mounds of fat. Lean and mean ran in her family along with coldness and sarcasm. She nestled her head against Shushu's velvety mommy-pillows and let Sushu pet her as if cuddling a beloved child.

Caressing Sushila, she was aware of the softness of a woman's body for the first time. *It's really nice*, she mused, *the silkiness of skin, the sweet scent, the gentle touch of Shushu and the intimacy of a creature like herself. This is the pleasure men find in our bodies. No wonder they pursue us, we're rather appealing and precious.*

She enjoyed Shushu's caresses, the sensitivity of her hands, but she wasn't sexually aroused, no fire, call to the blood, or the sexual delirium awakened by Ravi. Perhaps only male hormones could evoke a deep response in her body. Even when Sushila gently parted her legs to nuzzle her velvety lips and tongue under Garnet's mound of Venus until she achieved orgasm it was more an involuntary reaction than the culmination of passion.

Resting together afterwards, Sushila read her thoughts.

"You were a sweet experience. I won't forget your lovely body and spirit but you're not made for a woman. You need to be cherished and nurtured by a man."

Garnet put her arms around Sushila and kissed her cheek,

then fell back and smiled at her. "I won't forget you either. You *are Leela*, goddess of love!"

Sushila laughed and fed her a sweet cake and a sip of wine.

Garnet gazed at Sushila's shining face and sputtered through a mouthful of cake. "You're so full of spirit, Shushu - brimming with joy. The bible exhorts us to *be joyful unto the Lord* but it's impossible for me."

Sushila stroked Garnet's hand resting on the bed. "There's a dark side to my nature like everyone else," she said, her voice suddenly serious as she gazed into Garnet's eyes. "My bleak shadow isn't visible because I take care to avoid the abyss."

x

Garnet fell into a heavy, dreamless sleep and didn't awaken until noon the following day. She yawned and stretched, arching her spine and extending her legs and arms, then sank back into the soft bed and breathed a sigh of relief. She couldn't remember when she'd slept that well.

She felt oddly contented, Sushila's tender caresses lingering in her mind. Except for Winslow's hugs she had rarely been touched as a child. Francesca turned away and although her father might have wanted to show affection he feared the wrath of her mother.

She relaxed into the downy pillows and ruminated over the episode with Sushila. It was more a gift of love and healing than sex. An effort on Sushila's part to ease her fears. *Love is a tender mirror of compassion wiping out faults and reflecting only what is desirable and good,* Garnet thought. *A healing mirror held up to her by Sushila.*

She was half drowsing, watching the peacocks through the French doors near her bed as they strutted in the garden fanning their tails in the sun, gleaming shades of Egyptian blue, green and gold when she heard a tap at the door and turned to see Sushila tiptoeing in the room, carrying a breakfast tray.

"I'm up, I'm up. I can't believe I slept this long."

"Of course, you slept. You're exhausted." She propped the tray on Garnet's lap and sat down next to her for a moment on the edge of the bed.

"Come see me when you finish eating," Sushila said, blowing her a kiss.

Sushila was plucking the strings of an oddly shaped musical instrument when Garnet came to her room.

"Hmm, how nice," Garnet murmured as she stretched out on the chaise longue and made herself comfortable. "What are you playing?

Sushila smiled at her. "A ballad composed by *Mira Bai*, a young poet in the 15th century who was revered in Rajasthan as a *Vaishnava* saint. She was of royal birth but devoted her life to *Krishna*, dancing and singing before his carved idols and writing songs of mystic love to her beloved."

Sushila strummed the strings of the guitar-like instrument and began to sing in a low, plaintive tone.

"Thou launched the boat of love and then left it to drift in the wild sea. O Mira's lord, when wilt thou come? No longer can I live without thee."

Sushila's face shone like a young girl as she sang. The mask of age fell off, the years dropping away to reveal the young and glorious creature she had once been. *There is so much mystery to a life*, Garnet thought. *Sometimes one catches a glimpse.*

Sushila handed the *tanpura* to Garnet to examine.

"Such an elegant instrument," Garnet said, stroking the polished wood of the tanpura. "Not quite a lute, more like a *lyre* in a pre-Raphaelite painting. But the tones are so strange, as if vibrating from another planet."

Sushila nodded. "Would you like to learn the tanpura? I'm quite a good teacher."

Garnet laughed and reached out to hug Sushila. "I'd love it.

I played a bit of guitar in the Village but was bored by folk songs. I'd much prefer Mira Bai."

Sushila went into the closet, took out another *tanpura*, opened the case and handed the instrument to Garnet. "A present for you in remembrance of me."

"I can't accept this," Garnet demurred. "A *tanpura* is too precious to give away."

"Yes, you can and you must," Sushila said, pushing the tanpura onto Garnet's lap. "In India, we say the gift is a blessing on the giver so you dare not deprive me of *grace*. Take it, I insist."

"If you put it that way," Garnet said, kissing Sushila on the cheek. "How can I thank you?"

"I'll be repaid when I hear you play a ballad of Mira Bai."

Garnet plucked a string and hearing the tone cooed in delight. "Ooh, I can't wait to master this lovely instrument."

Sushila suggested Garnet come to her room in the coolness of early dawn to work with her undisturbed by her nephews and Niles who all slept late. "Lazy boys," Sushila called them, not hiding the fondness and pride in her voice.

The music lessons began in earnest. Garnet basked in the cool dawn and the dark-shadowed silence of the garden awaiting sunrise as a daub of titian crawled up the sky. She tiptoed into Sushila's room trying not to disturb her if asleep but Shushu was always awake, lounging on the chaise waiting for her.

Garnet was surprised to find Sushila an expert instructor and taskmaster. But being a perfectionist herself she relished the discipline, cramming in the lessons to conquer the *tanpura* and songs of Mira Bai. Sushila was a born teacher, specific and clear, which eased the difficulty of learning this ancient art of Indian music.

They worked several hours each morning until Sushila rang

for the servant who brought in a huge tray loaded with pitchers of inky-black South Indian coffee and hot milk, puffy hot breads to dip into *raita*, a creamy yogurt mixed with chopped cucumbers, and thick, juicy slices of orange papaya freshly picked from the tree. Sometimes Shushu ordered crispy samosas filled with spicy potatoes and peas or hot fritters.

"Not for breakfast," Garnet protested. But Sushila kept trying to stuff her with delicacies.

"Food is relaxing," Sushila retorted. "And you're tense. You work too hard at everything, like an over-achieving Americano. Food can *bring you down*."

Garnet was tickled. "Where did you pick up drug lingo?"

"Oh, I keep up with the times," Sushila answered, tossing her head. "Agra is crowded with hippies, sons and daughters of European friends whom I invite to the villa for a hot meal and a good wash. You could use more hot meals yourself."

"Forget it," Garnet countered. "I was born to be thin. And probably tense. Give up on changing me. I know all about that, one of my worst defects of character. *You* put in a lot of effort and *they* never change. I made that mistake with Niles and it was a disaster."

xi

Niles was still physically frail and despite his consuming liaison with Vijay was often moody and irritable. Occasionally, he suffered a seizure. Sushila mentioned her concern to Garnet. "I know Niles can't be forgiven for what he did to you but his life was tragic and he still suffers. Poor boy . . . I must do something for him."

Sushila searched for a way to infuse the gaunt, afflicted boy with health and strength. She began to coddle him, plumping up his bed with soft pillows, piling a feather bed on top of the mattress and a puffy eiderdown to pull over his head, and teasing him to eat by offering special Indian delicacies. Niles loved being spoiled and Sushila enjoyed pampering him as if he were a pet child, sitting beside by his bed when his head ached, telling him Indian fairy-tales and singing Hindu love songs.

After awhile her indulgence had an effect. Niles relaxed, content some mornings to rest on the window seat looking out on the garden without complaint while humming one of Shushu's Hindi songs to himself.

One night he slipped out of his room seeking comfort after a mild seizure and climbed into Sushila's bed where she lay naked and gleaming, like a giant *Khajraho* goddess. She woke in surprise but took him into her arms, aweing him with her great sepia breasts and soft stomach. He surrendered to her as if to a nursing mother, taking pleasure in the fat flesh wrapped around him like a warm blanket. Sushila caressed him but stopped short of a sexual overture, amused when Niles curled up in her arms like an infant, cuddled his face in her breast and barely breathing, fell asleep.

Vijay, more infatuated than ever by the strange American, was still in hot pursuit and becoming possessive while Niles enjoyed his undivided attention and intellectual stimulation.

Sushila discussed the affair with Garnet. "We can never make a path for another or decide their good. Right now, Vijay may be the answer. He's captivated by Niles, feels privileged to have a friendship with a fascinating eccentric and inflates Niles' self esteem."

Garnet agreed. Anyway, it didn't matter to her what Niles did as long as Vijay bore the burden of caring for him.

One morning after Garnet's lesson Sushila told her that Ravi and Vijay were returning home to Gajpur in a few days.

"Think about going to Gajpur with Ravi and Vijay." Sushila said. "The Gajpur palace can't be compared with our lavish palaces but the monarchy ruled there for hundreds of years. Gajpur is an oasis deep in the Thar desert where camel caravans crisscrossed the desert. Rich merchants built *havelis* there, houses of pinky-ocher limestone, soft stone carved into lacy facades and hardened by the dry desert wind. It's remote and secluded, a good place to work and quite interesting. Princely families in India abound in eccentric ancestors and bizarre events. An old Indian proverb warns: *Don't open a rajah's closet or you'll be crushed to death by the skeletons tumbling out.*"

"Decide quickly," Sushila urged. "Ravi and Vijay are leaving soon and will take very good care of you on the trip. Go! Don't miss the chance to see an aspect of India rarely encountered by outsiders."

In the evening, Ravi reiterated Sushila's suggestion to accompany them to Gajpur while Vijay pleaded, "Please, please come to Gajpur with us. We have so much to show you."

She fought the desire to go off with them but was tempted by Ravi's proposals of mouth-watering repasts of regional delicacies, and bizarre entertainments - maidens dancing with glass tumblers fastened to their feet, beautiful androgynous boys in *drag* dancing with pots of fire on their heads, sword-swallowers, magicians, or astrologers who could tell her fortune, even elephant or camel rides in the sunset but Garnet resisted all attempts to woo her.

"I don't see how I can leave," Garnet protested. "The work is going slowly and I need more time for research."

"No problem," Ravi retorted. "Cousin Vijay is an historian with thousands of fascinating facts tucked in his head and a reference library he'd be happy to share with you."

"Yes, yes, Garnet, do come to Gajpur," Vijay said excitedly, his eyes aglow at the idea. "I'd feel privileged to assist an artist like yourself."

"You see?" Ravi said, triumphantly. "And if you need books from the Taj museum, Auntie will pull strings so you can take them along to Gajpur."

"Ravi is right," Sushila said, jumping in to persuade Garnet to accept his invitation. "You must see the real India not the land of tourism and my beloved nephew is just the person to assist you. After all, you're writing about an empress. Why not add to your research by spending some days in a palace, even a minor one like Gajpur."

"You have a point," Garnet replied, hesitantly.

Niles was furious at the idea of moving on to Gajpur. "Absolutely no!" he growled. "I like it *here*. I'm sick of traveling. I don't want another long train trip or to be stuck out in the desert."

She didn't answer. She was sick of his problems but had some sympathy for his desperation, his anxiety at leaving Sushila and the attention she lavished on him, and his unwillingness to abandon any morsel of love. She understood but she had to remember her priorities.

Later in her room, Garnet took out the *tanpura* and sat at the window playing chords and humming to herself. There was a full moon rising over the garden and she thought again how blessed she was to be in India.

Why not go? she asked herself, her anxieties about Ravi wavering. *This is what I came to India to see. Why should I let fear spoil my chance to experience an ancient palace in the desert. Sushila is right. I'll travel to Gajpur, see it all."*

Sushila hugged her in excitement at her decision to join Ravi and Vijay on their journey.

"I'm planning a visit to Gajpur soon." she assured Garnet. "I haven't been back for years. A pity. So much of my youth, my memories and secrets, are held in the old stones of the palace. *Deja vu* is long overdue."

Ravi jumped up and down with excitement when he heard the news. He grabbed Vijay and danced around the room with him.

"The goddess Kali has saved us! Garnet is coming to Gajpur with us."

Niles continued to whine and complain about the long trip

166 | ELAINE WILLIAMS

166 | ELAINE WILLIAMS

and the discomfort he predicted they'd find in the desert but Garnet was adamant. Ravi assured him he'd be well taken care of and Vijay swore he'd make a better nanny than Auntie Shushu. Niles threw a pillow at him pretending to be insulted but in fact, was mollified by their reassurances so Ravi went ahead with the travel arrangements.

Sushila lounged on the chaise in Garnet's room while she packed and talked about Gajpur. "A word of warning about Ravi's mother. The Maharani is a tough old bird and a difficult one. She never got over being the *kumari* in the temple in Nepal, still sees herself as the *Living Goddess*."

"Do Virgin Goddesses often marry royalty?" Garnet asked.

Sushila laughed. "Never! But Ravi's father was a stubborn prince in love with beauty. He was visiting the king of Nepal when he discovered the exquisite Khalili. She was eleven years old and about to lose her reign as Virgin Goddess. The king was shocked at the prince's desire to marry the kumari, then laughed and patted his old friend on the shoulder. *"I have to admit, an exquisite creature like this is of use only to a king."*

"A strange story," Garnet said, shaking her head. "But how did the marriage turn out? Were they happy together?"

"Utterly miserable!" Sushila replied, with a chuckle. "My old friend, the maharaja, was bitterly disappointed but what could he expect after choosing a woman as an *object d'art*?"

"I wish I knew more about kumaris before meeting the celebrated goddess of the temple," Garnet said.

Sushila dragged herself up from the chaise and took a small book from the bookshelf.

"Take this book to Gajpur. It explains the kumari sect."

"Thanks," Garnet said, putting the book in her tote bag. "Ravi's father, the maharaja . . . When did he die?"

Sushila gazed out of the window and didn't answer for a moment. When she turned back her face was serious.

"I'm not free to discuss that and I'd avoid questioning Ravi. His father is a painful subject."

Garnet put her arms around Sushila and hugged her tight. "I've been very happy here, Shushu. You'll be sorely missed."

"I'm not dying," Sushila laughed, and pinched Garnet's cheek. "I'm still in my *late youth* as la contessa used to say. Not to worry. We'll meet in Gajpur and revel again."

IV

GAJPUR PALACE, INDIA

Raise me a dais of silk and down;
Hang it with vair and purple dyes
Carve it in doves, and pomegranates,
And peacocks with a hundred eyes."

Christina Rosetti

i

On the morning of their departure to Gajpur, Sushila bustled around the villa overseeing the servants as they piled up gifts, straw picnic baskets packed with cold food and five-tiered tin containers filled with hot-cooked delicacies. The chauffeur stacked the packages in the trunk of the Hispano-Suiza and they drove off with Sushila to the train station, Vijay with his arm around a nervously whining Niles and Ravi beaming at Garnet who hoped the trip wouldn't be a giant disaster.

They watched the chauffeur unload the mass of food provisions in amazement.

"This will keep you going between meals," Sushila said.

Ravi groaned. "You'll kill us with all this food, Auntie."

"Just make sure my steward warms it up properly. And don't dare taste the junk at station stops along the way or you'll be poisoned," she ordered, wagging her finger at them. "This means you, Garnet! Ravi and Vijay know better, but you can be too adventurous for your own good."

Vijay whispered to Garnet that Sushila was sending them to Gajpur in her private rail cars. "We're being hooked up to a passenger train en route to the desert which will drop us off at Gajpur."

Two pearly white rail-cars anchored to a shiny green engine puffing clouds of steam glistened in the morning light, the polished teakwood shutters closed tight against the heat. Entrances and verandas were red-carpeted, fitted with brass railings and filigree arches burnished to a glitter, the sides of the rail cars emblazoned in gold with Sushila's royal crest - her coveted title, *Kanwar Rani of Madhgaya* attained through a former husband. A strange contrast to the banged-up, rusted cars behind them.

Sushila swaddled them in bear hugs, kisses, and last minute instructions, then followed them into the train to give orders to stewards and porters in her employ, brushing by scarlet-coated attendants who stood rigidly at attention as she passed.

She hurried them along. "We have no time to waste, the train is about to depart."

Sushila hustled them into a rail car designed as a dining room, bar, library and drawing room, furnished with magenta velvet couches and soft plush seats. Then she pushed them through a second car pointing out sleeping compartments and bathrooms with showers, both cars embellished by crystal chandeliers, silk curtains and carved teak furniture. Several armed guards dressed in British Raj style uniforms saluted her at the entrances of the cars where they stood guard.

"We have to protect ourselves against bandits who force their way in to rob, even kill passengers," Sushila explained. "Sadly, rail cars must also be shielded from starving mobs who stampede onto trains in search of food."

Garnet leaned out the entryway of the train to wave goodbye to Sushila who remained on the platform waving and blowing kisses until the train disappeared from view. She saw the rail cars behind them were jammed with passengers, men hanging off the windows or balancing themselves on the roof just as she'd witnessed on the trip across the desert with Niles.

Traveling in private rail cars was light-years away from her journey with Niles on third-class trains. There were no bodies huddled on the floor of the car or wretched smells. Instead, obsequious stewards in white ballooned trousers and scarlet tunics greeted them with bows, bringing soft pillows, and trays of tidbits with tea in china cups to their cushioned seats while strains of Sushila's cherished music from the 1930s, Cole Porter, Lorenz Hart and Noel Coward, drifted through the cars on a state-of-the art stereo system. Toward evening, stewards served drinks and waiters hovered over a formal dinner set on Limoges china with gold flatware, then turned down the beds in their compartments for the overnight trip, leaving chocolates embossed with the *Madhgaya* royal crest on the silk pillow.

It may be more noble to be a proletarian, Garnet thought, *but it can't compare to traveling in the princely mode. No wonder people break their necks to get rich. Money takes the curse off the irritants of daily living, never more than when traveling.*

The trip turned out to be more pleasant than Garnet anticipated. For once, Niles didn't present any problems. Vijay fussed over him and ordered the steward to bring over the brass chess table inlaid with squares of green and white jade. Then he unlocked a cabinet and took out Sushila's silver chess set, its pieces hand-carved - a maharaja as *king*, a maharani *queen*, elephants as *knights*, palaces as *rooks* and soldiers as *pawns*.

"My God," Niles said, running his fingers over the pieces in amazement. "This must be worth a fortune."

"Probably," Vijay yawned. "But who cares? Not Auntie Shushu. She has money to burn. She had a little family money but the big bucks came from four rich husbands who remained devoted even after she divorced them."

Vijay set up the chess pieces on the board. "But as you

Americans say, let's *play ball*! Start the game rolling and let the slaughter begin! Killer-chess - spoils to the dauntless!"

"*En garde*," Niles answered, excited by the prospect. "A fight to the death!"

Garnet and Ravi watched the game for awhile. Then Ravi yawned and stretched in his chair.

"I'll let you fellows battle it out alone," he said. "It's bedtime for me. Rushing around with Sushila was exhausting."

Garnet nodded in agreement as she rose. "Bed sounds good."

Ravi led the way into the other car where there were four private compartments. He opened the door to Garnet's room, kissed her hand lightly and turned to his quarters at the far end of the car.

She waited in the doorway gazing longingly after him as he walked away. A vision of the Mogul prince kissing the throat of a princess in the miniature painting flashed into her mind and as Ravi disappeared into the compartment she could feel his soft lips on her throat. But the click of the lock reverberated in her ears.

Yearning and lust flows between us, she thought. *A million years of nature pounds in our blood demanding we respond and all I'd have to do is rap a faint tap on that doorway to bliss . . . But I dare not.*

She stretched out on the bed, munched on Sushila's royal chocolate crown and stared out the window into the blackness of a desert studded with an occasional dart of light as the train rolled through the small villages fringing the tracks. Pictures of the erotic Khajurao statues she'd found so disturbing in Agra danced in her head interspersed with the image of Ravi kissing her throat, her shoulders, moving his lips down to the soft flesh of her breasts. She peered out into the darkness trying to shake off the vision.

If only she could forget the trauma of Niles. *Get over it!* she scolded. *It's time. You can't live with that forever. Ravi bears no resemblance to Niles - he's a different planetary creature. Cast off*

the damaged past as if it were a filthy, tattered backpack, tossed in
a garbage truck to be ground up with rotten food!

She tossed and turned in the berth grappling with cravings and anxieties until exhaustion surrendered her to the rocking of the train and plunged her into a dreamless slumber for the rest of the night.

By morning, the train was twisting a path around the black mountains and arid desert Garnet remembered, pressing her face against the window as the dawn spread a wash of henna across a soot-grey sky. They were deep in a barren wilderness, a seemingly endless void swallowing living things in its dust.

Several hours later the desert turned pale, a pallet of whited-lemon and ecru dulled by dust drifting in the dry heat of the wasteland. Men were led to their deaths here when hot sands turned iridescent and shimmering light created the illusion of watery waves lapping on a distant lake. Desperate to assuage their thirst they struggled across blistering dunes to a mirage, dying cruel deaths as the sought-for oases and lagoons disappeared before their eyes.

Disappointment and death, mirages and the *sands of despond.* All too familiar.

ii

The train pulled slowly into the station at Gajpur to a noisy fanfare of music - drums, bagpipes and sitars played by turbaned musicians perched atop brightly decorated camels and elephants. Trails of rose-perfumed incense scented their pathway from the train as they disembarked onto the platform where they were greeted by a smiling cluster of girls in diaphanous scarlet saris who draped garlands of jasmine over their heads. As they walked through the rail station, Garnet noticed the floor was adorned with flower petals arranged in intricate patterns.

"Is this the requisite princely greeting?" she asked, trying to keep the conversation flippant to hide her struggle of the night.

Ravi rolled his eyes in mock despair.

"My dear Garnet, don't think for a moment these festivities are for my benefit," he answered. "No, princes don't amount to much any more. This bit of show is for tourists and visiting businessmen. Nineteenth century theatrics are strictly commerce in India and those who provide to the public expect to be rewarded."

He pulled out a handful of rupees, distributing them to the musicians and girls who smiled eagerly as they passed.

"Until there are enough proper jobs in India, free performances will remain a quasi-living for many. Luckily, Indians have a weakness for artistic gifts, consider it a blessing to pay for such balms to our spirit."

"Poets included?"

Ravi smiled and took her arm to guide her across the platform. "Poets above all," he replied. "We're sensitive spirits. Ask the hippies. Undying; limitless *soul* originated in India."

An ivory-lacquered Rolls Royce shimmered in the waning afternoon sun. At their approach a turbaned servant boy in a bedraggled wine tunic stood rigidly erect as he held open the door of the car.

Garnet caught her breath at the sight of the car.

"A *Silver Ghost!*" she exclaimed, running her hand across the pearly gleam of the fender. "I've never seen a real one before, only photos."

Ravi smiled, pleased by her appreciation. "Grandpapa bought her for my grandmother in 1931. Granny loved to drive and was fond of taking me to ruins and old temples for lavish English picnics. But the poor Silver Ghost has been sitting in a stable for years. Mechanically, she's in wretched shape from the climate and lack of use. Once in awhile Vijay and I take her out for a spin but the old girl would need a real overhauling if we wanted to do more than drive a short distance. She'll puff and chug her way home but don't worry, the Ghost has the heart of a lioness and won't fail us."

"Who could resist such a beauty?" Garnet shook her head in delight. "Or Shushu's *Hispana-Suiza*. Do all Indian royals collect vintage autos?"

"Only the smart ones."

Garnet stepped up on the lacquered running board and ran her fingers over the shiny silver sculpture mounted on the hood, a glittering figurehead of a woman, head tilted back, garments flying as she guided her ivory wheeled-ship.

"*Silver Fancy*, free and strong, a woman without chains," Garnet mused. "Later known as the *Spirit of Ecstasy.*"

"She captured my heart the first time I saw her," Ravi said, planting a kiss on the silver head. "I was a small boy of six when Granny held me up to see the shining, silvery woman."

Garnet smiled with pleasure. "The Silver Ghost was my uncle's dream."

"It's curious, but I think you resemble *Silver Fancy,*" Ravi said, squinting at the figurehead then back to her.

"She's the spitting image," Niles said, sliding his hands up and down the figure. "All chrome and no heart. Her uncle claimed Garnet's face was carved on facades of buildings, mantel pieces, and naked brass ladies languishing on *art deco* cigarette boxes."

Garnet ignored Niles and turned to Ravi. "If there's a resemblance it's only because I have regular features in the classic mode, blah, blah, blah."

"Who gives a shit?" Niles walked to the back of the car where Vijay was struggling with a pile of packages.

"But I've seen your face before," Ravi whispered to Garnet. "Five years ago your head hovered over the foot of my bed. A ghostly vision, a premonition. I recognized you when we met."

"A likely story!" Garnet laughed. "Is this how you lure unsuspecting maidens into your evil clutches?"

"Yes," Ravi answered, lowering his voice to a growl, "Eez

true. My name eez Count Dracula. Tell her, Vijay," he called out to his cousin. "Tell Garnet what a rogue I am."

Vijay chuckled. "I'm too tired, Ravi, she'll have to discover your evil qualities for herself." Then he directed the driver to place the boxes in the trunk of the car, helped Niles into the back and collapsed on the seat next to him, behind Garnet and Ravi.

Garnet stroked the cream leather of the seat and inhaled the scent of jasmine stuffed in silver vases at the windows. "How strange to journey all this way to realize a dream,"

"*And the end of our exploring will be to arrive where we started . . .*" Ravi murmured.

"*And know the place for the first time,*" Garnet added, looking at him in surprise.

"Don't be amazed I know a bit about poetry. You'll insult my Cambridge tutor who took pride in pounding literature into the head of a lazy Indian boy."

They dropped Vijay off at his home, an unimposing villa on the outskirts of the city, and waved goodbye back to him as he stood in front of the black iron gate and blew kisses to Garnet and salutes to Ravi and Niles.

"I'll visit with the family tonight but pick me up tomorrow morning," he shouted over the sound of the motor.

The Silver Ghost clattered down a rut-pitted road, the sand-drenched winds blowing up around them as they drove across the once princely state of Gajpur, now a near ghost-town imbedded in India's great Thar desert.

The sun began its descent splattering a drizzle of gold over the amber city shimmering in the distance.

"Gajpur," Ravi said, pointing out the city. "The golden jewel of the desert, a rare topaz whose amber hue comes from the sandstone houses and walls of the city. Seven hundred years ago there was nothing here but desert, rocks and sandy wastes until a rich prince, an eccentric fellow descended from Greek settlers in the Punjab, trekked down here in the twelfth century and established the area. Rich merchants crisscrossing the desert built up the city. Eventually my ancestors, whose idea of *noblesse oblige* was to confiscate territories, conquered the domain and established the princely state of Gajpur."

They drove through the gate to the walled city glowing golden against a sapphire sky, past pale ocher mansions carved in sandstone, thick-walled for coolness with lacy-etched *jali* screens where woman in *purdah* peered through tiny slits. Along the way, young women garbed in filmy scarlet saris, their honey-skinned arms covered in ivory bracelets, collected water in stone jugs, giggling and smiling as they walked like goddesses through the narrow streets balancing the water jugs on their heads.

Niles groaned in the back seat. "This ride is killing me. The jolting rockets through my body like an earthquake. For godsakes, when will the bumper-car ride be over?"

"Buck up, old boy, we're nearly there," Ravi answered, so doggedly cheerful that Niles moaned a few times more to make his point and fell silent. "You can see a glimpse of the palace rising above the walls of the city."

By the time the car rumbled past the walls the sky had darkened, the palace a faint silhouette in the evening shadows.

iii

Inside the palace, Ravi moved them quickly through the cool halls to his apartments occupying a wing of the palace. She saw no one. The great center hall and corridors were empty, the palace deserted. Perhaps servants took a siesta before dinner in the hot climate. Still, it seemed odd for a prince to arrive without being greeted.

Ravi rang for a servant to arrange for dinner and suggested they retire to their rooms for a bath and rest until the meal was served. He ordered the servant to show Niles to his room in the guest wing where Vijay would also stay, and escorted Garnet to her room in his wing of the palace, carrying her bags himself and placing them on a bench.

"Let me know if you need help unpacking. But first, I want you to see how maharajas indulged themselves in the past," he said, opening a door to the bathroom.

Garnet blinked. The bathroom was a pink grotto, its rosy marbled walls streaked in magenta, with a rose-quartz bathing pool sunken into the marble floor. Faucets and fixtures were crafted in gold, cut-glass urns were filled with bath crystals, and a mirrored make-up wall was framed by rows of pink lights. But the most extraordinary sight was the shower niche, a curve of pearl-pink marble carved and fluted like a sea shell plucked from Botticelli's *Spring*. A Hollywood epic *mise en scène*. Only Cleopatra was missing.

Garnet shook her head in disbelief. "I couldn't have conjured up this sight in my wildest fantasy."

Ravi laughed. "My father installed the bath in the 1930s. Show biz art deco, a Cecil B. DeMille fantasy to amuse chic harem ladies addicted to the new cinema craze. Like it?"

"I can't wait to take a shower and pretend I'm the darling of the harem, the maharaja's pet," Garnet teased.

Ravi patted her hair. "You're already the prince's pet in a palace full of surprises. Ironic, considering how broke we are."

"How did it happen?" Garnet asked.

"Extravagant living, bad investments, and the naive assumption that the State would support the throne when the monarchy ended. Such is *karma*. Today, there's virtually no money left in what's laughably known as the Royal Treasury."

"How do you manage?"

"We sell off treasures and Auntie Shushu helps the family out occasionally. But even she can't afford to invest the money needed to repair this crumbling edifice. It's a humbling reminder we aren't what we used to be, a tiny link to the plight of our impoverished masses although I wouldn't presume to equate our small inconveniences with their suffering."

"But you still have servants?"

Ravi smiled and shook his head. "We hardly pay the poor fellows, but they have nowhere to go and insist they're grateful for food and shelter."

"Is the rest of your family living here? The palace seems empty and quiet."

"My mother is still at our old summer palace in Simla playing cards with the ladies of the Indian aristocracy. Simla is the hill station in the foothills of the Himalayas where the wives of the British Raj and Indian royal families traditionally staved off hot weather and monsoons. The English left but we linger on."

"I'd like to see Simla," Garnet said. "Is it charming?"

"In a way," Ravi said, his face tightening as a shadow passed over it. "The setting of Simla is beautiful - a cool pine-forested town of waterfalls, streams and wild roses. The British chose Simla as their summer capital and recreated an English village with replicas of timbered cottages, tea shops, gardens of lilies and hyacinths. Then they built private clubs with terraces looking out over the mountains where drinks were served by white-coated *naukars* trained to imitate English butlers."

Ravi pulled the silk coverlet off the bed and folded back the top sheet. He looked tense. "British clubs in India were closed to Indians except for maharajas and royal families. But despite my mother's rank they snubbed her. Oh, they had to accept her on some level, after all, she was a maharani, but the ladies gossiped about the *Virgin Goddess*, scorning *kumaris* as quasi-whores, letting her know with that cold veneer of British *politesse* she was less than welcome in their well-bred society."

Ravi took the keys from Garnet, unlocked her suitcases, and shook his head. "Ironically, there were few aristocrats among the Brits. Most were ordinary civil servants who got off on feeling superior to people a few shades darker than themselves. Viceroys and high-ranking officials took care to be polite to our faces but no matter how noble our blood behind our backs they mocked us with the epithet, *royal darkies*. India under the Raj - an old, old story - one best forgotten."

Ravi opened the shutters and pulled apart the drapes.

"There's just enough moonlight to help you sleep. Have a good nap, and don't dress for dinner. Sushila's comfort law is strictly enforced at the palace! Rest well, and I'll drop by to escort you to dinner."

iv

Garnet slept, then woke and showered in the pink marble shell, amused to be washing her hair in this outrageous setting, imagining all the courtesans and lovers whose skin had touched the marble before hers. *Perhaps they made love against the rosy sea shell* but she didn't want to think about that. She slipped into a flimsy kurtah-pyjamah, the heat was heavy and she was sure there was no air-conditioning in an ancient palace. She was about to lie down for a few minutes when Ravi knocked.

"Are you ready? I hope I'm not disturbing you."

"This is it, for better or worse," she laughed, opening the door. "A wet-haired, no-frills Americano!"

"Suits me."

Ravi took her arm and escorted her through a maze of empty marble halls dotted with threadbare rugs and shabby settees. He paused at a carved teakwood door encrusted with silver and rapped loudly. A turbaned servant pushed open the heavy door, salaamed, and ushered them into a spacious gallery with marble pillars and fretted windows streaming in slivers of moonlight. The salon was nearly empty of furnishings but the air was scented with jasmine incense and a massive mahogany table in the center of the salon was set for dinner with candles burning in silver candelabra, fine china and two place settings.

"Niles left word he was too tired to join us so I had dinner sent to his rooms."

Garnet nodded, relieved not to have to deal with Niles without Vijay's protection. She could relax and absorb the atmosphere of the palace.

Clearly, this formal dining salon once represented the grandeur of the Gajpur dynasty. But the opulence of the past was long gone. The Oriental rugs were even shabbier than those in the halls, cushions on the dining chairs frayed, silk drapes worn, their mauve tint faded and stained. The velvet couches passed on their way had been threadbare and the blue satin on damask chairs scattered about the palace bleached white as a faded summer sky.

It was obvious the shabbiness could no longer be disguised. Garnet understood. The palace was in desperate need of repair much like her New England home; plaster crumbling, cracks in the walls, furniture decaying and no money to fix anything. But poverty didn't bear the same disgrace in India. It was merely a turn of the karmic wheel. Accepted. Neither shame nor blame. It was *karma*, or *Shiva* offering a chance for spiritual advancement through unlucky twists of fate.

Ravi regaled Garnet with jokes and stories during dinner while an ancient servant wearing the white *dhoti* of peasants hobbled around the room serving them. She couldn't help laughing. Ravi knew how to amuse and charm. It had been a long time since she felt so young and reckless, free to enjoy herself.

After dinner, Ravi walked Garnet back to her room.

"You need to have a good rest tonight," he said.

There was an awkward pause which Ravi broke by reaching out and kissing her hand. His lips felt soft against her skin, his palm so plump and reassuring that a sudden urge came over her to grab onto his hand and pull him into the room. *Are you mad?* she berated herself, blinking her eyes to get rid of the feeling. *Don't start anything you can't finish.*

Ravi stared at her intently for a moment as if he knew what

she was thinking. He began to say something, then stopped as if he thought better of it and released her hand.

"Tomorrow's another day," he said. "Let me show you the pleasures of the palace instead of the desolation."

v

Early the next morning the old servant brought a tray to Garnet's room piled with hot bread and a pitcher of strong South Indian coffee and soon Ravi appeared.

"Niles is still sound asleep," he said. "So there's nothing to hold you back from a tour of the palace. And the morning air is still cool."

He guided her through the courtyards to the other side of the palace. The heat and dust had not yet risen and the air was honeyed with frangipani and the tang of eucalyptus.

"My father grew up in this wing of the palace and I spent much of my childhood here with granny," Ravi said, as he led her into a large room filled with toys, rocking horses, train sets and books. "She kept a nursery for me and redid my father's old playhouse. Most of it is intact. Even my *tika raja* garments still hang in the armoire."

Garnet moved out to the courtyard to see what appeared to be a child-size replica of an English thatched cottage.

"Granny had the playhouse built for my father," Ravi explained. "The straw was imported from Devonshire and it was all made to order in England, the sofa, chairs, mantel for the fireplace and Spode tea set on the table. Now my father's old teddy bear and Granny's dolls in white dresses sit on mini Sheraton chairs."

Garnet peeked in the windows of the playhouse. "Ooh, I do envy you. What a lucky little prince to have a thatched cottage all your own."

"Granny's wing of the palace was my real home," Ravi reflected, his eyes soft and a bit moist. "Granny fused the best of two worlds. She was respectful of me as a child in the English way, unlike my mother who was intrusive and overbearing, yet expressed her love as well as any warmhearted Indian mother, showering me with hugs and kisses and making her lap available no matter how elegant her dress. She raised my father the same way. Perhaps it's why she was the most beloved woman in his life."

"Sounds idyllic," Garnet sighed. "A life protected from unpleasant realities. Not possible anymore."

"Not in India, anyway. But remnants of our royal past are preserved in the storerooms. Come see."

Ravi guided Garnet up a lengthy flight of wooden steps to an upper floor where a long hall was lined on either side with great cupboards and armoires preserving the garments of the royal household.

He opened the doors to show her the collection of maharajas' velvet robes and scarlet uniforms as well as pleated skirts worn by his great, great grandfather kings. A French armoire held his father's wine-red silk coats trimmed with buttons of 24-carat gold, and his white satin trousers.

"What fun," Garnet said, rummaging through the coats. "Try this on." She pulled out a long wine-red tunic with a high-buttoned collar and helped him into it pushing his arms in the sleeves like a mother dressing à child.

"You look splendid," she said, buttoning the last gold nugget, and stepping back to get a better look. "Practically unrecognizable."

"Hush, woman. Don't mock the Raja or he'll send you to the torture chamber."

"Where's that, I wonder? In the Raja's bed, perhaps?"

He tried to grab her to tickle her but she eluded his grasp and ran down the long hall with Ravi in pursuit.

"Promise not to tickle?" she asked, nearly out of breath.

"Yes, yes, I agree to all your demands. Sign the marriage contract and I'll give you everything I own."

"How much is that in dollars?" Garnet asked, breathless from running. "Rupees don't make it where I come from."

"Let me distract you from these cash negotiations by showing you granny's armoire."

He opened the cabinet and displayed the long white linen and voile dresses of his grandmother, embroidered and lace-trimmed, and large garden hats trimmed with ribbons and flowers and ruffled silk parasols. There was also a collection of exquisite gold brocaded saris gleaming like jewels in ruby, sapphire and emerald satin.

"Ooh," Garnet exclaimed, with a gasp of delight as she lifted the embroidered skirt of a voile dress so delicate she could see the veins of her hands through it.

"Now it's your turn," Ravi said. "Slip into one of Granny's dresses. She always wanted a daughter and would have doted on you, spoiled you unmercifully, just as she did me."

Garnet picked out a white batiste gown with a tucked and embroidered bodice, its waist sashed in pale-blue satin. She looked ruefully at a pair of delicate shoes, the silver mesh of the arch banded in gold with golden toes turned up in points. "I'm afraid I can't squeeze my big *step-sister* feet into these Cinderella beauties. *Quelle dommage!*"

"Who cares? Not this prince. There's a changing room across the hall," Ravi said. "Call me if you need help."

She came back in a few minutes wearing the gown but holding it together in the back.

"I'm afraid you'll have to button me up. You could break your arms trying to fasten these tiny buttons."

"I'm not too good at this," Ravi said.

"I thought men knew about buttons," Garnet teased, holding the dress together in the back as she twirled around. "Perhaps they only know about un-buttoning."

"What a naughty girl to talk of such things," Ravi chuckled

as he patiently worked on the buttons.

Garnet picked out a large straw garden hat trimmed with matching blue ribbons which hung down the back and pirouetted in front of a mirror for Ravi.

"Such a loo-vely life gone by," she sang, opening up a ruffled parasol and spinning it over Ravi's head. "What a change from my shabby black umbrellas, half busted, which turn inside out at the slightest breeze. I buy them cheap on the streets, they fall apart or I lose them but who cares? It would break my heart to lose this exquisite parasol. I'm sure it's wicked to lust after beautiful objects - one should hanker after more worthy causes - but my soul has its sinful desires."

"You're forgiven! Stand next to me in the mirror," Ravi entreated, linking his arm in hers. "See if we pass muster as a royal couple."

They gazed at their reflection in the long pier glass.

"We look perfect," Garnet said, bursting into laughter. "But you need a turban. Do you know how to make one?"

"Silly girl," Ravi said, wagging his finger at her. "We're descendants of Sikhs like most royal families in India. A Sikh who can't wrap a turban is thrown out of Sikhdom."

He picked up a length of ruby silk from the shelf, wound the yards of material around his head and swiftly twisted it into a perfect turban.

"I *am* impressed," Garnet said, twirling her umbrella.

"I'll even add an emerald," he said, rummaging through a carved ivory box. "Badly flawed and of little value but perfect to pin on my turban and convince you I'm a true prince."

Garnet curtseyed, fluttering a painted silk fan before her eyes. "I should kiss your jewel - like the pope's ring," she said, pursing her lips and reaching up to give the emerald a resounding smack.

"Ah, the beauteous princess mocks me," Ravi sighed, as if crestfallen. "Yes, reality is a little sad. We can only play at being princes now. But join me in the game and we'll live out our fantasies together."

As she looked into the mirror she felt as if she were stepping through her image into a dimension where reality faded and unreality became existence. She remembered slipping into that hazy place when she played *pretend* games as a child, a strange world providing her happiest moments.

Francesca had taunted her for her dreaminess. *"Wake up, Garnet, and stop daydreaming. One day, you'll walk out over the edge and won't be able to get back."*

Ravi pulled her away from the mirror. "We'll dream ourselves away with a waltz. I'll sing and you keep your toes out from under my feet."

He took her in his arms and hummed Strauss's *"Acceleration Waltz"* in her ear speeding up the tempo as he glided her around the dusty floor. In the whirl of the dance, Garnet felt as if she were no longer attached to earthly things, the cavernous room disappeared, pain and anxiety didn't exist and only the pleasure of Ravi's arms around her was real.

After the waltz, Ravi insisted on a polka, shouting out his version of a Polish polka and twirling her around the huge hall until laughing and breathless, she begged for mercy.

"What a playmate you are," she gasped in delight. "Why weren't you in Sailship Point when I needed you?"

"You're pretty expert at playing around yourself. Did you dress up as a child?"

"Only in secret, without a playmate like you to share it, and with all the anxiety of a CIA agent spying in enemy territory, expecting to be shot," Garnet admitted ruefully. "Francesca hated anyone to touch her things. But when she was out for the day with my sister I'd sneak in her room, try on clothes and jewelry, use her lipstick and makeup and stagger around in spike heels. It was all done in a state of terror. I was petrified she'd come back and find me so I'd dance around a bit in the mirror, then run to the window and listen for the sound of her car coming up the drive. Afterwards, I tried to put her things back, breathing hard, trembling with fear. Yet over and over again I felt compelled to repeat the ordeal. My mother always pushed me away - perhaps I thought putting on her clothes and makeup would bring me closer to her."

"Unfortunately, mothers like ours make intimacy impossible, Ravi said, closing up the cupboards as they got ready to leave."

Before they went downstairs, Ravi took Garnet into a room crammed with furniture and objects. He showed her a *palanquin* of gold, a carved-wood carriage coated in silver and gold topped by a canopy fringed in metallic-gold cloth and decorated with sculptures of silver and gold carved into elephants, tigers, goddesses and dancing Shivas. The coach was mounted on a litter to be borne by four servants.

"Step in," Ravi said, "and see how it feels to travel like a true princess."

"It's very tiny," she said. "I don't think a great, hockey-playing American girl can fit in there."

"Let's squeeze you in and see. You may have to fold yourself up a bit."

"I'll try," she said, half squatting as she bent her knees and head and stepped into the *palanquin* resting on a low bench.

"Actually, it's not too bad. Rather fun. Why don't you get the servants to carry me through the palace grounds."

"You'd kill those poor old arthritic fellows. Let me help you out before your muscles cramp up."

Garnet poked out her head and Ravi pulled her the rest of the way.

"Was that your cradle?" she asked, pointing to a polished teak cradle inlaid with tiny mirrors and a peacock studded with jade carved into the front. Animals sculpted in gold were set into the sides so the baby could watch them while being rocked, and nearby, Ravi's crib was ornately carved in silver, with a velvet coverlet and gold-threaded bolsters.

"This seems extravagant even for a Crown Prince," Garnet

teased.

"Gajpur was a real kingdom then," Ravi replied. "My grandfather was a rich and extravagant maharaja. We ate on gold plates, servants salaamed to me and obeyed my wishes and my ceremonial robes were woven of gold, my turban pinned with a huge emerald. We're Rajputs, literally *Sons of Kings*, our bloodline the purest in India, supposedly descended from the moon. In reality, our ancestors originated from Persians who invaded India from the 4th to the 7th century."

Ravi opened the door of a child's armoire, its polished fruitwood doors carved into a jungle of lions and tigers, elephants and giraffes, and showed Garnet the gold-brocaded vests, pearl-studded velvet coats, silk shirts and tunics he wore as a child.

"Ah, how the mighty have fallen," Ravi said, with a laugh. "Bred for a life which no longer exists. It wasn't easy to reconcile my upbringing in a world where we were deposed. Other princes and maharajas fared better. They went into business or tourism, turned their palaces into hotels and themselves into middle-class businessmen. But the thought of running this place as the *GajMahal Hotel*, taking on a horde of complaining tourists, was exhausting. I didn't have the talent or the stomach for it." On the way downstairs Garnet stopped to look through a triangular leaded window on the landing.

"Is that a lake in the middle of the desert?" she asked. "There's a white chateau floating on it, and a silvery bridge."

"It's an artificial lake," Ravi said. "The cobalt blue of the water is a reflection of blue cement at the bottom of the lake. My great grandfather dug out the lake and built a floating Summer Palace to cool his pampered princes in the heat-swamped years before royal families made the trek to Simla."

"That must be the palace where a spoiled prince demanded the cook bake a cake-palace?" Garnet said, shaking her finger at him.

"I'm afraid so," Ravi smiled. "Guilty as charged."

Garnet gazed at the floating white palace. "It's a fairy tale castle! When can we explore it?"

Ravi didn't answer for a moment but stared across the lake, his face suddenly tight and drawn.

"The summer palace is in dreadful disrepair. It's not safe to go there. Anyway, we should be getting back," he said, looking at his watch. "Vijay isn't here yet and Niles will be wondering what happened to us."

vi

Niles was stalking up and down in a fury, ranting and raging as they approached the Great Hall.

"I've been looking for you all over the bloody palace. This spooky dungeon gives me the creeps."

"It's my fault," Ravi said, patting Niles on the shoulder. "I didn't want to disturb your sleep, so I took Garnet to see our storerooms while we waited. Sorry. I lost track of time. Let me show them to you sometime. I think you'd be interested."

Niles muttered under his breath, turning his anger into a litany of whines and complaints. Garnet shrugged her shoulders and signaled Ravi not to respond. *Let him wind down by himself.*

Vijay arrived for lunch in a jubilant mood, brimming with smiles and jokes, and bearing a basket of sweets and flowers sent by his mother. Niles cheered up a bit as Vijay linked his arm and amused him with wild stories of Gajpur's royal scandals.

As they entered the dining salon Garnet paused at a portrait of a bejeweled potentate wearing a tunic woven in gold and a pleated silk skirt.

"I like his skirt," Garnet remarked. "I guess they didn't call it *drag* then."

"Are you speaking of Akbar the Great, our most exalted Moghul emperor and grandfather of your Shah Jahan?" Ravi protested, trying not to laugh.

He assumed an air of indignation. *"Drag*! Our emperor is garbed in the royal raiment of the 1500s. Remember your Scottish kilt is also a skirt."

Ravi paused before the painting and straightened the gold frame so that it hung properly.

"*Akbar the Great* was one of the most remarkable rulers of all time," he informed Garnet over his shoulder. "A patron of the arts who encouraged the famed artistic achievements of the Mughals. He was our great hero just as Napoleon was to the French."

"I'm sorry," Garnet said ruefully. "We joke about George Washington's wooden teeth."

Ravi patted her hand and winked at her. "We're not offended."

Vijay jumped in, eager to show off his knowledge. "For his tolerance and benevolence toward all religions Akbar was known as the *Guardian of Mankind*."

"But strong drink had been a problem to other emperors." Ravi said, shaking his head in dismay. "Akbar's father, Emperor Humayun, was an alcoholic who fell to his death on the circular staircase of his stone library. Akbar was forced to assume the throne at the tender age of fourteen."

"This was why Akbar warned his grandson against the *excessive use of lethal, alcoholic beverages*," Vijay interjected. "And Shah Jahan never touched alcohol before he was thirty. His qualms were intensified by his father, Emperor Jahangir, another alcoholic. But Jahangir advised moderation to his son . . ."

"Wine is a raging enemy, a prudent friend.

A little is an antidote, but much is a snake's poison."

"There's so much compassion in Akbar's face - the portrait shines with it," Garnet said, gazing up at the painting.

"One of the few paintings left in the palace," Ravi lamented. "We sold off the miniatures, even a Rembrandt wash of Shah Jahan. Sad, but we needed cash. Most of our treasures were swallowed up by this money-eating monster of a palace."

An old servant in a dusty grey tunic hobbled in from the

kitchen and seated them around the dining table.

Ravi poured wine into their glasses.

"So much for our *leçons d'histoire*," he declared, lifting up his glass. "As we're all moderate souls drink up and be merry - *à votre santé!*"

"I need a drink after that," Niles said, gulping down his wine. "I loathe history and I despise alcoholics!"

After lunch, Ravi offered to take them down to the stables to see the horses before they retired for their afternoon siesta. "I don't want to see horses," Niles complained. "Take Garnet. She adores horses, prefers them to people."

Vijay shrugged his shoulders as if helpless over Niles and walked away with him.

Garnet and Ravi raced down to the stables where she ran from stall to stall admiring the Arabian steeds, awe-inspiring horses, and stroked their shining necks feeding them the cubes of sugar Ravi put in her pocket.

Horses comforted her as a child, even an old swaybacked polo pony tethered in a nearby field whom she rode bareback. She often dreamed of horses, beautiful steeds galloping through her dreams as she cantered down a tree-lined bridle path in Sailship Point. She was soothed by the strength and steadiness of horses evoking in a funny way the love she felt for her uncle. At twelve she confided a dream to him of a shining russet stallion who leapt through a great window crashing the glass and soaring high, his amber-silk mane fluttering as he flew across the sky.

"The horse is you, Garnet," Winslow told her. "The dream means you must break through - fly like the wind and chase your destiny."

And she had escaped - from the coldness of the beauteous Francesca, the remoteness of her father and the torments of her sister - to find in India the horses and autos of her dreams. *What next?* she wondered.

"Only a prince could own such magnificent horses!" Garnet exclaimed.

Ravi smiled. "These fancy Arabian steeds don't belong to us. We make a bit of money raising or boarding them for polo-playing maharajas, who unlike us were clever enough to hang on to their money. Polo's the great Indian diversion and our own invention."

"They're exquisite creatures, especially this one," she said, rubbing her cheek against a stallion's chestnut neck. "I *know* him, I've dreamt of him since I was a child, a glorious russet steed with silken skin who flew like the wind. What do you call this handsome creature?"

"Emir, of course. He's an Arabian prince, *king* of the stable."

"Does anyone ever ride these beauties?" she asked.

"They need to be exercised so I ride quite often. Care to join me?"

"I'd be thrilled," Garnet responded. "I'm used to consorting with the proletariat, mostly old nags, not blue-blooded Arabian aristocrats."

"I take it you're a fair equestrienne?"

"Not bad. How about you?"

"Passable."

Garnet laughed. "Hmm, a modest prince. I'll check it out when you're in the saddle."

vii

A few days later, Ravi suggested they sneak away before Vijay and Niles returned from exploring the old fort and have dinner alone. "I'll leave word for them to eat without us."

"Sounds good to me," Garnet murmured.

"We'll dress in the garb of my ancestors," Ravi declared, as he scribbled a note to Vijay. "Then we'll time-travel back to the 17th century and *I weel take you to zee Casbah.* Veda will prepare a royal banquet fit for Mumtaz Mahal and Shah Jahan and we'll wind up the old gramophone and dance the night away."

"Where is the Casbah?" Garnet asked.

"Shhh, it's a surprise," Ravi answered, putting his finger on her lips.

They dressed in secret up in the storerooms, then tiptoed down the stairs to avoid Vijay and Niles in case they reappeared. Then Ravi led Garnet through a bewildering maze of passageways until they came to a courtyard edged in marble fretwork, the air heavy with the scent of jasmine. Cypresses and banyan trees, dotted with cobalt-blue parrots perched on gnarled branches, sheltered an astonishing tent of scarlet silk velvet, shimmering in the haze of a yellow moon.

Ravi untied the silken cords of the entrance, beckoning her to follow him inside. He salaamed as she entered. *"Bhärat äpkä swägat kartä hai*! Welcome to zee Casbah. Thees eez no *tente ordinaire, ma cherie,* but *la tente royale,* created by a Moghul emperor for his bride three hundred years ago so the empress could tarry at his battle-camp in palatial splendor."

Garnet could hardly speak as she looked around her.

"Is this Arabian Nights or what?" Ravi asked, pointing to the crimson silk drapings of the tent embroidered in gold flowers and slender pillars wrapped in ruby velvet curving over their heads.

Garnet gazed at the arched windows and huge Persian rug spread over the marble courtyard floor. There were tapestries woven with scenes of erotic lovemaking, lush women in sensual poses, and an ornate silver bed, sculptured with lions and dragons and draped with a gold-threaded coverlet of blue velvet, piled with silk pillows. The bed was suspended from the top of the tent by golden chains and swayed several feet above the rug while massive silver lamps carved with figures of maharajas and maharanis seated on elephants shed a glow over the tent.

"A reclining throne for a lazy emperor," Ravi quipped.

Garnet marveled as she ran her fingers over the emerald

velvet bolster, filigreed in gold and studded with pearls and rubies. "But how many poor Hindu girls went blind to create it?" she asked, only half joking.

"None," Ravi retorted. "The emperors and maharajas of our lavish past spared no expense, bringing skilled artisans to India from all over the world. It's what the opulence of India was all about and why they got rid of us," he sighed and kissed her hand."

The servant, Veda, brushed through the draped entrance carrying their dinner on silver trays, smiling at the sight of Garnet in Rani Elizabeth's white dress and Ravi in the maharaja's red military jacket, garments of the past he knew well having served the grandfather's regime as a young boy. Veda piled up pillows on the Persian rug and ladled out spicy curries, steaming samosas, vegetable stuffed triangles of crisp dough, tandoori chicken, dhal, hot puffed breads and mater paneer, Ravi insistent on dining Indian style.

"No forks or knives allowed," Ravi insisted. "Such devices were invented to stab your neighbor if he tried to steal your meat. We'll eat with our fingers and scoop up curries with *pooris* or *nan*. It's messy but strangely satisfying."

After a few tries and a good deal of champagne Garnet got into the spirit, licking her fingers and sucking on chicken bones. "Mmm, it's like being a child again but without a scolding parent calling you an ill-mannered little piggy."

Sated with food and wine Garnet stretched out on the bed and sank into the velvety cushions while Ravi lit sticks of jasmine incense in golden burners at the corners of the tent.

"Now I'm the Sleeping Beauty of my dreams," she murmured.

She gazed up at the erotic tapestries in the tent. "I can imagine the porno games played out in this seductive paradise."

"What?" Ravi protested, acting the outraged monarch. "Desecrate the blood of my ancestors and the artisans who created this splendor? This is a sanctuary of love, not debauchery."

"Well, where did the wicked pastimes take place while the

good prince hunted for Cinderella?"

"I'm hardly a saint," he replied, with a sardonic smile, "but those devilish games were played out in another part of the palace with call-girls supplied by my mother. Surprised? The maharani is a practical woman. Every year she drags in a bevy of young virgins from patrician families and tries to persuade me to marry a *pure, unspoiled* Indian aristocrat to strengthen the Asian blood of my children. When I refuse my mother fearing my robust nature, plies me with whores, high-class beauties trained to service the rich and princely. She worries I'll fall in love with a woman not of her choosing and terrified I might answer the call of my English blood by marrying a European."

"So she sends in more whores, each one exquisite, handpicked by her fine eye for beauty. I humor my mother by bringing them to my secret hideaway, feed them sweets and persuade them to watch television while I read a book or play the sitar until an appropriate amount of time has passed. To placate the maharani I occasionally let them spend the night, hush the girls up with extra money and insist they boast of my sexual expertise and wild erotic performance."

"Aren't you ever tempted?" Garnet asked, with a tug of jealousy as she envisioned Ravi amidst a cluster of beauties.

"I'm a normal man and when nature tugs I succumb," he replied, somewhat ruefully. "But for me, sex without passion is a bleak act and the next batch of girls have to suffer through a series of boring videos or reruns of old Hollywood films. They've all seen *"Casablanca"* so clever whores know how to give a parting shot as they leave with a wad of rupees in their hand. *We'll always have Paris*, they say with a snicker. But I'm too jaded to be insulted."

"I understand," Garnet said wistfully, stroking his hair. "Purely carnal sex is frightening. I bitterly resented the assumption of the sexual revolution that *lovemaking*, usually marked by the absence of love, is a casual encounter like a workout on an exercise machine. I hated the men who pressured me, calling me a prude for my reluctance or their hostile glares when they realized money spent for dinner was going down the drain without compensation. My hunger for love was something quite different, more akin to Mira Bai or Mumtaz Mahal."

Ravi nodded in agreement. He touched her glass with his and a light bell tone resounded from the fluted crystal. "You're the *beloved* of my palace. Now let us pleasure ourselves in this silken refuge trembling with the passions of ancient princes."

He cranked up the gramophone and they slow-danced to romantic ballads as he held her close, murmuring lyrics into her ear, "*I've got a crush on you, sweetie pie, all the day and night time, hear me sigh. I never had the least notion, that I could fall with such emotion.*"

Garnet giggled into his shoulder. "Don't laugh," he said, "*Those fingers in my hair, that sly come-hither stare that strips my conscience bare, it's witchcraft . . .*

"I know a few old tunes myself," she said, unable to control her laughter as she warbled . . ."*That old black magic has me in its spell . . .*"

Ravi held her close . . . *I've got you under my skin, so deep in my heart you're really a part of me* . . . Don't ever leave me, Garnet," he murmured.

Floating on champagne and dancing, Garnet whispered back, "Where would I find another playmate like you? A dress-up, play-acting pal!"

When they tired of dancing they fell on the bed to rest. Ravi burrowed his face in her hair and kissed her fingers.

Garnet smiled and lightly rubbed his temples with her fingertips. Ravi was captivating, the allure of a prince without the arrogance of power, like a handsome animal bred for elegance without bite or sting.

Ravi began to caress her and she felt his hands moving over her body through the silk of her kurtah. His hands were silky like the plump hands of a fat woman but the softness of his flesh was comforting, his touch as gentle as an infant stroking a mother's cheek. Ravi's sensitivity was a reminder of Sushila's tenderness and she was grateful to both of them as she felt desire spreading through her limbs. She yearned for surrender but when Ravi lifted her skirt and moved his hands up her thighs and she felt his nakedness she stiffened with fear.

She felt a wave of despair wash over her. She thought she'd *outgrow the graveyard of her childhood* like James Joyce but despite her efforts she was still imprisoned.

"No, no, Ravi, please, I'm not able to do this," she cried, pushing him away.

"Tell me, darling," Ravi said gently.

"I was molested, raped, left horrified by the sex act," she cried, weeping in Ravi's arms as she conjured up the bitter seduction and abortion endured by her girl-self. She sensed his shock as she related the details but he held her tight and cried with her, tears flowing down his cheeks as he listened to the painful events. She was taken aback by his response. No one ever cried for her before.

"I'm so sorry, my darling," Ravi said, wiping away her tears. "Forgive me if I pushed you too far."

Garnet sat up. "It's not your fault, it's mine. I shouldn't be here leading you on. It's not fair to you."

She started to get out of bed but Ravi caught her by the arm and pulled her back.

Ravi sat up, held Garnet's face in his hands and gazed in her eyes. "Not fair to me? I've been captured by your quirky, sensitive, beautiful soul. Of course, I long to make love to you but I can wait. As long as it takes."

Tears came into Garnet's eyes as Ravi spoke and she turned her head away.

"Don't be afraid," he whispered. "Just lie next to me knowing you're safe and protected. Shiva says pleasure is a tribute to the gods - being close to you is my pleasure."

"I know so little about pleasure," Garnet sighed. She was

sleepy but felt strangely comforted and sheltered. She gave Ravi a kiss of gratitude on his cheek and fell into a deep sleep.

Just before dawn, Garnet woke in fright to strange cries and howlings echoing through the tent. She was still in Ravi's arms, her shoulder and legs numbed and stiff.

"Wake up," she cried, shaking Ravi. "Someone is screaming as if they're being murdered."

He sat up in bed and listened to the muffled shrieks and growls. Garnet clung to him, terrified, but Ravi stroked her hair and reassured her.

"You're perfectly safe, my darling," he avowed. "Those aren't human sounds, only a desert lion howling as he roams through the rocks hunting for small animals to devour. But he won't come close to the tent. He's a reclusive breed and fears the human scent. You've nothing to worry about."

He put his arms around her and she fell back to sleep, curled up against him.

In the morning when the sun began to shoot blistering rays into the tent they dressed quickly to return to the palace. As they passed through the courtyard where the gardens were blooming with newly opened buds Garnet paused to gather an armful of pink roses. She heard sounds and stirrings coming from the French windows of the Lake Palace and looking up caught a glimpse of shadows moving behind white-louvered shutters. Curious, she turned to Ravi.

"Is someone living in the white palace?"

"Only some old servants," he replied, taking her by the arm, and hurrying her away. "Come along, I'm famished. Let's dash back to the palace and gorge on a real English breakfast. All this pleasure has given me a terrific appetite."

viii

After they ate breakfast Ravi took Vijay aside and asked if he'd find some amusement for Niles the following day.

"I'd like to take Garnet on a little jaunt to explore the old fort and temples and bring her out to the desert sand dunes at sunset to hear the musicians. As she's fond of horses I thought we'd ride out there. But I don't want Niles to bother her with his complaints."

"I'll see he's properly amused," Vijay responded, with a short laugh. "Niles is eccentric and a bit crazy but I've grown very fond of him."

The horses were saddled and waiting when they arrived at the stable the next day. The young groom, a sleepy-eyed boy roused from his nap on a straw bed in the corner of the stable, helped Garnet mount the gleaming russet steed who reared his head impatiently as he pawed at the earth.

"Emir is in bad temper today, missy-memsahib," the stable boy said hesitantly, looking back toward the stalls where the other horses were kept.

"Don't worry," she replied, feeding the horse a handful of sugar. "I can handle him."

"Why risk it if he's being difficult?" Ravi asked, drawing his horse up next to her. "Arabian horses can be temperamental, even dangerous. Especially stallions."

"Please, Ravi," she pleaded. "Emir is the horse of my dreams. He won't hurt me."

"Let's hope not. Stallions can be unpredictable. But it's up to you. As long as you're confident."

"I'm more confident about horses than I am about people," she replied, leaning down to kiss the horse's neck.

The sun was climbing high above the dusty horizon as Ravi and Garnet rode through the scrubby land to the entrance of the walled city and slowly made their way up the steep cobbled path leading to the fort.

As they passed under a huge stone archway, Ravi nudged Garnet with his riding crop.

"Sit up straight, Generalissimo," he commanded, affecting a rough military tone. "Conquering rulers passed through this *Gate of Kings* to celebrate their victories at the great Fort. We must salute the soldiers and greet the multitudes who bow down in homage."

Garnet saluted the arch. "*Victory is the beautiful, bright-colored flower* - Winston Churchill."

Ravi pointed toward a three-peaked hill. "Sushila would get a kick out of this. The handsome archway you see was built by the powerful *ganika* of a king, a *courtesan* who once ruled the city. Later, she rebuffed him and the angered monarch built a seven-story *revenge-palace* nearby for a harem of two thousand beauties."

They explored the Fort, climbed up on the temple roofs for a view of Gajpur, peered into elaborately carved Jain temples and visited the *Bada Bagh*, a garden oasis where they wandered around the *chatris*, ornate cenotaphs or empty tombs.

They rode through the thickets and brush of the patchy wasteland until Ravi stopped at a temple created exclusively for women, its entrance adorned by the statue of a half-naked pregnant female. He urged Garnet to light a stick of incense but she protested, insisting women came there for a fertility rite, a ceremony she couldn't participate in.

Ravi persisted and grudgingly Garnet waited behind two veiled ladies who knelt and prayed, mumbling incantations for what seemed forever. "Probably trying to bring forth a son,' Ravi whispered. Finally, it was Garnet's turn to light the incense and place it in the sand of the bowl held by the statue. She knelt, and mouthed a silent prayer, *Lord, keep me from acting like a damn fool.*"

They wandered through ravaged gardens and abandoned fortifications until the heat of the sun, a chalky blaze across the sky, became oppressive. By the time they rode on to the ruins of a temple overgrown with weeds and underbrush, Garnet was hot and exhausted. It was difficult to endure the constant haze of heat searing the desert no matter how she fought it. Her blood had a low boiling point, a defect impossible to change. When Ravi suggested they find a place to picnic Garnet gratefully assented. "I think we'd better unless you want a collapsed general on your hands."

Ravi helped her inside a crumbling temple and sat her down on a slab between ruined marble columns and broken statues of plump goddesses in provocative poses. He tied up the horses, unstrapped a leather bag and unpacked a picnic lunch and a bottle of wine, and spread out a cloth. After eating Ravi suggested napping on Dhurri rugs in the shade of an old banyan tree.

A warm breeze blew over them as they stretched out on the rugs. Garnet was tired and wanted to drowse but Ravi lay close to her and she could smell his scent, the sweet odor of his skin mingled with the faint residue of cologne and again fought the longing for him, surprised at the insistence of her craving.

She wondered if Ravi sensed what she was feeling and shifted to the edge of the rug. When he reached out to touch her hand, she stiffened. He gave her a consoling pat and quickly withdrew. For once, the warmth of the desert seemed comforting as she drifted off to sleep.

ix

"You've seen enough monuments," Ravi said, when Garnet woke. "It's time to ride off into the Indian sunset."

At the sand dune desert they took off their shoes and walked barefoot in fine-grained, powdery sand to the yellow hills.

"A mini Sahara!," Garnet exclaimed, digging her toes in the sand.

"It's a tourist attraction," Ravi chuckled. "Bus loads of sightseers come to ride camels over the dunes and watch the sunset.

Quite a kick for them - a bit of cinema, Lawrence of Arabia, Omar Sharif, etcetera."

"Dare we ride the camels?" Garnet asked, with a bit of trepidation.

"Dare?" Ravi snorted. "Riding camels is an adventure for middle-aged women in print dresses, not for dashing explorers like us."

The camels crouched in the sand waiting for their *keeper* to help the patrons mount. Ravi picked out a camel and climbed on to show her how easy it was but the camel balked and reared. Ravi laughed. "You mustn't take camels seriously. They think they own the place."

In contrast, Garnet's camel was placid and she sat comfortably as he raised his hump up to the sky and began to lope along the dunes. She remarked on his pleasant disposition to Ravi but at the sound of her voice the camel turned his head and growled at her, stamping his feet for emphasis.

"This camel is in no mood to be praised," she confided to the raggedy boy guide who smiled politely without understanding.

"Tell the beast in. Hindi, Ravi. Assure His Majesty I won't insult him again with my compliments."

The camels jolted them along the dunes until they reached the hilltop and disembarked. A band of red-turbaned musicians in rumpled white dhotis were sitting on the sands strumming an odd assortment of instruments. Ravi pointed out the seven-stringed *sitars* with their vibrating understrings and the guitar-like *Vina*, symbolizing the body of the goddess Parvati with its curved neck, gourds shaped like breasts and bracelet-like frets. *Sarasvati*, goddess of music, and her son *Narada*, musician of the gods, are depicted with the *Vina* in Indian paintings. There were the *bansuris*, or flutes dear to Krishna who enticed maidens by his tantalizing tones on the flute. *Tabla* drums pounded the beat, and a curious twang of music was created by rubbing gongs over brass pots and striking sticks against the gongs.

They sat cross-legged in the sands below the musicians as ragas and ancient folk songs echoed across the desert, the sky reddened by sunset like the cheeks of a maiden and sands hennaed with a tinge of rose. Garnet found the primitive yet complex tonal structure of the music oddly calming and was moved by the raggedy troupe of musicians, from shabbily clad flute-playing boys of six or seven to grizzled old men, all virtuosos of their instruments eking out a bare subsistence as they humbly offered their gifts to the sky and spirit of Siva.

After the musicians disappeared over the hills, Ravi and Garnet lay back in the sand. The sunset was fading fast over the desert, the glaze of titian and topaz melting to violet in the twilight. The sky had lost its edge of heat and with luck the dryness of the desert would cool the evening after the sun vanished.

They watered the horses and rode them at a slower gait to prevent straining the thoroughbreds after being tied up for hours. But when they came in sight of the fort, the amber sandstone gleaming gold in the distance, Garnet suggested they pick up the pace.

"I'm tired of poking along," she said. "These horses were born to run."

"We have time for a fast ride before the sky loses color," Ravi answered. "Race you to the old fort?"

"Try and beat me!" Garnet answered and prepared herself for the race, checking the stirrups, and making sure she was well seated in the saddle.

"Wait," Ravi said. "I'm not so sure you should race with Emir. Arabians can be unpredictable."

"Much like Indian princes, I suppose. But what chance would I have racing without such a horse? Unless you dreamed this up to keep me from winning."

"Not a chance. Haven't you heard about our Independence? We no longer fear the Ugly American."

Ravi clicked his heel against the rump of his horse. "Catch me if you can, my darling."

Garnet felt a rush of affection for Ravi but turned her head away to prevent his seeing the tender expression on her face.

She leaned down to kiss Emir's silken mane before she gently touched the heel of her boot to his rump and let him gallop away, exhilaration rising in her as the wind rushed by.

"Race your heart out, Emir," she whispered in the horse's ear. "We can do it. Go, Emir, go!"

The stallion responded to her touch, flying across the stony desert like a mythical winged beast, the evening air cool on her cheeks, the setting sun blurring a blaze of saffron before her eyes. She felt fearless but safe, as if lifted across the desert in the hands of angels.

Ravi's horse bolted ahead but Garnet pushed her graceful stallion to extraordinary effort, urging him on, begging him. When the wall of the fort came in sight Emir spurted forward, outdistancing the other horse by a length as he reached the gate.

"You're a glorious rider." Garnet gasped to him, her hair flying, her face flushed with effort. "A desert Sheik! I can't believe we beat you."

Ravi shook his head. "I didn't have a chance," he snorted. "Emir is an Arab prince and a woman lover. He won to please you and get the best of me."

Garnet laughed and reached over to pat the neck of Ravi's horse.

They slowed the horses down to a trot to cool them off as they made their way back. From a distance, the palace scaled the horizon like a fairy-tale castle as the last vestiges of sunset washed over the crumbling stone of walls and turrets, decay and deterioration restored in the rosiness of the setting sun.

At the palace Vijay and Niles were already eating dinner. Ravi suggested joining them but Garnet begged off, pleading a sudden attack of exhaustion and the onset of a headache.

"Let me run up to my room and take a shower first. This *pisces-fish* needs to be drenched with water to revive. I'll be quick, and then we can stuff ourselves."

x

Garnet rested for a moment on the bed before taking a shower but when she tried to get up she was too exhausted to move. An hour later, when Ravi knocked on the door she was still lying down.

"You look tired, Garnet. Let's skip dinner in the salon," he suggested. "Veda can prepare something light and bring it here."

She relaxed in a soft armchair in his sitting room while waiting for dinner but felt too ill to concentrate on what Ravi was saying. By the time the servant set out the food the smell of spices which usually whetted her appetite, overwhelmed her with nausea and she ran into the bathroom to throw up. She hoped she wasn't going to be really sick but once it began, she couldn't stop and spent the rest of the night alternately throwing up and having severe attacks of diarrhea, half-fainting from weakness.

The real miracle was to be in India for months without getting sick. Realistically, she knew it was bound to happen with her physical sensitivities in the sweltering, germ-ridden climate of India ridden with bad plumbing and lack of sanitation. Remembering her mother's revulsion at illness she was embarrassed for Ravi to see her this way. But Ravi was different, holding her head when she vomited and comforting her when great cramping pains left her shaken and weak. Still, she wanted to cry out, *How can you? This is too disgusting even for me to bear* but she was too sick to voice her shame.

"Poor darling," he said, carrying her into the bed from the bathroom and sponging off her hot forehead with a cloth dipped in ice water. "You're burning up. I'm afraid it's a bit more serious than *turista*."

When morning came, Garnet was worse. Her temperature had risen, vomiting and diarrhea intensified and her skin took on a gray pallor. She was too prostrated to speak and as the illness worsened it was clear this was no simple case of Delhi-belly or food poisoning. Her condition deteriorated quickly and Ravi realized medical help was needed, hopefully a competent doctor, a scarce commodity in Gajpur. Vijay became alarmed as well, both hoping against hope the illness wasn't the plague they feared.

The phone lines were out of order again so Vijay offered to drive to the local hospital and fetch the best doctor he could find. This was no case for the bumbling, white-haired Dr. Bhwagham who fawned over the maharani, bowing and scraping with '*Your Highness and Your Majesty*' ad nauseum, pandering to her hypochondriacal complaints. Dr. Bhaghwam couldn't diagnose or treat a real disease if his life depended on it.

Luckily, Vijay retrieved Dr. Karawalla, the most eminent physician in the area. A wiry, intense young Indian in his thirties who'd grown a beard to disguise his youth, he had graduated from Harvard Medical School and interned at a top New York hospital.

Dr. Karawalla shook his head after he examined Garnet, and pronounced their worst fears had proven true.

Garnet was too ill to talk but could hear snatches of whisperings, '*Cholera . . . yes, severely ill, dangerous situation . . . don't dare move her . . .* '

The doctor motioned Ravi out of the room to discuss the prognosis. There were complications, signs of pneumonia making the case more difficult to cure. He warned that the patient had only a 50-50 chance of recovery but promised to try everything to save her. Antibiotics were available and he'd begin medication at once, along with intravenous saline and mineral solutions to replace loss of water, sodium and potassium. However, he warned such cases did not always respond to treatment. Besides the pneumonia there was the danger of renal failure and the risk that reduction of plasma volume would lower the blood pressure, resulting in a fatal collapse.

Ravi paled when he heard the diagnosis - cholera victims

were wiped out by the thousands during India's plague epidemics.

"I'll arrange to send over a nurse in the next hour or so," the doctor assured him, as he wrote out several prescriptions.

"I prefer to nurse her myself," Ravi replied.

"It's far too risky," the doctor answered, raising his eyebrows at the very idea but not wanting to offend the prince. "You'll need a nurse who's a specialist in infectious diseases."

"Send her if you like," Ravi said, firmly. "She can assist me but I intend to take care of Miss Lawler."

The doctor shrugged his shoulders. "As you prefer," he answered, pressing his palms together and bowing in an obsequious fashion. He hated his falseness but his practice was dependent on Gajpur's upper-class and he wasn't about to endanger it by being inflexible or disrespectful to a member of the royal family, no matter how eccentric.

"Then you must take precautions," he warned. "You'll need a shot of serum to give you some protection. Cholera is extremely contagious and quarantine is a necessity. You must cordon off this wing of the palace. The nurse will explain other safeguards and convey my instructions to aid you in the treatment. I'll check on the patient daily but call at once if an emergency situation develops."

Ravi kept his fears to himself and insisted Vijay keep Garnet's condition secret as Niles suspected she was seriously ill and was beside himself, frantically begging to see her. But Vijay took charge, keeping Niles in their wing of the palace and devoting himself to reassuring and distracting him.

Ravi stayed with Garnet day and night, refusing help from Dr. Karawalla's cheerful, plump-cheeked nurse. He sponged Garnet to bring down the fever, held her head when she vomited and changed her nightdress when it was soaked with perspiration. He waved off her embarrassment, insisting such delicacies were unworthy of her.

A week passed but her condition hadn't improved. Dr.

Karawalla was troubled as he reviewed her chart and checked her lungs and pulse.

"The pneumonia has not responded well to treatment," he told Ravi. "There's still a good deal of fluid in her lungs. I'm sorry but you must be prepared for the worst. We're dealing with a delicate young woman though youth is on her side. Hopefully, that factor might enable her to bounce back. Right now she's nearing a crisis. Her recovery will turn on that axis and give the definitive answer."

Tossing feverishly in the desert heat on sheets damp with perspiration, in her delirium Garnet had visions of the cool sea edging the rocky peninsula of Sailship Point. But there was no comfort there as unwanted memories intruded into her dreams, flashing through her mind as if she were drowning and obliged by gate-guarding angels to account for her days on earth.

For the next few days Dr. Karawalla spent his nights in the palace in a small room adjoining Garnet. He remained in the palace, leaving only intermittently for consultations at the hospital. He experimented with a new antibiotic and a serum flown in from the Tropical Disease Center in New Delhi but to no avail. Garnet's temperature escalated and her weakness became profound, nearly comatose, barely responding to touch.

"The crisis approaches," Dr. Karawalla whispered to Ravi, dropping his Harvard manner and reverting back to his Indian origins. "Now we wait, and pray."

Servants and sweepers gathered in the halls with Ravi's old servant, Veda, who was wringing his hands in despair, while Vijay waited helplessly, running back and forth to check on Niles. Dr. Karawalla instructed Ravi that if they held a vigil during the night they must be restricted to the Great Hall.

When the hour grew late and the crisis neared, Vijay tried to slip away alone but this time Niles, frantic at being left behind, had a small seizure and became hysterical. Vijay decided it might be more calming for him to join the others gathered in the Hall, lighting incense and candles and praying before massive brass statues of *Shiva*, god of regeneration symbolized by his large and erect penis, and *Ganesh*, the elephant god, remover of obstacles and *Krishna*.

Dr. Karawalla checked her temperature and adjusted the intravenous infusion aided by the nurse, her jolly face now anxious and sad, then let Garnet rest without disturbing her as they waited for nature to take its course.

Garnet was barely conscious. Although she heard the sounds of voices around her she couldn't connect the words. She was floating beyond the planet to a place of drifting and dreaming, her body melting away.

Ravi sat by Garnet's bedside and held her hand, his head bent in prayer as she seemed to slip farther and farther away from him.

Hours passed in silence. Ravi looked at his watch. Four o'clock, he thought, the *hour of the wolf when death bares his fangs*. He could hardly breathe.

As the darkness of the long night began to lift and a scrawl of vermilion scribbled its way across the black sky, Dr. Karawalla leaned down to feel Garnet's forehead with his hand, then tapped Ravi on the shoulder to give him the news. Her fever had broken.

The doctor checked her heart and lungs with his stethoscope, greatly relieved to reassure the prince. Losing this patient could have seriously damaged his reputation and practice.

"Her vital signs are 'stronger and her lungs are clear." His voice was triumphant. "She survived the crisis and won the battle. She's perspiring profusely and the fever has passed. The young lady needs a good deal of care, she's quite weak, but I have every reason to believe she will recover."

Ravi put his hands over his face and wept. Dr. Karawalla patted him on the shoulder. "You need rest. Get some sleep," he said. "The nurse will watch over her."

xi

In the morning, Garnet emerged from the delirium of fevered sleep, soaked with perspiration but grateful to be out of limbo. Ravi was sitting next to her, wringing out a cloth in a bowl of ice water.

"The doctor assures me the crisis is over," he said, bathing her face with the icy cloth as Garnet shivered. "We watched over you waiting for the fever to break. You were burning up. Then you began to perspire, the first sign of recovery and we all breathed with relief."

As he spoke, Garnet felt the nightmares dwindle away. She tried to smile but her face felt heavy and it was difficult to hold her eyelids open so she fluttered her fingers at Ravi and drifted off to sleep again. Although the worst was over Garnet slept on and off for days intermittently sipping broth, eating bites of bread and yogurt, then collapsing back onto the pillows and falling back to sleep.

"Not to worry," Dr. Karawalla said cheerfully, his confidence in his role as *the great doctor* restored by her recovery. "Sleep is healing. Nature's cure."

A week later Garnet woke up, smiled at Ravi, took his hand and placed it on her forehead.

"As cool as a mango," he assured her.

"No cucumbers in India?" she teased.

"The princess must be better if she argues with the *tika raja*," he said, vastly relieved by her improvement. "You gave us some scary moments, wicked girl, but we'll soon have you well. *If* you follow my orders!"

"I'm too tired to resist," she said, sinking back into the pillows. "The Ugly American capitulates."

When she was well enough to sit in a chair for short periods and take a few steps, Ravi said, "I'll bet you're dying to take a shower instead of being sponge-bathed by the nurse. Do you feel strong enough to try?"

He tossed a big towel onto the bed and suggested she pull off her nightgown under the sheet and wrap herself in it. Then he helped her up and brought her to the pink marble shell.

"I'll get you into the shower, turn on the water and promise not to look," he said.

Garnet took off the towel inside the shower and handed it to him through the pink translucent curtain but in her weakness she staggered against the shell and nearly fell. Ravi stepped in, grabbed her and steadied her against the wall, and was about to step out again when she held onto to his hand.

"Please stay, Ravi, I'm dizzy. This is no time for modesty."

He tore off his shirt and got under the shower with her wearing his thin white kurtah pants.

"Ah, my elusive maiden of the forest, now I've captured you."

Garnet fell into his arms, soaking wet, her hair dripping water onto his chest, laughing as he held onto her. For a moment she clung to him.

"Watch out you haven't caught the *Queen of the Willies* instead of the Swan."

"I'll take my chances," Ravi answered. "Since I just saved you from breaking your neck you might even be sweet to me."

Ravi held her up and soaped her with the sponge. She didn't resist as he turned the shower up to full force and a cascade of water rushed down, drenching her body.

She closed her eyes imagining herself in a primeval forest perched on a rocky ledge under a mountain waterfall while cool streams gushed over her and washed her past away, dissolving torments and doubts and baring a hunger to surrender as willingly as God's first woman.

There was a sweet, perfumey scent clinging to Ravi's skin and she leaned down and kissed his shoulder. She had tried to stifle her infatuation for him, fearing it was too risky, but Ravi had saved her life, nursed her through disgusting physical episodes repulsive even to her. He had cared for her in illness with the tender hands of a loving mother. Remembering him at her sickbed evoked an even greater desire for him and melted away the barriers she'd erected to protect herself. It seemed pointless now to evade her longing. She took Ravi's hands in hers, kissed them and placed them on her breasts.

After the shower, Ravi swaddled her in towels and carried her to the bed. He was leaning over her trying to straighten out the bedclothes when she wrapped her arms around his neck and pulled him toward her.

She wasn't entirely conscious of the act when they made love, still a bit dizzy so the experience felt surrealistic as if she'd relapsed back into illness yet it was those sensations of weakness and delirium that allowed her to surrender to passion for the first time.

Afterwards, Garnet stroked the silky skin of his shoulder.

"I think you cured me."

"I hope so. You were a very sick girl and caused me a good deal of anguish when we came close to losing you. I'd waited for you to appear for such a long, long time," Ravi said, insisting again their meeting was predestined and he'd been prepared by a ghostly vision.

"When you floated around the foot of my bed five years ago, a faint sound emanated from your ghostly head. '*Wait for me, wait for me,*' you whispered. '*I'm on my way, slowly, slowly.*' I was haunted by the apparition, couldn't shake off it off, and consulted the family astrologer."

"The pundi reassured me. '*Your vision was a glimpse of the soul you've waited for, the one who brings completion, who connects the past with the present.*' It didn't make sense to me and gradually the feeling of being haunted faded. But I began to experience an inner thirst as if my soul had gone dry and was consumed with longing to find the spirit who would fulfill me."

Garnet drew him close to her. "I could never have imagined a man like you."

"There were signs I'd stumbled on my destiny when we met," Ravi said, kissing her fingers. "The garnet is the spiritual jewel of India, a gem imbued with mystical powers, and it's my birthstone. I'm a Capricorn goat born on the fifteenth of January, the same day as Shah Jahan."

Ravi handed a velvet box to Garnet. "The Greeks named garnets after pomegranate seeds and claimed they would *draw a heart close and keep it faithful*."

"Mmm, a present?" Garnet smiled happily. It was fun to feel well enough to tease Ravi again. "Or payment in lieu of two hundred dollars on the bureau?"

He shook his head. "What a wicked girl you are. And such high prices!"

She opened the box. A rope of garnets was nested in the velvet. In the light the gems glinted scarlet sparks as she caressed them with her hands. She rubbed them against her cheeks with a repentant look at Ravi.

"The garnets are beautiful but I don't deserve them."

"Yes, you do," he said, taking the rope of garnets and fastening them around her neck. "They belonged to Granny and were precious to her. She'd want you to have them."

"I love them even more because they were hers," she said, kissing the garnets.

Ravi held her tight and kissed the top of her head. "Thank God you were saved," he whispered.

Ravi devoted himself to Garnet during her convalescence. He helped her bathe, read to her, sang the English lullabies his granny sang to him as a child, told silly jokes to cheer her up and cajoled her into eating delicacies he invented to tease her appetite back into existence.

"It's time we fed the poor convalescent her breakfast," he said, pointing to the window where the dawn flooded the worn silk curtains with color.

When Veda arrived at the door with the breakfast tray Ravi took it from him and carried it to the bed. He plucked a rose from the silver vase, tucked it in Garnet's hair, then propped up the pillows behind her and poured the coffee.

"Now this is what I call princely service," Garnet said, biting into a hot puffed *puri* and sipping her coffee. "But aren't we depriving some chaste princess of a royal mate?"

Ravi took a bite of her bread. "It's a tradition in my family beginning with my grandfather not to marry the designated princess but to rebel with a love-bride of one's own choosing."

She laughed and rubbed her cheek against his, feeling safe and comforted as he lavished on her the nurturing she'd craved as a child. *How strange*, she thought, to find her longed-for affection in the palace of an Indian prince. She'd hoped to grow beyond such infantile hungers but for now she needed Ravi, not only to convalesce from her illness but to recover from her past.

xii

Some weeks later, in an early dawn of mists and sand-drenched winds blowing across Gajpur, a fireball of red sun splattered the sky with color and crept through the windows of the palace.

Garnet stirred and sighed in Ravi's massive bed under the canopy draped in velvet and swathed in white mosquito netting, like a virgin bride at the altar. It seemed as if she'd been lying in bed with Ravi forever, making love, drifting and dreaming through the days as if she were still the invalid in the throes of cholera floating in and out of consciousness. But instead of the doctor's cold probing instruments the plump lips of an Indian prince were sucking on her toes. She laughed to herself. It was an Arabian Nights tale, a fantasy, like the old films she and Imelda giggled at, gobbling Hershey's kisses:

Prince of ancient days captures maiden, binds her with silken ropes, flings her over his swift Arabian steed and imprisons her in a palace where she awaits his pleasure idling the days away nibbling on nougats and Turkish Delight.

We do make an odd looking pair in bed, she thought ruefully, contemplating her delicate shoulders, lanky legs and sharp hip bones contrasted with Ravi's fat belly and soft hands. She smiled to herself and turned around to nuzzle Ravi's ear.

"You're my tawny tiger," Ravi teased. "A rare Bengal beast," admiring strands of topaz hair piled against the pillow and skin honeyed from summers tanning on the beach. "I should shoot you, mount you on the wall and worship you from afar as you'd make a wretched rug with those sharp bones of yours."

Garnet laughed and raised her head to catch a breath of air rustling through the window. A light breeze was blowing across the indigo lake created to cool indulged princes in summer.

Her poor de-throned prince rubbed his cheek into her hair and sucked up a strand with his lips. "Your hair tastes like flowers," he murmured. "I may eat you up, bones and all. Legend claims my cannibal ancestors feasted on slender girls, an ancient delicacy based on the theory that the tenderest meat is close to the bone. You of course, are not such young meat but you might make a fair meal. Perhaps you've grown tastier with the years like a great Burgundy wine."

Garnet stuffed a pillow in his laughing mouth and straddled him, pounding her thighs on the side of the bed.

"You go too far, my prince," she squealed. "Try to remember, my beloved, I'm the conqueror here. In me lies the secrets of American know-how, consumer addiction, and expertise on how to run crummy little factories as well as germ-kill, clean-up, and magic methods to sanitize raunchy toilets."

"For that you die, imperialist monster." Ravi twisted out from under her legs and wrapped his arms around her. "Fiendish tortures were invented in India for women who commit such heresy. In archaic times it was the rack but over the centuries a subtler method evolved. We call it *jihwajuddha*, loving a woman to death! Endless sensuality until she dies of exhaustion."

Garnet jumped out of bed, wrapping a sheet around her. "You already tried that, you beast. But instead of dying, I'm getting fat and healthy. Worst of all, I've become fond of my captor, a clever brainwashing technique favored by terrorists. But you can't fool an American."

Teasing, teasing, playing games to hide the deep sense of contentment and pleasure she was experiencing.

"Bravissima!" Ravi cheered. "The princess is cured and back to her old tricks."

He tugged at the sheet and pulled her toward him covering her face with kisses until she succumbed, laughing helplessly as she sank into the soft feather bed.

xiii

Now that Garnet was stronger Ravi brought her the books she needed for research and had the servants carry in a small French desk belonging to his grandmother, *Rajmata* Elizabeth.

"Granny wrote on this desk every morning," Ravi said, rubbing his palms over the polished top. "Letters to arrange help for the poor or begging the Viceroy to commute some poor fellow's unjust sentence, always helping someone. She liked me to be in the room while she worked, let me play under the desk, rummage through the box of *treasures* she collected for me and gobble up the English *toffees* in the silver bowl meant for visitors."

Garnet thought of Rani Elizabeth as she worked on the small fruit-wood desk, trying to sense her presence and feel the spirit so loved by Ravi. There was a framed photograph of her on the desk and when Garnet paused in her work she pored over the image of the young woman in a white dress, fitted and ruffled *turn-of- the-century* fashion, perhaps the very frock Garnet tried on in the storerooms with Ravi. The fresh and innocent smile of the bride-to-be in the photo taken shortly before her elopement made Garnet reflect on this sheltered Viceroy's daughter. Rani Elizabeth had the courage to fight for marriage to an Indian prince who, though a future king, was scorned by the British for his shade of skin.

The days slid into each other without definition. Mornings she slipped into the 17th century palace of Shah Jahan and Mumtaz Mahal absorbing herself in their lives, afternoons she was in Ravi's bed where time disappeared.

She'd never been touched so lightly yet each caress reverberated through her as his fingers slid along her skin, barely grazing her body reminding her of healers who move their hands in circles above the patient without touching.

She reveled in the feel of Ravi's flesh, plumped up as if stuffed with the softest of goose down, embarrassed by her boniness, hip bones sticking up when lying on the bed, pelvis hollowed out like a bowl with her stomach hidden in the cavity.

But Ravi reassured her. "You're perfect," he said. "We were made for each other. My round tummy fits into your lovely hollow and my fat cushions your delicate bones, the fragile underpinnings of your beauty which make you even more precious."

He covered her body with kisses, plump squishes puckering up her skin with pleasure, reverberating through her like the shocks of an acupuncture needle.

She woke each day longing for the feel of his plump flesh on her skin wishing it could melt into her bones and spread over her body. There was so much pleasure in his touch - the delicacy of Sushila's caress fused with robust male hormones, female and male in one, rugged and sweet, the lovemaking of *Lord Krishna*.

Nor was he remote. Garnet was moved by the sensations and depth of feeling she evoked in him. He shivered at her slightest touch - sliding her fingers across his arm raised goose bumps on his skin and he was unashamedly expressive in lovemaking, moaning, crying out, even weeping in ecstasy.

She'd been a lost girl holding herself together by sheer will, pretending to the world she was strong while hiding hurt and

vulnerability under a flimsy shell. Ravi was offering the unconditional love she craved as a love-starved child, a chance to
recuperate from a lifetime of lovelessness. She drank in the comfort of Ravi, savored the solace and let the damage of the past
fade away.

xiv

The sudden appearance of Ravi's mother set the palace in
an uproar, sending servants scurrying about sweeping and dust-
ing what had been sorely neglected in her absence. The maharani,
as was her yearly custom, had spent the hot summer months in
the Simla hills where once the British Raj held court. It was here,
in their longing for king and country, they stubbornly planted an
English village of frame cottages and tidy gardens, paradoxically
adopting the Hindi *bangla*, anglicized as bungalow, to describe
their homes while rejecting all else in the culture including the
natives. But that was long past and Simla now had a somewhat
desolate quality, a forlorn town living on past glories as the tim-
ber of English houses rotted and there was little interest or money
to restore them.

Still, the large summering houses of the maharajas remained,
a vestige of former extravagant lives. The old royal families flocked
to the hills, relieved to escape the brutal heat, unconcerned about
the shabbiness of comfortably built summer palaces set amidst
lush green hills. In the cool dawns of mountain summers, parrots
and cockatoos twittered morning songs as days were whiled away
playing bridge and lunching at the palatial country club where
once only the British Raj and a handful of Indian crowned heads
were welcome.

The maharani held court here, gathering friends about her,
entertaining as lavishly as she dared on her limited income, demanding deference as the ex-maharani and gathering sycophants

among the refugees escaping India's blistering heat to satisfy her greed for adulation.

Her hasty return to Gajpur, some weeks earlier than expected, was the result of a flurry of gossip carried up to the Simla circle by jealous acquaintances who despised Khalili's pretensions and seized the opportunity to jab the maharani's overblown ego. The word was, they whispered surreptitiously, confident it would soon reach her ears, that a comely young woman from the West had taken up residence in the palace apartments of the crown prince.

"The maharani is back from Simla and commands us to appear before her this evening," Ravi reported with some amusement.

"You see, my infamous mother refuses to accept the ending of royal reign in India, over for twenty years, insisting she still has power over her mythical subjects. The family and servants indulge these illusions to prevent her bad temper from disturbing our lives but you mustn't take her seriously. When you consider my poor mother's childhood, bred and fed on illusion, one can forgive her rejection of reality."

Garnet nodded in assent from the chaise longue on the balcony where she stretched out lazily watching the rippling of the lake in the afternoon breeze. "Sushila gave me a book on kumaris," she said, handing him the slim volume. "It's hard to believe this ancient cult still exists."

Ravi skimmed through the pages, nodding his head as he read. *Kumari puja*, or *virgin worship* is an ancient sect which worships feminine energies through Shakti, female consort of the god, Siva. The sect is maintained by the monarchy of Nepal and the king worshipped as the living descendant of Lord Vishnu, god of protection."

The *kumari, or Living Goddess* who presides over the temple is selected at the age of four or five. Only a flawlessly beautiful child is eligible and she must pass thirty-two stringent tests of perfection including silky and unblemished skin, radiant health with no unpleasant body odors, and a test of bravery to prove her fearlessness where men in demon-masks feign monsters and brandish the severed, bloody heads of buffaloes."

The child goddess is secluded in the Royal Temple, dressed in red as a symbol of power, energy, and the blood of life. She leaves the temple only for religious festivals and ceremonies which parade her through the streets, carried by attendants as religious law decrees her feet must not touch the ground.

Pilgrims travel great distances to be healed or blessed by the goddess for the kumari is considered the mystical symbol of creation. She is petitioned to foretell the future and indicates by various signs her pleasure or displeasure. If the Kumari rubs her hands after eating it is a sign the pilgrim is destined to become ill within the month, if she laughs aloud or weeps during prayers he may die. When a Kumari trembles the seeker will be imprisoned, if she claps her hands he's in danger from the king.

The kumari reigns until her virginal perfection is blemished by a serious illness, or even bleeding from a cut. At puberty the first drop of blood ends her reign and removes her from the small throne.

After her reign, the most ravishing of ex-Kumaris faces a bleak future. Although the temple endows her with a sum of money and allows her to marry superstition clouds the life of a former goddess. Many believe a Kumari retains divine powers endangering the man who marries her, some say a bridegroom who weds the Living Goddess will die within a year.

"I became curious about my mother's bizarre childhood while at school in Dehra Dun," Ravi said, tossing the book on the table. "So I traveled to Nepal to see the reigning Kumari. She was pathetic, a dressed-up little doll locked in the temple. At the age of five or six the child looks forlorn closeted away behind the balcony, watching street urchins playing in the courtyard, her face wistful as they jump and squeal."

"But as a kumari grows older the role takes hold and she changes. Pride and arrogance emerge in her face and in the imperious manner her small hand waves people away. Ironically, by the time she grows fully into the vision of herself as a goddess, puberty arrives and it's all over. She's pushed out and another child takes her place."

Garnet shook her head in disbelief. "Leaving the goddess as what? It seems barbaric."

"That's why I pity my mother," Ravi replied, "despite the difficulties she creates for everyone around her."

"What about your father - was there an end to his obsession?"

Ravi pressed his lips together and looked away. "Someday I'll tell you that unhappy story."

After dinner Ravi escorted Garnet through the maze of pearly marble halls, past the threadbare rugs and shabby settees into the reception area of the palace where the maharani awaited them. Smoky wisps of sandalwood incense swirled by them as they entered a large salon nearly empty of furnishings whose chill marbled walls gave off a coldly formal air.

The maharani was seated at one end of the drawing room on a settee of silver, the curved back sculptured in flowers, leaves, and tiny dancing figures. On the wall behind her, a faded tapestry depicting scenes of warriors and women in sensual and provocative poses was flanked by huge sconces, flickering candles casting an eerie light over the barren room.

His mother did not rise nor greet them when they entered. She motioned them closer, scrutinizing Garnet intently and pointed them toward two chairs placed directly opposite her.

Set up like a job interview, Garnet thought. *Her way of keeping the wrong young woman at bay, off the back of her precious prince?*

The maharani folded her hands in greeting and bowed her head slightly. Ravi returned the greeting and Garnet followed suit. His mother was silent, as if calculating her next move.

Her skin was the color of old bone, ivory-smooth, cheekbones high with a tinge of Nepalese broadness, eyes ice-black. There was no doubt about her beauty, it was evident in remnants of past glories even with parchment skin now aged, fine-wrinkled.

There was nothing commonplace about her, certainly not her gaze, a forbidding mixture of severity, remoteness and arrogance.

She sat motionless, creating a hush of serenity around her, an impenetrable aura of silence as if she were encased in a glass dome. A trick perhaps of the child Virgin Goddess, a theatrical maneuver designed to control crowds who came to gape. After a moment, the maharani waved her hand in a vague gesture of reconciliation drawing the thick silence around them. She stared at Garnet. Time seemed to stop.

It's pure sorcery, thought Garnet. *Magic and wizardry transporting us into a mountain shrine, a Buddhist temple perched on the roof of the world, the maharani as head-honcho controlling our very breath. All that's missing are the beating of gongs and the clang of temple bells.'*

She dared not break the silence and looked toward Ravi who sat slumped in his chair, his eyes half-closed as if disinterested in the magic powers displayed by his mother. Finally, when it seemed no longer possible to endure the heaviness the maharani spoke, her voice cold, sharp-edged.

"May I ask where you met?"

"In Agra," Ravi answered, "at the Taj Mahal, introduced by Guru Devand. Garnet is a poet, the recipient of a literary grant. She's in India to write a book on Mumtaz Mahal."

Ravi's mother waved her hand away, dismissing the subject. "Such nonsense. Too much has been made of that woman. A cruel and selfish moghul of little interest."

The maharani's iron-black eyes blinked as she examined Garnet with a look of unconcealed contempt.

Then she spoke, slowly, choosing words as carefully as a jeweler selects rare gems to set in a ring. "My concern is about the woman living with my son in the palace."

"Garnet is here at my invitation," Ravi answered, his tone clipped as if to brook no further discussion.

"I understand that," his mother answered, her voice harsh and icy. "But as the affair has continued for months, I would like to make a few things clear. Miss Lawler is unsuitable and her presence here is a deterrent to your future."

Garnet sat silently in her chair. *Had she traveled ten thousand miles only to encounter another Francesca?*

"This is none of your business," Ravi said, his face red with fury as he started to get up from his chair.

"Sit down!" the maharani ordered sharply. "Of course, it's my business. A relationship between an American woman and an Indian prince of marriageable age is unacceptable. Impossible. An alliance with an adventuress, certainly not a virgin and far too old. Twenty-five, my friends tell me."

"Too old for a man ten years her senior? Don't be ridiculous," Ravi said, flushing with anger.

The maharani turned away from Ravi and spoke directly to Garnet. "Prince Ravi has evaded the issue of marriage long enough. It's time he chose a proper wife and carried out his duties to the royal line of Gajpur."

"I think I have something to say about that," Ravi interrupted.

The maharani ignored Ravi, fixing on Garnet's face with an intense stare as she spoke. "As Crown Prince, he must take a young wife, a pure, unspoiled Indian princess to bear his children and raise them in our royal tradition."

Garnet looked away. *It was pointless to answer. She could see the maharani was into her kumari act. The Virgin Goddess terrorizing pilgrims. But she learned from Francesca, that other beauty and master manipulator, how useless it was to engage in this sort of combat. A no-win situation for their victims.*

The maharani glared at her. "I want you to promise to leave the palace at once."

Garnet looked toward Ravi. This onslaught of hostility was making her feel ill and weak but she tried to garner her strength and hold back the tears, not wanting to give the maharani any satisfaction.

Ravi saw the expression on her face and got up quickly.

"Come along, darling," he said.

He folded his hands and bowed to his mother who sat in silence, her face tight and inscrutable. Then he helped Garnet up from the chair and took her arm as they walked slowly across the drawing room to the door, casting long shadows behind them on the marble floor.

XV

Garnet paused at the door of her room and leaned against the carved ivory of the frame, her body limp as if her spirit were wilting away.

"We're not stopping here," Ravi said firmly, pulling her away from the door. "You're tired and upset. *Come back wiz me to zee Casbah*, my beauty. We'll indulge our senses and pleasure ourselves in the silken tent."

Garnet shook her head. She was too upset to think about pleasure.

"Nights when I need consoling," Ravi persisted, "when black moods grab me by the throat and misery stomps down the dark passages of my soul, I seek solace in the ancient tent."

He rang for the servant and when Veda knocked Ravi stopped him at the door and whispered his orders into the old man's ear.

She took his hand reluctantly as he led her through the corridors. But in the tent she collapsed on the bed and sank into the pillows, her cheeks wet with tears.

Ravi leaned over to kiss her drenched lashes. "Is this my brave warrior?" he asked. "The General in his camp tent, dissolving in tears? This was a minor skirmish, *mon capitaine*."

Garnet sat up and wiped her eyes with a handkerchief. "The hate in your mother's eyes was a mirror-image of Francesca. Suddenly, this funny little world we've created, so pleasurable and comforting, was shattered in a thousand pieces."

Ravi stroked her hair. "Yes, my darling, there are life-spoilers who take pleasure in inflicting misery. But we won't let it happen."

"My mother was also a beauteous *dragon-lady* and I know what it is to live in that scenario," she whispered, trying to pull herself together.

Ravi hugged her and rubbed his cheek against hers.

"Matching monster mothers," he agreed, and brought out a bottle of champagne. Then he sat with his arm around her while they sipped wine and she told him about Francesca.

Just as Garnet's character had been influenced by the rugged seacoast where she grew up, Francesca was shaped by a landscape dissimilar in every way from that austere New England coast. She grew up in the honey-suckled land of Spain, in a voluptuous countryside blooming with purple bougainvillea and scarlet hibiscus, air heavy with the scent of frangipani, wild roses and lemon trees. Sensuality of climate and culture infused her blood with heat although she buried her lust and passion to maneuver a calculating, loveless marriage to Garnet's father.

Her family were wealthy Spanish aristocrats of Madrid society but during the Franco takeover in 1936 her parents, who opposed the dictator, were assassinated by a car bomb. Graciela, the old Spanish housekeeper and Francesca's nurse since birth, escaped with her eighteen-year old charge to Tangiers, then to America where Graciela labored as a domestic to take care of Francesca.

"Beauty was all I brought with me," Francesca admitted ruefully. "My parents regarded me only as an *object d'art* to be shown off and admired by their friends in Madrid - *as exquisite as a French china doll!* Men were the same, all they cared about was my beauty."

In America, Francesca came close to making a fatal mistake. The *shadow* in her scheming nature was a primitive lust excited by a brutish man, and she was drawn into a brief but passionate affair with a coarse peasant, a rough lout who deserted her in brutal fashion when she became pregnant. In spite of his unsuitability Francesca was shaken by the abandonment.

But gifted with a shrewd grasp of reality she rallied and sensibly turned her mind toward richer stakes. Still obsessed with Valdez she spurned the idea of abortion, pretending religious qualms, and boasted she would get a prosperous man to take care of them.

"Nothing blinds men like beauty," she told Graciela. "Beauty can reel a man in like a fish. *La pez muere par la boca!*"

Graciela shook her head. "*Puta!* You think like *puta.*"

"Don't be stupid, what else do I have to offer?" she retorted.

Francesca met Edward Lawler, an eligible young lawyer, at a dance and coolly studied the way his face lit up when they were introduced. Seeing herself through his eyes when he took her in his arms to dance she noted his disbelief as he held the exotic creature who tangoed like a delicate bird against his chest, a willowy white-throated dove with almond eyes and the glossy black hair of a raven. As they danced his breath grazed the top of her eyelids, smoked blue by veins traced under fine skin, and she sensed Edward's legs weaken with desire as he tightened his grip. Visualizing Edward as protection for herself and father for her unborn child Francesca set out to seduce and marry him. Blinded by infatuation and enamored by the uniqueness of her beauty Edward was oblivious to the vanity and opportunism concealed under the creamy skin of the enchantress, never dreaming he would one day grow to hate and despise Francesca.

"Our mothers are two peas in a pod," Garnet said angrily. "They lost their status in life at a young age and compensated by making everyone around them miserable."

"I should think about leaving Gajpur," she murmured, her eyes filling with tears. "Before your mother destroys us."

Ravi shook his head. "I'd never allow that."

Garnet held out her goblet for Ravi to refill. "You saw how determined she was to get rid of me. Women like our mothers always get their way, no matter the cost."

Ravi kissed Garnet's hands. "I'll protect you."

"If you can," Garnet said sadly. "I'm not sure how much I can bear. Remember the mermaid who loved a prince? Neptune turns her fishtail into legs and she's blissfully happy but when she takes a step it's as if knives are stabbing the soles of her feet. She's in agony, torn between excruciating pain and her great love for him."

Ravi listened intently as she spoke but didn't interrupt.

"Nothing gives me more joy than *dancing* with the handsome prince," Garnet said, looking away as she spoke. "But there are knives about to cut into *my* soles - or *soul*. I suffered my mother's malevolence as a child, I don't dare risk it again. This is reality."

"We're happy," Ravi protested. "I call that reality."

"No, my darling," Garnet demurred, caressing his cheek with her hand. "We've been dreaming our days away in a crumbling palace as if we were Mumtaz Mahal and Shah Jahan. It's not that I don't love it. What could be happier for a lost child than to dream her life away? But we're living in the past, as if it were 19th century India."

"There's no place for ex-princes to live except in the past," Ravi said, kissing her on the forehead. "I was a boy twenty years ago when the monarchy ended, forced to relinquish the royal entitlement brewed in my blood for a thousand years." He gave her a rueful look. "It didn't help my sense of reality that in India's so-called democracy discarded royalty was still addressed as *Prince* or *Maharani*. Unlike Russia and France, when India turned socialist they were too polite to machine-gun us into a ditch or chop our heads off. They allowed us to live on in impoverished gentility. Like the *castrati* of Italy our testicles were removed, but our lives spared. We could no longer sing Grand Opera, only bit parts in comic operettas. There were princes who turned to tourism or trade but some of us couldn't make the transition. We were bloodless aristocrats whose time had come and gone, a dying breed who lacked energy to move toward the 21st century. So, as monarchy and aristocracy are anachronisms in a world hanging by a nuclear thread I'm content to play the fairytale prince in a ramshackle palace."

Basking in the daydream was pleasurable for her as well but the maharani's hostility had shocked her into reality. *Had she escaped Francesca only to be tormented by a witch at the other end of the world?*

"I can't help loving your beauty and vitality," she confessed. "What woman could resist you? Or your indulgence in pleasure, foreign to me but irresistible."

"Mea culpa, mea maxima culpa," Ravi pleaded, nodding his head from side to side. "Take pity on a spoiled ex-prince."

Garnet sat up in the throne bed and laughed. "I'm afraid I've been a willing accomplice."

xvi

Ravi salaamed, opened a Chinese lacquered cabinet and removed a stringed instrument similar to Sushila's *tanpura.* "Forgive me for the pain my fiendish mother caused and let me soothe you with Indian love songs."

Ravi's face was serious as his fingers plucked the strings and he began to sing, his eyes half-closed in concentration. As Garnet watched him a flood of love coursed through her. She wanted to interrupt his singing, smother his soft mouth in kisses, bite his round cheeks, devour his sweetness like an adoring mother who threatens to eat up the plumpness of her baby.

She was still worried. Poor Ravi was an innocent who never had to confront the devil mother before and had no idea the extent of treachery and tactics such women were capable of. She knew she should leave Gajpur. But what if Ravi was her destiny, the mystic lover her soul was seeking, the karmic lover whose fate was entwined with hers?

She sat in silence listening to the reverberations of the strings as Ravi ended the last chord. When he paused to rest she took the *tanpura* from him.

"Now I'll play for you," she said, running her fingers over the strings, idly picking out a few chords.

Ravi lay back and rested his head on the velvet bolster. He smiled up at her.

She strummed on the tanpura and began to sing, "*I am maddened with love for thee, Lord Krishna but to whom shall I tell of my suffering? Only he who has felt the pangs of love has suffered.*"

She stopped singing as tears filled her eyes and spilled over her cheeks.

"Mira Bai! The Vaishnava saint," Ravi cried. "Where did you learn to play the tanpura? He laughed with delight and shook his head as if he couldn't believe it.

He turned and saw her tears. "No, no, my darling, you mustn't cry," he said, leaning over to kiss her tears away. "I won't let anyone spoil our happiness."

Garnet wiped her eyes with a handkerchief. "Shushu taught me. It was meant to be a surprise."

"Sing more, my beloved, your voice is so sweet," he murmured.

For once live in the moment! she rebuked herself. *Stop obsessing about the maharani and bliss out with Ravi.* She blew her nose, then smiled at Ravi and resumed singing.

"*Wounded, I wander from forest to forest, but have not found the healer yet. O my Lord, I will be cured only when thou shalt be my physician.*"

"You do love me! Then allow *me* to be thy good doctor," Ravi said when she finished, kissing her neck.

"First, more champagne," she teased, putting down the tanpura and reaching for the wine to refill their glasses."

"I feel close to Mira Bai," she said. "Not just any man would do. She searched for Krishna, singing to a *god*, but she's not the only one who hungered for a spiritual love. Your tenderness nursing me through my illness was as appealing as your candy lips."

She took his hand and kissed his fingers one by one, then buried her lips in his palm. "Mmmm," she murmured, "*Muy delicioso.*"

Ravi held out his arms and Garnet fell into them as if in a dream. The night air sifting through the tent was perfumed with jasmine and bougainvillea, curls of incense heavy with musk and sandalwood wafted a fragrant web over the velvet cushions of their bed, and reality disappeared.

She was Mira Bai searching for Lord Krishna as she felt the delicate touch of Ravi's fingers slide across her body, the twang of the tanpura reverberating in her head as she whirled in the pleasures and longings of the exotic saint. Afterwards, lost in the dream, she fell asleep entwined in Ravi's arms.

xvii

Garnet was awakened as the dark severed itself from the dawn with a river of carnelian flowing across the somber sky. She was still wrapped in Ravi's arms, her long hair twisted around his face, when there was a pounding on the courtyard door just outside the tent, a voice shouting in Hindi and broken English.

"Wake up, wake up! Come quickly, your Highness."

Ravi sat up in bed and tried to rouse himself from sleep, rubbing his face and shaking his head violently.

"Yes, yes, Veda, I hear you," he called back.

The velvet drapes of the tent parted and the elderly servant hobbled into the room. Garnet was fond of Veda. Although now a servant he'd been nurse and teacher to Ravi in his childhood.

His brown face, normally serene, was agitated. "Please, Sir," he pleaded, holding his folded hands up to his face in a placating gesture. "There is trouble in the summer palace. The old one threatens to kill himself."

Ravi shook himself awake and jumped out of bed, instantly alert as he gave orders to his old *ayah*.

"Fetch my clothes and bring me water for washing."

Veda filled a china basin and held it before Ravi who hastily splashed his face. Then the servant helped him into his white kurtah, admonishing him to *hurry, faster, faster*, as he wrung his hands and nodded his head from side to side in that odd little motion of Indian servants and shopkeepers. A nod which seems to say no, no, but means yes. *Yes, I understand, yes, I agree, and even if I don't, I'm obedient to your superior will.* Veda's life of service had confused his sense of himself as a separate entity. Long ago he merged his identity with this patrician family taking on their problems as if his own.

He politely avoided looking in Garnet's direction as she wrapped herself in a sheet and ran into the dressing room. She washed quickly, ran a brush through her tangled hair, slipped into her gauzy white dress and hurried back just as Ravi and Veda were leaving.

"Wait for me here, darling," Ravi said, planting a hasty kiss on her ear as he turned away. "I won't be long."

She was startled see Ravi's face had paled, his eyes tense with a mix of pain and fear.

"I'll come with you."

Ravi waved her back. "No, no, you mustn't."

Garnet followed him into the passageway.

"Garnet, please, I beg you. This is a difficult and private family situation. I prefer to handle it alone."

"Stop right there," she said, blocking his path. "You can't shut me out, Ravi, hide your life from me and treat me like one of your mother's whores. Am I really unworthy to share your pain?"

Ravi stared at her. Tears welled up in his eyes and he touched her face with a trembling hand.

"Come along then. If you're frightened, I'll send you back

with Veda."

He took her hand and they hurried behind the servant along the cool twisting halls to the courtyard facing the Lake Palace.

"What's wrong? Why should I be frightened?

Ravi didn't answer but held her hand tightly as they ran across the silvery bridge in their bare feet. When they came to the end and stepped onto the terraced gardens she could hear muffled cries and moans coming from behind the palace walls.

"Unlock the door," Ravi ordered Veda as the elderly man fumbled at the chain around his waist searching for the key to the carved teak and silver door.

"Here, let me," Ravi said impatiently, grasping at the bunch of keys in Veda's hand.

"Patience, Your Highness." The old man spoke softly, his tone at once reverent and admonishing. "*Krishna* says *Maya* controls all, what moves, what is unmoving. The key will turn the lock at the time ordained for it, not one moment sooner or later so all haste and anguish is for naught."

Ravi nodded his head in deference to the childhood nurse and spiritual teacher who taught him the scriptures of the Bhaghavad Gita. He remained silent as Veda opened the heavy door.

They stepped inside an inner court and Garnet paused for a moment, caught by the beauty of walls inlaid with semi-precious gems, opals, garnets, carnelian and amethysts patterned into delicate flowers, and a pearly marble floor whose center was carved into a shallow pool in the shape of a lotus flower. Tiny fountains, hidden in the petals, sprayed streams of mist while water-filled channels circling the edges of the room created a unique cooling system perfected by Mogul architects centuries earlier.

As the door opened a boy servant ran to usher them in. He, too, was wringing his hands, his face grimacing in anxiety as he bowed a greeting, and folded his hands in an imploring gesture.

"Namaste, Your Highness. We can do nothing with him today, sir. Please, quickly come."

He led them down a twisting hall and as they moved closer the noises grew louder. No longer moans and cries but great shouts of rage and the clatter of smashing glass.

"His Highness has much anger today," whispered Veda. "He goes from fits of violence to great weepings."

Garnet looked questioningly at Ravi but he ignored her, rushing ahead and flinging open a door at the end of the corridor.

As they hurried behind him, Garnet caught Veda's arm. "Who is *the old one*? What is he to Prince Ravi?"

Veda looked surprised. "Why, he is Maharaja, father of prince."

"Then he's alive?"

"Of course, otherwise Prince Ravi would be maharaja. But the old maharaja is ill, he lives in seclusion."

He hurried to the open door but Garnet caught him and pulled him back toward her.

"What's wrong with him?"

Veda's eyes filled with tears and he bobbed his head back and forth. "Please, memsahib, it is not my place to discuss such matters. You must speak to the prince."

Veda tiptoed into the room, bowing, barely dodging a glass vase flying across the room. Garnet waited, half hidden, at the edge of the door.

The sound of a deep voice, hoarse with violence, hurtled out of the room into the corridor.

"I'll fix those lying snakes. I'll get every one of those infidels and smash them! They destroyed my father's throne and turned me into a broken peasant leaving me to rot for eternity."

A great crash followed this outburst. Garnet peered around the edge of the door frame into the room. Tables and chairs were overturned and broken vases and glasses were scattered over the floor. An old man wearing a gold-embroidered red velvet coat over a long pleated skirt was whirling wildly around the room, slashing at the air with a saber, threatening servants who were trying to get close enough to take away his weapon.

Veda came out of the room to where Garnet was hiding behind the door and reassured her.

"Now that Prince Ravi is here, all will be put right."

"Why does the maharaja wear a skirt?" she whispered.

"He is garbed in the royal costume of his kingly ancestors," Veda replied stiffly as he hurried back into the room.

"Out of my way, you beasts of prey. Take one step nearer and I'll cut your heads off your shoulders, cleanly, in the manner of a true king!" the maharaja shouted as he chased a servant around a table, waving his sword over the cowering fellow's head.

It was a frightening sight until it became apparent to Garnet that the old man was enjoying himself immensely, reveling in his power, roaring with laughter as he taunted the terrified servants. His actions seemed half in pretense, the act of a charlatan aware of the role he was playing and its effect on his captives, and half the delusions of a man submerged in madness.

"Execution by the hand of the maharaja himself, truly a great honor," he cackled, rejoicing in their terror as they tried to escape him. "Come, come, who will be the first to die like a man?"

The servants cringed in corners or skirted around him ducking his wild slicings of the air with his saber.

She saw Ravi standing just inside the door. He looked upset and angry but as he approached his father he straightened his back until he stood erect, calming the expression on his face. He bowed to the maharaja, his hands folded in the traditional greeting.

"Namaste, father, my spirit bows before you."

"Out, out!" his father bellowed. "I want no part of a wretched family who longs for my death. You're a pack of animals trying to devour the lion but he is not yet conquered. You won't find him lying dead at your feet for some time to come. Lord Krishna has decreed it."

Ravi walked to the center of the room, ignoring his father's words and the chaos around him. The maharaja watched him furtively, his eyes sly, his lips twisted in cunning as Ravi held out his arms to him. He shook his head, his voice thick with self-pity, as he whispered, "I should not fear the end but rather embrace Death as my ultimate lover."

"Soon he will ask me to surrender to his heavenly wings." His voice grew wistful as he watched Ravi out of the corner of his eye. "Perhaps he awaits me now, longs for me, yearns for my breath to be consumed by him. Are you calling, Lord Krishna? Shh, shh, I hear the rustle of wings outside my door."

He glanced at Ravi to observe the effect on him, then closed his eyes as if in pain, "Is the spirit ready to take me? Lord, let me drink of your beauty, swoon with ecstasy in your arms to be forever adored by you."

With that, he turned the sword toward his body, arching his back and lifting his face to the ceiling. "Now, now? I come, do not despair."

Before he could plunge the sword into his body Ravi moved swiftly toward him, grasping his wrist and twisting his arm until the sword clattered to the floor. The maharaja's body went limp and twisted in a slow spiral to the floor.

He lay motionless on the floor for a few moments, then raised himself up on one elbow and glared at Ravi, his face contorted with rage, his voice a harsh growl. "Then kill me by your own hand, ungrateful son, and seize my throne for your own. A cruel fate to be destroyed by the flesh I created but I accept the Divine Will. Stab me, monster, and may the gods take pity and release you from your karma."

Ravi knelt beside him, gathering the frail body into his arms, and gently pressed a kiss on his father's cheek. The old man sobbed brokenly.

"No one understands my pain, cures my broken body or brings solace to a heart shattered by an ill-fated existence."

"You've every right to be angry with me," Ravi said, stroking his father's head. "I've been a neglectful son."

His father nodded, momentarily appeased by his son's abject expression.

"I've been away for some time, in Agra with Cousin Vijay," Ravi said, his voice soft and soothing. "We stayed at Sushila's villa where she regaled us with tales of her adventures. It seems she was more than a little in love with you."

The old man sat up, his face brightened and a broad smile spread across his tear-stained cheeks. "You saw Shushu? Ah, there was a woman, a wild and beautiful creature who could make any man feel like a king. Gone to fat now. Too much appetite and not enough restraint. But once a goddess with breasts as ivory as the moon. You can't imagine what it was to swim naked with her in the lotus pool, bathed in moonlight under the shadow of the Taj Mahal. Shame on me, an old man spilling secrets. No matter. Memories keep me alive. When the gods allow me to drift in dreams I forget I'm imprisoned in this dungeon."

"You need more distraction," Ravi said gently. "Are you bored with television and the films I brought?"

The maharaja pushed Ravi's arm away roughly. "Staring at flickering images, trash blinking out of a box? Show me where there's life in such an existence. I call it a living death, another empty invention by the hollow men running the planet, drugging witless idiots so they question nothing."

"Or perhaps," he continued, his face blistered red with rage, "you suggest I spend my days watching cheap films like your mother, the maharani, who sits for hours engrossed in plots nearly as inane and outrageous as the soap opera of her life. I think there must be a better way to endure the last days of my poor existence."

Ravi was silent, trying to hide the conflicting emotions churning inside him. Anger at his father's past of arrogance and self-indulgence was mixed with compassion for the torment of a once proud king. He quietly helped his father up from the floor and the maharaja collapsed in his throne chair, leaning his head back and rolling up his eyes, an expression of acute suffering on his face. Yet Ravi noticed a crafty glance under nearly closed eyelids, a shrewd appraisal of the effect he was achieving by his outbursts. He was part charlatan, rich with cunning and manipulative powers, but also a pathetic old man broken by disease.

The maharaja had been a lover of beautiful women but his unbridled desire revenged itself and he fell victim to the dread sexual disease of his generation. Syphilis, gifted by Carmela Agoya, a ravishing Spanish dancer met by chance in Europe who carried the plague from a string of sordid cafes beginning in Valencia and ending in Madrid where as *La Carmelita* she achieved acclaim for her flamboyant execution of the Flamenco as well as notoriety for her remarkable skill in unusual sexual practices learned in the Orient. The maharaja was drawn into a tempestuous affair, his greed for sexual pleasure finally satisfied by a dazzling *maestra* of eroticism.

When it came time to leave Egypt he could not bear to relinquish the miracle of voluptuous gratification appearing so unexpectedly in his life and decided to bring Carmelita back to India and set her up as a second wife. Tired of dancing, a good deal older than she admitted and fearing the dismal prospects ahead, Carmela grasped at the chance to escape a future eking out a meager existence in cafes as her charms faded or prostituting herself at the lowest level.

The maharaja took Carmela to India, traveling in style on a luxurious ocean liner, with a coterie of servants who indulged her every whim. She spent some weeks in the palace at Gajpur and wedding plans were in progress when the maharaja developed certain symptoms which court doctors recognized as an early stage of syphilis. Without telling his bride-to-be what transpired, the maharaja informed her it was necessary to undergo a medical examination before the marriage could take place. Doctors corroborated the feared diagnosis. Although she was without symptoms Carmelita was a carrier of the disease.

The doctors explained the gravity of syphilis to him. In that pre-antibiotic era mercury, arsenic and other methods of cure were primitive, often toxic, and usually ineffectual. There was little hope for recovery. They would try to arrest its virulent progression, an unlikely prospect considering the crude methods available.

The maharaja was enraged at the prognosis of his disease and dismissed his Spanish dancer brutally, beating her and shouting obscenities. Aides were ordered to search her quarters, retrieve money and jewels and threaten her with imprisonment or worse.

"Pay her fare to Spain and throw her back in the gutter where I found her. May she never rise to destroy another."

The Minister of State made it clear Carmela had reason to fear for her life unless she quietly acceded to the maharaja's demands, hustling her out of the palace in the dark of night. Two military guards accompanied her on the royal train with strict orders to remain at her side until she was safely boarded in Bombay and the ship embarked for Europe.

Khalili relished the news of her husband's downfall with intense pleasure as revenge brought about by the Goddess Durga on her behalf. She reveled in his misery, taking malicious comfort in hurling the disease in his face, claiming it retribution by the gods for his carnal adventures.

"You see how Divine Power punishes?" she gloated. "My beauty and spiritual powers weren't enough for you. No, your debased lust craved dirt from the lowest of the low. Now you see where vile desires end."

It ended with the aged, once impetuous maharaja terminally ill in the last stages of syphilis, the disease having spread to his brain causing uncontrollable rages, fits and seizures. Doctors eased his physical pain with morphine but could not assuage the suffering of his spirit.

xviii

Ravi took Veda aside to question him, "Did something happen to bring on the attack?"

"Yesterday morning," Veda whispered, "the maharaja insisted Rani Elizabeth was in the courtyard picking roses. He cried out, *She's wearing a white dress and her hair is shining in the sun!* He was much agitated and we could not quiet him. He thought the spirit of Rani Elizabeth had come to bring him a message, unless the apparition was Death disguised as his mother to carry him away without protest."

"I see," Ravi said, realizing the maharaja had mistaken Garnet for his ghostly specter.

Ravi thought for a moment. *If his father met Garnet it might calm his fears. But dare he subject her to this? Would the maharaja feel humiliated by his debilitated condition, a king whose power ended in shame and despair? Perhaps it was kinder to keep him hidden like an animal crawling away to die.*

Yet his father exulted in beauty, took pride in his reputation as a roué and could derive pleasure from the sight of a lovely young woman.

Ravi decided to chance it and motioned Veda to bring Garnet into the room. The old servant hurried outside the door where Garnet leaned against the wall trying to calm herself as she heard the noises and commotion coming from the room. Veda whispered Ravi's message in her ear.

She hesitated a moment, caught between fear of violence, or intrusion, then followed Veda to the door where she waited silently, trying to get courage to enter. She'd seen the prancing figure of the old man, heard him wheezing and panting, galloping around the room. Now as she neared the door she caught a glimpse of his ravaged face mottled with purple blemishes.

As she paused in the doorway, Ravi stopped his father with a hand on his shoulder and pointed toward Garnet. "Look, father, I've brought someone to see you."

The maharaja turned and looked at her as the light from the windows shimmered overhead blurring the edges of her white dress into a luminous aura, circling her long hair with an aureole of gold. The maharaja rubbed his eyes in disbelief and sank into a cushion on the floor.

"Spirits. You've brought spirits. So, this is the end, death in the form of a beautiful woman. Maya spreads her veil across my eyes to ease passage into the world beyond, beckons me with the merciful hand of my mother to step across the threshold.

Looking toward Garnet, Ravi understood why his father was confused. In the diffused light there was an uncanny resemblance to Granny Elizabeth as a young woman, the similarity startling to the maharaja whose diseased brain retained little of the present, his clearest memories fixed in childhood when his mother was but a girl herself. For a moment Ravi allowed himself to be caught up in the illusion as well, recalling his grandmother's loving nature in a wave of nostalgia and pain. He motioned Garnet to come forward, his finger on his lips signaling her to be silent. She moved slowly into the room, light flooding over her in a haze of white, a near ghostly apparition.

As she approached the maharaja his eyes filled with tears and his body seemed to melt and collapse as he sank to his knees. Garnet stood quietly, horror and pity stirring in her at the wreckage before her. It was obvious his pain was real yet she was aware he was a superb manipulator, expert at faking emotions to evoke guilt and compassion. She wondered why she was drawn to him, clearly he was an old crook, selfish and spoiled, but felt impelled to bend down and gently stroke the top of his head.

When the maharaja felt her touch, he wrapped his arms around her skirt like a small child and began to sob, great heartbroken cries of "Mummy, mummy," weeping, clinging to her skirt as if the beautiful young mother of his childhood had returned to him. He was dimly conscious the young stranger was not that

mother but embracing her near-image released pent-up yearnings, memories of himself as a petted child. He had searched for
his mother's comfort through sexual encounters hoping to reexperience her warmth with other women but to no avail. Now he
took pleasure in pretending Garnet was his mother as he reached
up to stroke her long silky hair and cover her hands with kisses.

Ravi lifted his father from the marble floor and half carried
him to the silver throne chair, propping him up againstthe velvet
pillows.

He kneeled on a cushion at his father's feet. "This is Garnet
Lawler, an American poet who's staying at the palace."

"English, you say?" his father answered craftily, trying to
bend reality for his own pleasure.

"Ah well, if you like," Ravi said, smiling at his father as if to
let him know he was onto the game but willing to play it with him.

The maharaja beamed at his son. Ravi's indulgence toward
him was reassuring, another reminder of his doting mother.

"May I, my dear?" he whispered to Garnet, lifting the ends
of her silky hair to his lips, kissing the golden strands and breathing in the perfumed fragrance.

"Of course," she answered, kneeling at his feet and smiling
up at him with a look of such acceptance and compassion the
old man had to bite his lips to prevent real heartbreak from consuming him.

The maharaja leaned on the throne and closed his eyes, his
face exhausted but peaceful like a child who empties himself of
violence in a screaming fit and then lies soothed in his mother's
arms.

"Rest well, father," Ravi murmured in his ear.

Impulsively, Garnet bent over the throne and held the old
man's head in her hands. "Perhaps Ravi will bring me back to
visit you again," she said softly, and lightly touched her lips to
his temple."

The old maharaja did not stir but his lips moved in a slight
smile.

"I think he's asleep now," Ravi whispered, and taking Garnet's hand, stepped quietly back from the sleeping maharaja. At the door, he turned to look at his father who was breathing heavily, his head lolling back against the velvet of the throne. "Can you find your way back to the other side of the palace?" he whispered.

Garnet nodded.

"I should wait a bit longer to make sure he's all right."

"I'll stay here with you if you like," Garnet whispered.

"No, no, I'll leave soon myself," Ravi responded. "He needs quiet and solitude."

He kissed her cheek and smoothed back her hair. "Rest, my darling. Go back to our rooms and try to get some sleep. I'll join you before long."

But as Garnet retraced her steps through the courtyard she knew sleep wasn't possible after the painful scene she witnessed. Shaken by the maharaja's anguish she felt submerged in bleakness as she moved into the dusty air thickening the landscape.

V

GAJPUR, INDIA

Deserts bleached death-dry under a cruel
sun defy plants to grow. The old banyan tree turns
his gnarled and twisted limbs to the light and
sighs.

But in the Garden of Desire tangled vines
and burnt leaves studded with rocks stab the soil,
suck up moisture from the fertile earth and a mad
blooming bursts forth.

Life begins. Butterflies flutter in excite-
ment with wings spread open, buds explode.

Entwined in happiness, we weep.

e.c. stewart

i

Garnet reached the marble wall of the courtyard and pressed
her face against the pierced fretwork. She peered through the
tiny holes, squinting to see what lay beyond the atrium. In the
distance, only faintly visible, there appeared to be the remains
of a walled garden. Turning away from the maze of corridors go-

ing toward their rooms she pushed open the heavy wooden door leading to the grounds behind the palace.

She began walking across a patch of stony desert studded with scrubby brush, searching for the garden until she came to a wall entwined with vines and dried brush. Hunting for a way to enter she discovered a rusted iron gate hidden beneath a mass of dried brush and struggled to push it open until the gate gave way and she stepped into the tangled mess of an abandoned garden. The parched ground was strewn with dried leaves, flower beds were choked with debris and roots of great old trees had exploded up through the earth. Overhead, broken branches cracked from the trunks of remaining trees hung grotesquely as if in shame at their decay while a slatted bench circling the banyan tree had broken in half and fallen to the ground, the wood rotted from the years of monsoons and arid heat.

The ground was crusty with a light layer of sand sifted across its surface. Garnet knelt down and brushing away the sand began digging into the dirt with her fingers as if burrowing into the earth could blot out and heal the pain from the world above. But the hard soil was immovable. Looking around, she noticed the remains of a garden tool missing its handle under the broken garden seat. By using the rusted blade she was able to break through the crust, surprised to strike a flagstone path crisscrossing the center of the garden.

She propped up the shattered pieces of the tree seat against the banyan tree, viewed her surroundings and realized she was in the English garden created decades earlier by Rani Elizabeth. Ravi remembered it as an enchanted sanctuary, a lush English oasis planted by his granny in the arid Indian desert.

Garnet rested, then scraping the knife through the soil followed the stone path to the end of the garden. The brick walls enclosing that side of the garden were barely visible under the debris but by running her hand along the wall while pulling off vines, she discovered gaping holes where bricks had loosened and fallen back into the garden. She searched for another exit out of the garden, fighting her way through a mass of underbrush until she found a second gate. Tugging at a snarl of dead vines she saw the gate was secured by a wire stiff with rust and corrosion, twisted around a post. It was impossible to budge but by wrapping a bunch of leaves around her hands for protection she painstakingly twisted the wire back and forth until it dislodged.

When the wire finally came loose the gate fell backwards onto the ground. The hinges were gone, the gate propped against the wall with a single wire to keep it in place. *Ah India,* she thought with a rush of love, *you're as patched up and unworkable as I am.*

As she climbed through the underbrush and stepped over the fallen gate she saw a small white temple shaped like a beehive at the far end of the field. She squinted and observed the Sikh in the distance sitting cross-legged in the shadow of the doorway. The swami had been a life-saver on the train but she hadn't seen him again since Agra. She hoped he wouldn't turn into the new breed of *pied-piper* gurus rampaging through middle-class America spouting simplistic spirituality into the minds of unwashed, over-indulged hippies. Scores of sons and daughters who rejected the materialism of prosperous parents willingly begged money as disciples of spiritual Masters who were not averse to tucking away a flock of Rolls Royces in the Ashram.

Sri Devanda was Ravi's guru, discovered by him in the holy city of *Puri.* When he learned the swami was searching for the right spot to build his temple Ravi urged the swami to bestow the honor on the palace grounds at Gajpur.

The swami agreed, drawn to the idea of an impoverished desert, but on condition the temple be built by his own hands. He invited his new disciple to join him and as they struggled to construct the beehive structure the guru taught him the spiritual principles of the ancient sages. *Work is prayer*, he assured Ravi as they sweated together in the scalding sun.

When Ravi became restive at the slow progress of the work Swami urged patience with the words of Mahatma Gandhi, *He who is ever brooding over result often loses nerve in the performance of duty.*

The guru was meditating under a tree when Garnet reached the whitewashed temple. He was surrounded by garlands of jasmine and marigolds gifted by devotées making homage to the master. She approached silently, not wanting to interrupt his contemplation but ventured close enough to note the peace and purity of spirit in the sadhu's face.

The swami glanced at her and she felt compassion in his benign gaze as if he understood everything, her shyness, insecurities, her existence from beginning to end. He smiled at her, enveloping her in benevolence, but did not move or beckon, only raised a hand in blessing and closed his eyes in meditation.

As her light footsteps neared the mound of fruit and flowers, the guru opened his eyes and beckoned her to come closer. She knelt before him, bowing her head to accept his blessing.

"I'm sorry I've no fruit or flowers to lay before you," she said.

The swami nodded, his face suffused with kindliness as he reached for a circlet of white jasmine on the ground beside him and placed the fragrant garland around her neck. "Please, sit down. How can I help you?"

Garnet hesitated, her voice trembling and uncertain as she spoke. "There's so much suffering . . ."

"Wipe everything from your mind," he responded. "Rid yourself of all thought. Only breathe, slowly, slowly."

The scent of jasmine rising up from the garland around her neck and the peace emanating from the swami soothed Garnet after the disturbing events of the morning. Sitting cross-legged to the best of her ability, considering the stiffness of limbs unused to a contorted position, she felt sleep creeping up on her. A twinge of guilt mixed with the calm. I should be talking to him, absorbing his wisdom, learning, not lazily drifting off. The swami's voice was edged with knife-clean lucidity. "The doing of non-doing is the strongest action we can take. No guilt."

Most of her life had been spent in effort, little had come

easily. The idea that one could just *be* and still achieve seemed extraordinary to her. She'd pasted the words of Krishnamurti above her typewriter. *Stay absolutely alert, and make no effort,* often stared at them but *not making an effort* took a great deal of effort on her part.

"There is purification in suffering that brings peace. Grieve your wounds and surrender to your pain. Have no fear. Your healing has already begun."

The guru's voice was a light, clear bell echoing against an ice-blue sky.

"But you can heal only yourself. You cannot solve the life of another."

He paused and Garnet felt the beat of her heart throbbing through her veins until he spoke again.

Silence. It seemed an eternity before he spoke again. "Wash everything from your mind. Wipe the mirror clean and surrender to the infinite."

Time floated in the shadow of the banyan tree below the white sky. There was no tomorrow or yesterday, hardly the present as she had known it. Only cool infinite space where nothing existed. She was no longer concerned with time. It was enough to exist in the moment forever. Perhaps this was the bliss of saints.

When she opened her eyes, the sun had shifted position and the guru was smiling at her.

Garnet felt a smile rise from the core of herself, blooming and blossoming as it rose to her lips. She folded her hands before her face in reverence to the master.

Sri Devanda's voice was gentle when he spoke. "It is time to turn inward for happiness. *Be ye a refuge to yourself.*"

The angel Winslow must be smiling at that. The swami took her hands and held them and she could feel his serenity flow into her arms and stream through her body.

"Return to the palace," he said. "Rest and sleep, let go of fear. Remember joy and don't allow events to disturb your serenity."

He raised his hand in blessing and waved her away. She moved cautiously feeling as if amnesia had swept through her brain wiping it clean of memory and thought. But her footsteps were light, nearly floating over the ground and her movements effortless, propelling her forward without exertion on her part. She hardly knew how she got to the palace, it seemed only a breath of time before she was back in the bedroom. She rested on the bed for a moment but her eyes closed and she fell into a dreamless sleep so profound she didn't hear Ravi when he returned. Hours later, she woke in surprise to find him asleep in the bed, his arms wrapped tightly around her.

* * *

Ravi was deeply asleep, his breathing slow and soundless. Garnet waited motionless in his arms for awhile, savoring the comfort of his flesh and the warmth of his breath against her cheek. Then, trying not to wake him she gingerly disengaged herself and slipped silently out to the stone terrace facing the blue lake where a tiny ball of amber sun was beginning its nightly dip below the ancient hills. She watched it bounce lightly on the horizon before making its descent. Like so many ceremonies in India the sun played out a ritual, nodding and bowing onto the distant skyline before disappearing with a flourish, stippling the lake with streaks of lavender.

When Ravi appeared on the terrace with a glass of papaya in his hand he found Garnet staring out beyond the lake, her face subdued in twilight.

"Chock full of enzymes," he said, handing her the glass. "Not that you need it. The color is back in your cheeks - you've been reborn a rosy baby."

"Let's hope so," Garnet said, greedily gulping down the fresh sweetness of papaya juice. "Your mother thinks I'm an aging crone."

Ravi shook his head. "She wants to put me on a slave-block

and sell me off to a princess."

Garnet finished the fresh juice and fell back again on the chaise.

"You looked a bit sad when I came out." Ravi asked from behind the lounge chair as he bent over and kissed the top of her hair. "Bad dreams?"

"*Au contraire.* I was lost in a lovely dream, floating in the silken tent rose-perfumed with incense, listening to the twang of a sitar and drowning in pleasure. I hated to come back to earth. Swamiji urged me to find joy and it was in my dreams."

Ravi pulled up a chaise and held her hand and they rested together watching the darkness creep over the lake.

Garnet broke the silence. "Why is the maharaja living in the Lake Palace?"

"He's been hiding away," Ravi said sadly. "When his syphilis reached the symptomatic stage he retreated, moved into the Lake Palace and refused to see anyone. He insisted we spread a rumor that he died during a sacred pilgrimage to the holy city of Varanasi. My mother verified that the sacred ritual performed by a son was fulfilled by me in the holy city and his body burned on the traditional funeral pyre. People gossiped as no one saw him in death but when they questioned me I refused to answer, inferring it was too painful to discuss."

Garnet lifted his hand to her lips and kissed his fingers. She decided to put aside the question of leaving Gajpur for now. After the troubling encounter with the maharaja and her experience with the guru, it occurred to her there might be a divine purpose in remaining . . . *Every person is your teacher and every experience is your lesson.*

ii

Several days later, Ravi woke and discovered Garnet was

nowhere to be found in the palace. He searched the courtyards but the elusive Garnet had disappeared. He decided to circle the grounds and came across one of the young servant boys carrying a load of dry brush in his arms. When he inquired whether Miss Lawler had been seen the boy pointed toward the ruined garden.

"The memsahib works in the garden," he answered, shaking his head from side to side in dismay. "We help her since early morning, but job difficult."

Garnet had been thinking about the walled garden since she'd stumbled on it. At first, she dismissed the idea of trying to restore the ruined oasis of the ghostly Elizabeth, now a hopelessly ravaged patch of desert, but she kept seeing the garden as it might have looked years earlier and the vision wouldn't leave her in peace.

One morning she rose at dawn, dressed herself in a coarse cotton kurtah and woke two young servant boys and took them to the garden. When Ravi found her she was working alongside the servant boys, like a boy herself, raking up dried leaves, clearing away dried-out brush and loading her arms with broken branches, ordering the boys to follow her directions while laboring beside them.

"Want to help?" she asked Ravi, smudging his cheek with a sooty kiss.

"Spoiled princes have no energy for this kind of effort," he laughed, sitting on the ground, and watching her in amazement.

Garnet gave him a tolerant smile and went on with her work, taking up a hammer to nail a broken portion of the bench to the tree.

"We need a new seat built around the tree," she said, and looking around the garden added, "Also a table for picnicking and chairs for lounging under the trees."

"Are you planning to make a habit of hard work?"

"Why not? A bit of work would do you good. At least, find me a handy fellow who can build a bench."

"That's no problem, there's a woodworker in the palace. But take it easy. You're exhausting me."

Garnet showered an armful of dried leaves over his head.

"Work is prayer," she said. "I thought your guru taught you that. Perhaps you found it difficult."

"Alas, my sins are revealed. I hope my laziness didn't come as a shock."

"I've seen nothing else since I met you," Garnet retorted, as she picked up a broken shovel.

"You go too far, American slave driver," Ravi shouted as he jumped up from the ground and ran towards her.

But Garnet was too quick for him and slipped out of his grasp. Ravi chased her around the garden until he caught her and brought her down to the ground with him, holding her tightly and kissing her. Garnet protested, trying to fight him off but she was laughing too hard to get away. The servant boys exchanged smiles and turned away pretending not to notice as they went back to the work of gathering piles of branches and tossing them over the top of the walled garden.

Garnet rose early each morning leaving Ravi sleeping in bed while she roused the servant boys, the carpenter or whomever else she needed and dragged them, grumbling at the early hour, to the garden. But she also brought the cook who carried out trays of coffee and hot baked breads for them to breakfast on. The servants sat on the ground in a circle munching their food and staring at her in wonderment while she planned the work for the day and gave orders to the workmen, insisting they follow every direction to the letter. They obeyed meekly, treating the *memsahib* with respect, regarding her more as a tough *pukkah* boss than a prince's lady. But she was kind, saw they were well-fed and encouraged afternoon siestas under the trees.

Garnet had read about the garden spirits invoked with such success in Findhorn, Scotland by mystics who grew huge cabbages and vegetables at the edge of the Scottish sea where sand and salt prevented the growth of vegetation. They called on nature spirits or *devas* to create *feng-shui,* the Chinese word for an environment in balance. When in harmony it links with wavelike *ch'i* currents in the earth, and planting thrives.

The Findhorn mystics intuited messages from the *devas* and claimed their miracle garden bloomed and flourished with the help of tiny plant spirits, elves, fairies, gnomes, nymphs, wood sprites and fauns.

Garnet decided to try it. She needed a miracle to revive this lifeless place and felt driven with a stubborn determination to restore the garden, as if the ghost of Elizabeth were urging her on. She took time each day to sit in meditation under the banyan tree, legs crossed and palms open on her knees as she focused on invoking the *deva* spirits of landscape, begging them to fly into the desert and show her how to make the garden bloom. The servants stopped work to gape at her, trying to figure out what she was doing but Garnet was quick to open her eyes and shout, "Go back to work, lazy bones!" The young servant boys relished her American lingo and imitated her. *"No sloff off, lezzy buns!"* they cried out to each other. *"Get back on j-o-b!"*

She drove Ravi's Silver Ghost into the village, enthralled by the stick shift and hopeful her American license would suffice if she were stopped, hauling back piles of seeds and plants, bushes, young trees and huge bags of soil which she lifted out herself to the dismay of the workers.

But she insisted servant boys lug pails of water out to the garden while she planted. They rolled their eyes and groaned at the effort, acting as if the work of laborers was beneath them but Garnet shouted crossly when they slowed down, "Work is prayer, work is prayer!" laughing at herself, sure they regarded her as a *crazy American lady* who labored like a coolie instead of a Raja's princess.

She repaired and painted the broken trellis, planted climbing roses to crawl up the slats and made the boys scrub the marble pool, fill it with buckets of water and float lotus flowers and water lilies in it. She oversaw the trimming and cutting back of the dead branches of the banyan tree to allow for new growth, and helped plant young neem trees, flowering cork, mango trees and hibiscus bushes. The flower seeds she planted herself, blessing the earth as she dug up the soil and placed in the ground grains of frangipani, poppies and amaryllis lilies and the seeds from packets of unknown flowers, their Hindi labels untranslatable.

Garnet spent mornings in the garden and afternoons writing about Mumtaz Mahal. Ravi complained she was working too hard and neglecting him but she insisted days were for workaholic Americans and evenings for Indian princes, promising him Scheherazade nights of bliss.

iii

The maharaja sent for Ravi and begged to see Garnet again. Ravi was reluctant, afraid her resemblance to his mother would stir him up.

"Don't be an idiot," the maharaja rebuked him. "I know she's not my mother. What kind of fool do you take me for? But she's a reminder, a gateway into the Shangri-la of my childhood. When I saw her I was taken out of my misery for a moment, brought back to the idyllic days in my mother's garden playing in the shade of the banyan tree."

"Remember how granny adored you?" he reminisced, his eyes wet with tears. "She sat on the wooden seat circling the great tree with her little prince on her lap and read English nursery tales aloud, the same ones she read to me, stories that carried me out of the sweltering desert into the cool green hills of the English countryside. Can't you recall the sweetness of her voice? Its music still echoes in my ears."

Ravi was hesitant but discussed it with Garnet. "The maharaja pleads to see you again but I feel uncertain. His syphilis has reached the terminal stage. At times he can't control his muscles, suffers agonizing pains in his legs lasting for days, is attacked by blinding headaches, or falls into such a state of exhaustion he can't lift his head from the pillow. He has lucid moments, periods of brief remission when he appears rational, nearly the father I remember. At other times, grandiosity and megalomania over-take him and he thinks he's still ruling Gajpur, insists he must hold Court in the Great Hall and demands the appearance of servants long dead. He longs to see you because you remind him of his English mummy, the only woman he ever loved."

"It's so sad," Garnet said, overcome with pity. "I'd like to visit him."

"Actually, except for the beauties who aroused his lust, he showed little affection to anyone but granny," Ravi said, a little bitterly.

"Poor darling," Garnet said, with a kiss on the top of his head. "Not very nice for you."

"I suppose. My father was too busy keeping journals of his lust, writing of *naked asses and breasts urging caresses from his hands*. My mother tried to burn the journal when she discovered it but he caught her in the act. He struck her, slapping her face so hard she flew across the room and into the wall. Then he pulled the diaries out of the fire with his bare hands, screaming, *'These books are my soul. How dare a gutter whore burn the soul of a maharaja! Not even the title I bestowed on you wipes away your pettiness and greed, your ganika mentality. Get out of here before I strangle you with my bare hands.'"*

"And now he drinks heavily," Ravi warned. "But Dr. Karawalla insists there's no point stopping him. *'Let him forget, allow him to sleep in his house of dreams.'*

"He's right," Ravi went on, "but servants tell me that by dinnertime he's so drunk he slumps over the table and lets his head fall into the curry."

Ravi shook his head in despair. "It's depressing, tragic, but it's not your tragedy. You didn't come to India to take on the problems of a dying man."

But Garnet was moved by the maharaja's loneliness and isolation and persuaded Ravi to let her see him.

Ravi tried to dissuade her, then relented. "Veda can take you over to the summer palace and after that you'll be able to find your way alone if you choose to go back. I'd bring you myself but sometimes my father's not in the mood to see me."

The maharaja was sitting up in bed drinking a cup of tea when she entered with Veda. At the sight of Garnet in a filmy white dress, wearing a pale, straw hat with a blue ribbon, and carrying a ruffled parasol to keep off the sun, he smiled with pleasure. The maharaja had a clear memory of his mother's face when he was a child, that young fair English face so different from the darker skinned faces around him.

As Garnet approached, his mind became confused and his mother's features seemed to switch back and forth on Garnet's face. Syphilis had made inroads in his memories and perceptions so that what was real, past or present, merged into a collage of images he couldn't separate.

Veda brought a chair for Garnet, offering sweet cakes and a cup of tea, but he seemed reluctant to leave her there alone.

The maharaja waved him away impatiently. "You can go, Veda. Stop looking at me like a fool. I know who she is, I'm not crazy. Go, go, go. She's in safe hands. Hurry, before I get angry and hurl this teapot at you."

Veda salaamed and backed out of the room, mouthing to Garnet, *'If you need me, call me. I won't be far away.'*

At the end of her visit the maharaja begged her to return, and realizing how lonely he was, Garnet took time to call on him every day. At first, she was sickened by the sight of the maharaja's skin, the eruptions and pustules on his face and hands, and tried to avoid looking directly at him. But as she grew fond of him, compassion overcame revulsion.

She sat with him on the terraces of the white palace overlooking the lake, and walked in the gardens with the maharaja leaning on her shoulder for support. He became dependent on her daily visits, watched for her arrival and become upset if she were late. In his lucid moments he told her stories of his family and the extravagant days of royal India in which he'd been raised, but he liked best to talk about his English mother.

"Mummy loved India more than anyone. We Indians complain about our country but Mummie embraced it uncritically."

Garnet was fascinated by his stories. The Viceroy was a distant cousin of the British royal family and hoped to educate Elizabeth in England. At the age of ten, they sent her to a school in Kent but the child could not tolerate the stringent regime of boarding school after the ease of life in India, or exist without her loving family and doting nurse, her beloved *ayah*. She became ill, close to dying of what was termed *brain fever* in those days.

The country doctor who attended children in the school wrote a stern letter to the Viceroy. *"Your daughter's condition is exacerbated by the heartbreak from which she suffers. She cannot bear the chill of our English climate, the separation from all she loves and lack of homely affection which nurtured her in India. Please, if you wish this child to regain her health, see that she returns to India at once."*

The Viceroy's old auntie accompanied her, touched by the child's pain. When the ship docked in Bombay and Elizabeth realized she was back in India, tears streamed down the child's cheeks and her face lit up like the colors of a sunset.

'The poor little thing was transformed,' the aunt reported. *'Her pinched cheeks filled out and bloomed like pink roses and for the rest of the journey she smiled like a beatific angel.'*

Afterwards, any attempt to raise her as a proper English girl failed, from stiff-necked British governesses to formal teas and white smocked dresses. She circumvented such notions by sustaining an intense attachment to her Indian ayah who bathed her, crooned Indian songs and filled her ears with tales of Krishna and the Bhagavad Gita.

She ran after the gardeners to the flower beds insisted on helping with the plantings, listening to them talk in Hindi, trying to learn the words, and absorbed India into her blood as eagerly as a pilgrim embraces *mecca*. At the age of eleven she announced she'd no longer eat meat, declaring the practice cruel and inhuman. Henceforth, she'd be a vegetarian and insisted her ayah prepare Indian food for her. The Viceroy and his wife approved of her independent spirit and indulged her, ordering kurtah pyjamas when she rejected English dresses and providing tutors when she asked to study Hindi and Sanskrit. She picked up Tamil from servants and later studied Urdu, the language of poets.

Some days Garnet arrived to find the maharaja in the throes of his illness, shouting and weeping, or hallucinating that she was his mother magically restored to him. She described his delusions and furies to Ravi.

"Sometimes his pain is real," Ravi explained. "And sometimes it's a game my father plays to hide his despair, a way to make people pay attention. Dressing up, playing in the world of lost dreams. A bit sad. He was used to power and when it was over there was nothing left for him to care about."

Real or not, in his worst states Garnet was able to soothe him by reading from his old storybooks, or playing Elizabeth's gilded white piano and singing tunes from her tattered songbook.

"Your hair is so like my mother's, the maharaja sighed, as he lifted a lock of her hair and let it slip through his fingers. "The same silky strands of gold and brown and red."

The maharaja wiped a tear and looked away. "Those enchanted days childhood are still vivid. Nothing since ever seemed as real."

The maharaja enjoyed hearing Garnet's research on Shah Jahan and Mumtaz Mahal, especially their marriage described in the journals of Qwazini . . . *She was his intimate companion, colleague and close confidante in distress, joy and grief* . . .

Tears flowed from the maharaja's eyes as she read.

"A fusion of two souls, like the marriage of my parents. What I always longed for," he wept. "But obsession with beauty and lust was my downfall. *Maya,* veil of cosmic delusion, pulled me towards a ravishing kumari with no more substance than a porcelain doll. When beauty mocked and scorned me I became bitter but the sins were mine for pursuing empty dreams. There's no escape from karma or a beautiful witch with the heart of a ganika. In *Lessons of a Whore* Damodaragupta wrote, *Ganikas and bees coax their victims open, then leech them to the dregs.*"

Garnet wiped away the maharaja's tears and bathed his face with cool water.

"There are even worse devils of legend," she said, hoping to distract him. "The wickedest was Lilith, first wife of Adam who predated Eve. She was a vampire-like demon formed by God out of sludge and grime instead of the pure dust used to create Adam. A rageful and evil creature, Lilith, a word meaning shriek, was known as *the monster of screeching.*"

"That sounds familiar," the maharaja grunted.

"Enticing and hideously evil, Lilith leads men to destruction," she continued, as she adjusted the pillows behind his head and held a glass of water to his lips.

"Robed in scarlet and bedecked with baubles like a whore, Lilith waits at crossroads to entrap fools with scarlet lips honeyed in sweetness and words slippery as oil," Garnet resumed, holding the maharaja's hand in hers.

"The mad fool follows Lilith and she takes him to her bed where they fornicate. He sleeps but when he awakens and longs again for sex she is garbed in robes of blazing fire and menaces him with a sword. Her malevolent eyes strike terror into his soul. He quivers and shakes and pleads with Lilith but she kills the fool and casts him into Gehenna, the place of hell."

"I know *Gehenna* well," the maharaja said ruefully. "I dwelt there many years."

"I'm so sorry," Garnet said, deeply moved by his anguish and helplessness.

She sprinkled eau de cologne on a handkerchief and laid it

across the maharaja's forehead, then sat by his bed until he fell asleep and slipped quietly away from the white palace.

But she found herself haunted by him. To her surprise she'd come to love the old man. Perhaps he was a substitute for the grandfathers she'd never known - both dead before she was born. Or simply a pairing of two oddly disparate souls, *simpático* for no particular reason.

iv

The maharaja was failing, his bad periods increasing, his unhappy moods shifting into maniacal rages and uncontrollable fits. Dr. Karawalla explained the syphilis in his spine had invaded his brain inducing seizures and psychotic episodes. In her affection for the old monarch Garnet made an effort to be cheerful but it was increasingly painful to witness the progression of his devastating disease.

Garnet searched for a way to assuage the maharaja's despair and recalling how fondly he spoke of Sushila hoped a visit from her might cheer him up.

"Shushu was a luscious young woman, full-breasted and slim hipped," the maharaja reminisced, his face lighting up as he envisioned her. "Abandoned and passionate, uniquely satisfying as a lover. Never another like her."

Garnet sent off a note to Sushila reminding her of the promised visit and begging her to come to Gajpur soon. The maharaja was now critically ill. She decided not to tell him about Shushu's visit fearing shame about his appearance would cause him to retreat. But she was sure once Sushila was there he'd forget his dread of being seen.

Sushila arrived several days later loaded down with bundles and packages of delicacies for the family, and an abundance of cheer. They celebrated their reunion, avoiding Khalili by having a festive dinner in Ravi's apartments laughing over old times, Garnet much comforted by Sushila's presence.

Garnet planned the picnic for the maharaja the next day in the garden.

"Why don't we dress up in royal costumes," she suggested to Ravi. "Would the maharaja go along with this?"

"He adores dressing up," Ravi laughed. "But he'll want the most splendid regalia for himself."

The next morning they trundled upstairs to the storerooms. Ravi opened an *armoire* brought back from France by his father.

"Voila!" he cried, pulling out a glittering coat of metallic gold-threaded fabric, the gold glowing in the dull light.

"These are my grandfather's royal vestments with matching trousers, and turban. And a sword with a jeweled handle and gold scabbard." Ravi pulled out the sword and thrust it forward, his knee bent in fencer position.

"*En garde!*" he shouted, as they all laughed. "Never mind," he said, putting the sword away. "The maharaja will enjoy being decked out like my grandfather, picnicking in granny's garden."

Vijay and Niles were impressed by the goldthreaded garments and Sushila was nostalgic as she held up a jeweled tunic.

"This was the India I remembered as a child. Finished now. Perhaps for the best but those are sweet memories."

Ravi opened cupboards and armoires, directing them to choose among the mass of clothes and objects stored there. Garnet selected the white ruffled dress and straw hat, Ravi found a jeweled crown and scepter to complete his father's costume. He chose for himself a long, gold-threaded coat and white silk pants worn by his maharaja grandfather on state and diplomatic occasions with the British, and pinned an emerald on the matching gold turban. Sushila opted for a gleaming gold sari while Vijay turned Niles and himself into Indian princes with emerald satin tunics and pants. Vijay wrapped their heads in silk turbans and linked arms with Niles facing the mirror.

"The two most appealing princes in all of India," Vijay

laughed, squeezing Niles close to him.

Garnet didn't let the maharaja know where they planned to hold the picnic or of Sushila's presence. *Better to surprise him*, she thought, *not give him time to object or retreat*.

Ravi dressed the maharaja in his gold garments and the servants carried the monarch across the bridge to the grounds behind the palace in the gold palanquin, the small windowed coach mounted on poles he'd shown Garnet. As they neared the garden Garnet sent the servants back to the palace, Ravi lifted his father out of the palanquin and the old maharaja leaned on Garnet's shoulder as she guided him through thickets growing on the path.

Ravi followed behind burdened with the picnic basket, Vijay and Niles carried bags of dishes, wine glasses and a myriad of things Garnet insisted on. She'd forbidden them to bring servants into the garden to help.

"The garden must be private. For us alone," she insisted, tweaking the maharaja's ear and smiling at him. "Picnics are best when you do it all yourself."

The maharaja patted her hair and shook his head. "Playing at being poor, a favored game of the rich, enjoyable for a brief period. Feeling ennobled by picnicking on the lawns of a great estate."

Ravi pretended to grumble. "How did I get mixed up with this wild creature, a radical Americano who wants to take away the few princely pleasures left to an impoverished raja. It isn't necessary for me to pretend to be poor. Divine Wisdom has ordained that."

As they approached the gate of the garden the maharaja began to tremble. His eyes filled with tears as he paused to look at the old brick walls grown over with ivy and the fallen bricks scattered on the path. He stooped down to pick one up, held it in his hand and wept, tears streaming onto the broken brick.

"I'm not sure I can go into the garden," he said, covering his face with his hands. "I thought these memories would be sweet but they are bitter beyond belief."

"Perhaps we should go back to the palace and picnic in the courtyard," Ravi suggested, his face showing concern.

"It's too late to turn back," Garnet objected, reaching out for the maharaja's hand. "I promise you won't be disappointed."

"Garnet's right," the maharaja said, wiping his tears on the sleeve of his gold tunic. "Let us embrace each new experience, even those built on ashes. If we have been led to this path by the Divine with Garnet as our heavenly messenger, we must not fear to walk on it but embrace the lesson as sacred."

Garnet pushed open the heavy iron gate and the maharaja made his way slowly into the garden. The last time he'd seen the garden was when his mother died and he ordered the garden locked, forbidding anyone to enter.

The planting and restoration of the garden was nearly complete. The woodworker in the palace had built a new bench to circle the great banyan tree and a long lacquered table for picnicking. Wood-frame steamer chairs with caned backs, seats and leg-rests, purchased by Garnet in Gajpur were bright with handloomed fabrics covering pads and cushions, the work of village craftsmen.

"There it is!" the maharaja exclaimed, excited by the sight of the wooden bench. "The same seat where my mother sang nursery songs to me and made me laugh with her funny English stories."

He wiped his eyes and looked around. The garden was beginning to come to life. The trees were budding, branches sprouting tiny green buds were nearly open, flower beds bloomed with crocuses and pansies, and roses still tightly closed, had started their climb up the trellis of the rose arbor.

Sushila was hiding behind the arbor. She tiptoed behind the maharaja and wrapped her arms around him. When he turned and realized it was Shushu he broke down and wept in her arms. "I thought I'd never see you again."

Sushila hugged and kissed him. "Where did the years go?"

"Finished, gone forever," the maharaja replied, regaining

his composure. "We're in the last act of a bad play. Ring down the curtain, I say! Let's not linger for applause. Get off while they're still laughing, like a couple of vaudevillians."

Ravi and Vijay helped the maharaja into a steamer chair under the banyan tree, propping his legs up on the footrest while Garnet and Sushila set out the picnic on the table, unwrapping packages of delicacies and unpacking china plates and crystal glasses. Sushila had brought a case of French champagne and made sure there were several bottles chilling in a bucket of ice on the table.

The maharaja was lying back in his chair looking up at the sky through the branches of the banyan tree. He was serene and smiling as he held onto Sushila.

"You see before you a goddess men dream about but never experience."

"Don't forget what a lover *you* were," Sushila laughed, squeezing her arms around him. "*Le roi d'amour!*"

"There was no way to hold onto this elusive creature," the maharaja chuckled, furtively fondling her breast. "Too sought after in the great world by kings, poets and scores of exalted men vying for her affection."

Niles enjoyed the picnic although his old whines and complaints had lessened since he was with Vijay. He was fascinated by the maharaja, recognizing a majesty in him not destroyed by the deformities of disease which gave Niles a little more tolerance for his own infirmities.

The maharaja noticed him staring and realizing it was not in dread but in awe smiled at him. "When I was a boy I used the kurtah you're wearing for ceremonial occasions. Now we picnic together in an enchanted garden."

Ravi poured the champagne and they drank and gorged themselves on the delicacies spread across the picnic table. The maharaja's face was flushed and excited. He was laughing, relishing the occasion, holding court as he regaled them with amusing stories. For Garnet, it was a glimpse of the charismatic monarch he once was and in his energy and high spirits she saw Ravi's resemblance to his father.

When the maharaja became tired Ravi called the servants to carry him back to the Lake Palace and accompanied his father along with Vijay and Niles while Sushila and Garnet rested for a while in the setting sun, then gratefully allowed the servants in to clean up the picnic and made their way back to the palace.

They were too full to eat dinner but Sushila persuaded Garnet to come to her room for a glass of *porto*. Garnet happily agreed, gratified to be reunited with Sushila.

"I don't know if we'll have another chance for a private talk before I leave," Sushila said, and questioned Garnet about Ravi.

Garnet confided she was frightened by her growing attachment and love for him. "It can only end badly," she said.

"What does it matter?" Sushila chided. "Love is life's greatest pleasure. Why not revel in it?"

"But the situation is insane," Garnet said, and described her meeting with the maharani. Sushila roared with laughter.

"The woman is a monster," Sushila agreed. "Only Rani Elizabeth knew how to handle her. Elizabeth was a lovely, warmhearted woman but when confronted by Khalili's fishwife attacks her English blueblood turned to ice. The Brits don't chop with an axe, they wound with a stiletto. One quick thrust. She'd cut Khalili off with a sharp word delivered calmly, and the dragon-lady was vanquished. If the incident were truly offensive Rani Elizabeth would *send her to Coventry* - ignore her, refuse to speak personally. Khalili grew more and more afraid of her."

"It's a British thing," Garnet said, reaching for the bottle of port to refill her glass. "My father had a bit of that. Very effective with my mother in a crisis."

"We Indians secretly admired the British character," Sushila reflected. "They planted the Union Jack over India, refusing to yield or be defeated, willing to die for their principles. Who but an English poet would glorify six hundred bedraggled cavalrymen hurling themselves into certain death? But such lessons by the British Raj taught *Mahatma* and his followers strategic tactics to seize back our country."

"So, to deal with the maharani, I should chill out, take a English pill?" Garnet asked, dubiously.

Shushila put her arm around Garnet's shoulder and kissed her cheek. "You fought some battles in the past and have a few weapons of your own. Khalili might discover she's no match for you."

Garnet nodded but looked troubled at the thought of dealing with the maharani.

"Stop worrying," Sushila said, ruffling Garnet's hair. "Follow your bliss and see where it leads."

Sushila stayed in Gajpur for several days after the picnic but Garnet was saddened to watch Shushu pack her bags to return to Agra. Before leaving she cautioned Garnet.

"I know you're fond of the maharaja, but don't break your heart over him. He's a dying man and you can't change that. You're still recovering from a serious illness. Spend your time with Ravi, he can put the bloom back on your cheeks."

They drove Sushila to the station in the Silver Ghost and waited in the car until they saw the train pull in with Shushu's white rail-cars gleaming behind the steam engine. Garnet boarded with Sushila while Ravi and Vijay supervised the porters as they unloaded the Rolls and carried the bags and boxes aboard. Sushila hugged her goodbye and Garnet wept, feeling bereft at losing Shushu's loving support.

"Don't forget there's always a home for you in Agra," Sushila said, drying Garnet's tears with a lace hanky.

Garnet was quiet on the ride back to the palace. There was so much loss in life. Her father lost the life he loved in South Africa and England, her mother lamented the devastation of the affluent society she was born to in Spain, Winslow died when she needed him badly, just as he lost Sibley. Now Sushila was gone, the maharaja was dying, and soon she'd have to let go of Ravi.

v

The maharaja grew steadily worse in the next few weeks and the end seemed to be drawing near. Garnet redoubled her efforts on his behalf for she'd grown to love the old monarch despite his moods and eccentricities.

When it was clear the maharaja was dying, Khalili demanded to meet with her husband before his death. Garnet was sitting beside the maharaja's bed reading to him when there was a knock on the door. Without waiting for a response the door flew open and Khalili burst into the room. The maharaja flew into a rage when he saw her, the pustules on his face turning bright red.

"How dare you enter my palace without permission?" he screamed. "Leave here at once and don't show your face to me again."

"As Maharani of Gajpur I have certain obligations," Khalili retorted, stepping forward.

"Maharani?" he snorted. "I'd advise you not to put on airs with me."

He gazed up at the ceiling avoiding the fury in Khalili's eyes and calming his voice.

"*Nanak*, the great Sikh saint, repudiated *caste*, defining evil-mindedness as the *low-caste* woman, a slanderous heart the *sweeper-woman*, and wrath the *pariah woman*. You're the *Highness of Nothing* despite your fine clothes and lust for power. Yes, I was blinded by your beauty but I paid dearly for my pact with the devil. Return at once to *my* ancestral palace, poisoned by your malevolence, with this warning. Invade my privacy again and you'll die."

"How dare you humiliate me!" Khalili shouted, her face distorted with rage.

"A dying man has no shame. He speaks the truth without remorse," the maharaja answered. "Please escort the *maharani* to the door, Garnet. If she refuses to leave, ring for Veda and have the servants throw her out."

Garnet stood up uncertainly, and looked toward Khalili.

"Perhaps it *would* be best if you returned to the palace."

The maharani glared at Garnet and pushed past her, shoving her out of the way as she stalked to the door. "You presume to order me around - an American slut living in sin with my son? You'll regret this," she screamed, storming out of the room and slamming the door behind her.

The maharaja looked at Garnet and shook his head. He was trembling, gripping the sides of the bed as he spoke.

"A marriage from hell. Poor Ravi. A hateful, *schadenfreude* mother and a neglectful father who reveled in his power and the pleasures of the flesh. As the poet rued . . .

In this world, there is an ancient tradition:
Sweet pleasure is not without bitterness.

"My prince deserved better but regrets always come too late. "Take care of Ravi when I'm gone," the maharaja said, wiping his tears away with his sleeve.

Garnet hoped to bring the maharaja back to the garden but he remained too ill and weak to make the effort. Dr. Karawalla warned the end was near but a few days later the monarch suddenly regained strength. Garnet was surprised one day to find him looking hearty and energetic, greeting her with vigor.

Veda served them an English high tea and Garnet relaxed, pleased at his improvement. The maharaja was resting in his chair after finishing his cakes and tea when he leaned close to her and in a barely audible voice asked, "Forgive me, but before I die I need to feel the body of a young and beautiful woman. Just once more."

Garnet hesitated, realizing Ravi would be horrified, then nodded her head in pity. She refused to remove her clothes but allowed the maharaja to touch her through the thin white kurtah, standing still while he fondled her breasts, then fell to his knees and caressed her thighs, kissing her across her hips as he held her around the waist.

The maharaja smelled of death and the stench of dying, of pus and blood and excrement and she could feel the pustules of his skin burst wet against her dress as he squeezed his face against her body. But despite her nausea at the sickening odors the experience seemed strangely spiritual as the maharaja ran his hands all over her body, touching her as if caressing a sacred statue or worshipping *Chiti Shakti*, goddess of creation and consciousness."

Afterwards, the maharaja collapsed onto the bed and wept, then reached out a trembling hand to bless her, "*Bhagwan bhalla kare* - may God do good to you."

The next day he was weaker, as if his spirit had begun to fly away. The maharaja appeared to be dying, his face had paled and his breathing was labored.

But he begged Garnet to read about the death of Shah Jahan. "The dying image of a great emperor will inspire me to leave this wretched planet as a king."

Garnet patted his hand and picked up the journal of Shah Jahan's Court Historian.

"Incarcerated in the great Fort for the last seven years of his life by his ruthless son, Aurengzeb, who seized his throne, Shah Jahan was a patient prisoner. He passed his time in devotion and prayer, reciting the Koran, copying its verses, and reading about the lives of saintly persons of the past.

'Talk of his passing away from this stage of transitoriness and decline became the cause of his joy and pleasure.'

Garnet looked up to see if the maharaja was listening. He seemed weak but nodded for her to continue.

"At the age of seventy-six Shah Jahan became deathly ill. The Court Poet wrote of his passing . . .

'His most Exalted Majesty, Shah Jahan, departed from this abode of gloom to the garden-house of the Holy Gardens.'

The maharaja suddenly sat up in bed. "The garden. Please.

I want to go to my mother's garden."

Garnet sat helplessly for a moment staring at him in dismay. There was no way he could be moved such a distance.

"I demand to drink in the sweetness of my mother's garden before embarking on my celestial passage," he cried. "Arrange it, Garnet. One last pleasure!"

She sat in silence trying to think, then forced a smile. "If His Highness commands, we will go to the garden," she answered, trying not to show her fear.

He's so weak, she thought. *I hope he can stand the long haul*, wondering how to accomplish the move in his condition. Then she called for Veda and the servant boys and explained.

Veda's face showed his shock and horror. "No, no, madame. Such a thing is impossible."

"Well, impossible or not, we're going to do it. And say nothing to Prince Ravi," she ordered, fearing Ravi would not permit him to be moved. "I'll take full responsibility."

"But Madame . . ."

She interrupted him before he could finish. "No buts, Veda. Just *do* it, and quickly."

She directed them to rig up the *charboy* and after they lifted the old man off the bed she helped strap him securely onto the cot. The boys carried him out of the Lake Palace and over the bridge while Veda hovered fearfully over him as they made the trek to the garden. By the time they reached the garden wall the maharaja was gasping for breath but Garnet instructed the servants to lift him onto the chaise under the banyan tree. Then she ordered them away.

Veda objected. "But you may need me, madame."

"Please, Veda, I beg you. Leave us in peace. I promise to call if I need you."

Veda reluctantly left the garden with the servants, shutting the gate behind them. Garnet sat close to the maharaja on the bench circling the banyan tree and wiped the perspiration off his forehead with a handkerchief.

"Don't be afraid," she whispered, "I won't leave you."

The sun-washed garden was serene and blooming, alive with the perfume of jasmine and the bright odor of newly green leaves on trees and bushes. The climbing roses had made their pink ascent up the trellis, irises bloomed purple, and water lilies and lotus blossoms floated on the scented waters of the pool. A peacock crossed in front of the maharaja and fanned his tail into a shock of blue-green and gold, shining brilliant in the sun. They sat in silence listening to birds singing back and forth from tree to tree as if chattering and responding in bird language. A day for living, not dying.

The maharaja reclined peacefully on the chaise. She watched as his face brightened, color came back to his cheeks and his eyes looked clear. *Perhaps he won't die soon after all.*

"*There is no armor against fate, death lays his icy hand on kings*," the maharaja murmured, his eyes filling with tears. "A journey to darkness or the bliss of *nirvana?*"

The maharaja's eyes closed. She listened to his breathing hoping he was resting, trying not to disturb him by talking. They sat quietly in the tranquility of the garden. After awhile, the maharaja grew restless, his face paled, his breathing was irregular. She wondered if the end were near but as she felt his cheek with her hand he reassured her, patting her on the wrist.

"We lived in arrogance as monarchs, my dear, infatuated with power as if protected from the laws of heaven." His voice trailed off and Garnet bent closer to catch the words. "*But Pale Death with impartial tread beats at the poor man's cottage and the palaces of kings.* My fate is shared by *pariahs* sweeping the streets and the bearer boys who carried me here."

The maharaja sighed and lay back in the steamer chair with his eyes closed. "I was neither a good man nor a good king," he whispered, his words now barely audible. "But despite my sins the *Bhagavad Gita* promises salvation . . .

Even if thou art the chief sinner among all sinners, yet by the sole raft of wisdom thou shalt safely cross the sea of sin."

"I know you will," Garnet breathed.

She reached in her bag for *The Tibetan Book of the Dead*, held his hand in hers and read . . .

"*O child of noble family . . . you are not alone in leaving this world, it happens to everyone so do not feel desire and yearning for this life. You cannot stay, you can only wander in samsāra.*"

He didn't respond or ask about the source with his usual curiosity. She wasn't sure he was listening but continued reading in a soft voice close to his ear.

"*O child of noble family, when your body and mind separate, the dharmatā will appear, pure and clear yet hard to discern, luminous and brilliant, with terrifying brightness, shimmering like a mirage on a plain in spring . . .*"

She paused when the maharaja opened his eyes and pulled himself up, pointing to the gateway of the wall in excitement, Garnet surprised by his sudden strength and vitality.

"A woman is opening the gate and entering the garden!" he cried.

Garnet turned her head to look but saw no one. The maharaja's face was perspiring, sweat running down his forehead into his eyes. She took out a cloth and wiped his eyelids but he brushed her hand away impatiently.

"Her hair shines in the sun and her eyes are a sea of blue. Ask her to draw nearer."

Garnet motioned with her arm in the direction he was pointing as if she could see a woman entering the garden.

The maharaja squinted his eyes and smiled, his face bright and alert. "Now I see her clearly. Look over there. See? She is my mother, come to fetch me. So young and radiant. Ahhh," he breathed, turning his face up to the sky. "Listen . . . she is singing." He moaned, as if in pain. "Ohhh, the songs of angels cannot be as sweet as her voice."

Tears came to Garnet's eyes. She tried not to show the maharaja she was crying as she leaned over and kissed him.

"Your mother's hands are outstretched," Garnet said. "Walk

towards the light and into her arms."

"She begs me to come quickly. But how? Help me, Garnet."

Garnet turned her head away to hide her weeping. "Just go!" she whispered, her voice breaking. "Into the light, one step at a time. Don't keep her waiting."

"Perhaps." For a moment, he looked uncertain. "I can try." Then his face brightened again. "Why not?"

He smiled at Garnet, stretched out his arm as if to take his mother's hand and shut his eyes. He gasped once as his head rolled to the side but the smile lingered on his lips.

Garnet kissed the top of his head and laid it gently against the caned back of the chair. She leaned her face against his cheek and whispered, *"When beggars die, there are no comets seen; The heavens themselves blaze forth the death of princes."*

Then she walked to the gate and called out to Veda to come and bring the servant boys with him.

vi

Ravi took charge of the traditional funerary ceremonies making sure his father's body was properly washed, perfumed, and wrapped in linen. The body was then tied to a bamboo litter, strewn with flowers and carried out to a patch of forest behind the palace grounds to the small royal temple where cremations took place. Ravi, as son and chief mourner, led the procession into the woods carrying a firepot bearing the consecrated fire preserved by maharajas for the lighting of their funeral pyres. The family was accompanied by musicians playing bamboo flutes, *bansuris, tanpuras,* while others beat *tabla* drums.

Garnet tried to reach Sushila in Agra hoping she'd attend the ceremonies but Sushu had gone off to Paris and sent a note. *"Ashok and I said our good-byes in Gajpur. No regrets. I pleasured my lover in the early years, and gave my friend a few laughs*

at the end. Don't fret. The maharaja had a good enough life.
Pursue your own happiness now."

The servants built a funeral pyre with six hundred pounds of sandalwood, fueled the fire with *ghee* and heaped flowers on the pyre. The priests chanted invocations and Ravi recited prayers. Then he walked around the pyre three times and lit the sandalwood with a flaming torch from the ancient firepot to begin the burning of his father's body.

Khalili insisted on accompanying them but Ravi would not permit her to approach the pyre.

If only she'd jump on the fire and commit sati, Garnet thought, with a twinge of guilt. *Fat chance!*

After the body was burned, Ravi flung a potful of water from the sacred Ganges River over his shoulder onto the charred pyre and in accordance with religious ritual, walked away without looking back.

Garnet whispered prayers at the edge of the smoking pyre, visualizing the spirit of the maharaja as pure joy, bounding over the clouds with his sword and waltzing with his beloved mother. Then she caught up with Ravi.

On the way back to the palace Ravi stopped in at the temple where some of his father's ashes would be interred in an urn, engraved with his birth date, death and the years he ruled as maharaja, and placed in a niche in the wall along with the urns of his ancestors. The rest of his ashes would be scattered in the Ganges River at the sacred city of Benares and buried under the rose bushes in his mother's garden. Ravi pointed out the array of recessed urns holding the ashes of his forbears dating back to the 16th century.

"A majestic past," Garnet mused, running her fingers over the engravings as she read the names of maharajas and princes who preceded him. "No wonder your mother wants to get rid of me."

"My mother lives in a dream world," Ravi scoffed. "Royal

dynasties are a joke in India. Princely lines ended with my generation, the titles we still use are purely imaginary."

Garnet glanced again at the rows of urns engraved with crowns. *His mother will never accept me now. She'll insist on Ravi assuming the role of maharaja, no matter how ersatz.*

Ravi fell silent and didn't speak again until they reached the palace. Garnet dropped the subject but was sure a crisis was coming.

Ravi decided to hold the month-long mourning ceremonies to a minimum with sacred rites performed in secret as there was no way to explain observances for a maharaja long believed dead. The maharaja despised hypocrisy and would have laughed heartily at efforts to revive him to society only to kill him off again.

She was saddened by the maharaja's death. She realized his passing was a release from suffering but their friendship had meant a great deal to her. In a strange way, he nurtured her, even cherished her, and shown her that within us those we love never die. Elizabeth remained alive to him and Winslow would always be alive to her, his vitality and encouragement a part of her forever. Now the maharaja had a place in her heart.

Ravi regretted he hadn't been closer to his father but in the philosophy of his forbears accepted he was not in control of his destiny. Divine Powers took charge of fate and adjured him to detach from mortal grief.

Garnet wasn't wrong in her predictions about the maharani. Not only did Khalili insist Ravi play the role of maharaja but she began pressuring him to marry a suitable girl from a princely family. In the next few weeks she put out feelers among her friends and contacted several elite marriage brokers to arrange an advantageous match for Ravi.

Finally, Khalili received an offer she couldn't refuse. A former maharaja, scion of a princely family who turned to commerce to make his fortune when the monarchy ended, was faced with the difficult problem of finding a husband for his beautiful but slow-witted youngest daughter. The family was planning a move to

England for business purposes and the father hoped to marry her off before their departure. He was prepared to offer a sizable fortune as dowry to a princely family providing background and protection.

In view of Ravi's royal heritage and newly acquired title of maharaja, he agreed to restore and refurbish the Gajpur palace, furnish a comfortable living for Khalili and build a modern villa on the palace grounds as a retreat for the young couple.

Princess Jali was an agreeable girl, quite beautiful, who liked to laugh and dance but whose intelligence remained at a twelve-year old level. She could function to a degree in society, behave charmingly at social events and with her wealth would not have to deal with everyday problems. She could bear an heir as her deficiency didn't stem from genetic inheritance and didn't need to assume responsibility for children who in privileged classes were customarily raised by *ayahs* and servants.

Ravi responded to Khalili's scheme with amusement. He, who valued intellect in a woman was being pressured by his mother to chain himself to a dim-witted princess.

"Are you crazy? The girl is retarded."

"What difference does that make?" Khalili snapped. "You have brains enough for two. You don't need intellectual stimulation. We need money to keep the palace going."

Ravi's face flushed in annoyance. "It's time you stopped pimping for me. I've no intention of accepting a marriage arranged by anyone but myself."

"Don't be a fool, Ravi," Khalili answered, squinting icy black eyes at him. "They've offered a huge financial settlement. A merger with that family would restore the palace of your ancestors."

She ignored her own avarice and greed for lavish living which Ravi knew was part of the bargain but let pass.

"There can be no more excuses, Ravi," Khalili snapped irritably. "It's time you married a highborn Indian girl and produced a son for the royal line."

"Get it through your head," Ravi said, opening the door to leave. "The *royal line* has ended! And when I marry I'll do the choosing."

"Don't worry, you can still keep your English whore on the side," she sneered.

Ravi's face tightened and his voice was icy when he replied.

"I think you know she's an American poet. Remember that granny's English blood runs in my veins and be careful. Jealousy and hatred could create a rift with your son you'd regret."

"Please yourself," the maharani answered, shuffling through papers on her desk to hide her uneasiness at Ravi's outburst. "As long as you continue to hide her in your apartments."

Ravi slammed his fist on the table. "Garnet is my guest," he shouted. "Where she stays in the palace is my business."

He stood up to leave and looked down at his mother sitting on the gilded armchair, once the maharaja's throne. His voice was cold and deliberate.

"As you were quick to point out, with the death of my father I've ascended the *throne* as maharaja of Gajpur. Bogus as the title may be, one thing *is* clear by law and inheritance. The palace, its contents and lands are now mine. You're here at my sufferance, so take care."

When Garnet saw Ravi later he looked upset, his face drawn and his lips tight, but he did not reveal his meeting with his mother.

Toward evening, he suggested they have supper in the silk tent and spend the night there.

Might as well, she thought. *There may not be many nights left for them if the maharani had her way. Perhaps the time was drawing near for her to leave Gajpur. Why not enjoy another idyll of pleasure before it all falls apart.*

Ravi escorted Garnet through the marble courtyard, silvered by a rising moon, and led her into the silk tent. Inside, Veda had set out curries, tandoori chicken, and Ravi's favorite Indian sweetmeats on silver dishes, champagne sparkled in crystal glasses, the gramophone was playing old dance music and the tent was ablaze with light from candles flickering on the low dining table, in sconces and candelabra suspended from rod supports, and tiny oil lamps gleaming over chests and tables.

Garnet looked at the profusion of lights glittering against the scarlet silk and velvet of the tent and felt her throat tighten. The silk tent was an Arabian fairyland and Ravi the fabled, alluring prince. She caught her breath, realizing how painful it would be to leave Gajpur and Ravi behind.

"Look out on the lake," Ravi said, pulling aside the drape of a window-like opening. "There are hundreds of lights from tiny oil lamps made out of leaves floating on the waters."

"Divali begins tonight," he explained, smiling at her. "The Festival of Lights, celebrated on the darkest night of the month. Divali augurs the sowing of seed invoking *Lakshmi*, goddess of prosperity. Even the most impoverished villager lights a clay oil lamp beseeching Lakshmi not to overlook his hut but enter and bring good fortune."

They toasted Divali with champagne and fed each other bites of food from their plates. After Ravi dismissed Veda for the night, he refilled their glasses and gave Garnet tastes of the remaining delicacies. When finally they lay back on the velvet bolsters, stuffed with food and a little tipsy, Ravi kissed the palms of Garnet's hands.

"I can't bear the thought of your leaving," Ravi whispered. "I'm desperately in love with you. Stay in Gajpur and marry me."

"Remain in India?" she asked in astonishment.

"I'm afraid so," he sighed. "An impoverished prince with no aptitude or enthusiasm for work would be run over on America's fast track. No one feels sorry for deposed crowned heads unless they're rich. And what about you, my darling? Do you want to swim in those shark-infested waters?"

It was true. The last thing she wanted was to fight for a place in that world. She was free, homeless, rootless, without ties to

family or country. But it was madness to think this would work
out.

"What could be more amusing than marrying an impoverished prince?" Ravi persisted. "The ragged beggars in town and
our bedraggled servants would address you as princess, even
maharani."

"Oh, Ravi, I'd be a disaster for you," she responded, her
head swimming at the idea. "You deserve a sweet, sheltered princess accepted by your mother who'd give you a son. No little
prince can reach the planet through me."

"Forget children. I'll be the little prince. Cuddle *me*, sing to
me, rock *me* to sleep," he pleaded.

Ravi sat up against the bolster and lit a *Gitanes*.

"People aren't replaceable like machine parts." he said, blowing smoke rings over her head. "Why not take a chance on me?"

"And your mother?"

"I'll handle her," he said, his face tightening.

"It's madness, Ravi," she said, rubbing her cheek against
his. "My brain is too dizzy to think straight. But I *could* make
love if it pleasures the prince."

Ravi laughed, stubbed out his cigarette in the champagne
glass, and buried his head in her shoulder.

In the morning when the sun rose, Deva returned laden with
trays and served them breakfast. They left the silk tent reluctantly, hating to break the spell of the night but Deva needed
Ravi to drive him into the village to pick up supplies. Garnet
decided against the trip and returned to the palace to continue
her writing on Mumtaz Mahal.

vii

She put aside her worries and sat at Rani Elizabeth's desk
reading Qwazwini's Court Journal.

In 1631, Shah Jahan and Mumtaz Mahal had enjoyed nine-teen years of a happy marriage and were still inseparable. She often accompanied him on military campaigns where lavish tents were erected to provide her all the comforts of the palace. On a campaign in June, he set up camp outside of Buranpur awaiting the birth of their fourteenth child. Mumtaz Mahal was thirty-eight.

Shortly after midnight she gave birth to a daughter but her doctor was concerned when he discovered she was feverish. He already feared the worst for Mumtaz disclosed she heard the child cry in her womb, a sinister omen in those days. When her temperature rose dangerously high the doctor realized the life of his royal patient was threatened. Mumtaz was likely a victim of *puerperal* fever, a rampant *childbed* infection resulting from unsanitary conditions or unsterilized instruments. But doctors knew nothing about infection in the 1600s, the awareness of germs and bacteria still centuries away.

As her illness worsened, Mumtaz sensed she was in danger of dying and sent for Shah Jahan who hurried to her bedside in great distress. In the last hours, Mumtaz Mahal expressed her final testament to Shah Jahan and entrusted their royal children and her mother to his care.

Qazwini wrote . . .

The world is an extremely pleasant paradise
But it is a garden hedged round with thorns.

and faithfully recorded her dying hours . . .

The Lady of angelic nature summoned His Majesty to the hour of farewell. He presented himself with a grieved heart and sorrowful mind at the bed of his life-long companion, and as the night waned, the dying queen responded to the comforting summons: Allah beckons thee towards the Abode of Peace . . .

This heartrending event sent tremors through the Emperor.

His heavenly dignity could not keep from lamentation and mourning, the eye of the world-conquering king was flooded with tears.

Garnet sighed as she finished Qazwini's account and shut the book. She felt tired and rested her head in her hands. Such a marriage had little in common with the tormented union of the maharaja and Khalili, or Francesca and Edward.

She heard the sound of footsteps clattering down the hall, then a sharp rapping on her door. She opened it a crack.

"I must speak to you, Miss Lawler," she heard the maharani announce in a high-pitched, imperious voice.

. Garnet held her hand on the door. "Not right now, I'm busy," she answered through the crack, dreading to emerge from the bliss of the night before. Talking to the maharani would be like putting her head in a noose and begging to be choked.

"Too busy to have good manners?" Khalili sneered, as she flung open the door and pushed Garnet aside. "I don't intend to await your pleasure. I have something to say to you."

She walked into the room and stood in the center glaring at Garnet like a witch, her black eyes blinking and her face contorted with fury.

Garnet cut her off. "I know, I know - *Leave my son alone!*"

The maharani tried her old hocus-pocus, fixing Garnet with a stare - temple bells chiming across the Himalayas, mystic goddess invoking Divine Powers - but the magic was gone. Once we see though a magician's tricks we know the coins are up his sleeve.

Garnet remained silent. *Detach, detach*, she warned. *The maharani has talent for an atomic bomb attack but lacks finesse for a Cold War. Don't let her engage you in battle.*

The maharani changed her tactics when she saw her wizardry had no effect on Garnet.

"This affair has gone on long enough and I intend to put a stop to it," she snarled.

"Yes, yes," Garnet replied irritably. "The royal dynasty is at stake! What else is new?"

The maharani walked around the room examining objects on Garnet's desk, taking note of the silver-framed photograph of Rani Elizabeth and the mounds of papers, files and research books piled on the desk and tables. She moved to a small table where there was a photo of the maharaja with Ravi when he was a boy of ten, a perfect little prince in satin tunic and trousers with a jeweled turban wound around his head, his round brown eyes sparkling with mischief. Khalili picked up the picture, glanced at it and dropped it face down on the table.

The maharani examined her reflection in the gilded pier glass. Then she straightened her shoulders, smoothed her hair as if it were a crown and raised her chin in a queenly fashion.

Garnet watched Khalili as she scrutinized her image in the mirror. *The woman has playacted all her life, first as child goddess then as queen. She has no idea of reality beyond empty role-playing. Just don't play her game. She can't harm you if you step back and stay with your truth.*

The maharani turned back to Garnet and began to berate her. Garnet was silent. Angered by her lack of response Khalili began to rant and rave, shouting ugly names and cursing her. Garnet stood transfixed as Khalili's rage rained over her like a torrential cloudburst. *The maharaja was right. Under her pretensions prowled a street-woman ready for attack.*

Every so often, the maharani's words jumped out at her.

"My son was better off with whores," she hissed. "Girls for hire know their place. If they make trouble they're easy to get rid of but you amateur sluts are insidious."

Garnet rolled her eyes but kept her silence. *I plan to flee your crumbling castle as soon as possible, bitch, but I've no intention of giving you that satisfaction until I'm ready.*

"Prince Ravi has been amusing himself," the maharani sneered. "But he'll never marry you despite any rash promises made to the slut whetting his sexual appetites."

Now Garnet was shaking with rage but tried to control her voice as she retorted.

"Boss your son around if you can, but don't tell me what to do. I don't take your orders."

"I'm in charge of the palace now and I demand you leave Gajpur," the maharani barked, her black eyes glittering at Garnet as if they were lethal weapons.

Garnet said nothing but stared back defiantly.

"There's nothing here for you in India. Go back to America or I'll make your life a living hell!" the maharani shouted, raising her arm as if to strike her.

She took a step toward Garnet who stretched out her arms as a barrier.

"Touch me, and I'll knock you to the floor," Garnet threatened, her voice stern, her knees melting like water. "I've no compunction against hitting back so I suggest you make a graceful exit before I lose control."

Khalili hesitated for a moment, then moved toward the door.

"Take my advice and leave Gajpur. Insist on staying and you'll live to regret it."

She turned on her heel and left, slamming the door behind her.

Garnet staggered into the adjoining bedroom as waves of nausea shuddered through her body. Her head was whirling and she felt faint. Khalili's attack was upsetting but the sickness she was feeling had to be the aftermath of cholera. Too dizzy to stand she clung to the bed post and pulled herself up on the bed, then drank a glass of boiled water and rested.

She jumped up when a surge of anger replaced the nausea, ran to the closet and pulled out all her clothes, throwing them on the floor, then emptied the shelves and threw the rest of her belongings on top. There was no way she'd stay in Gajpur under the thumb of this monster.

When everything was piled on the floor she sat down on top of it, looked around at the havoc she'd created in the room and began to laugh. She tried to stop but the laughter turned into sobs and hysteria. *I've got to get out of here before I go stark raving. Imelda would call this a bad acid trip with a harpy from hell.*

She stood up feeling sick and shaky again, relieved Ravi hadn't returned from the village to find her in this state. She was still weeping when she ran out of the room and down the halls. She passed Veda who tried to stop her, calling out, "Madame, madame, what is wrong?" with great concern in his voice.

"Nothing, Veda, nothing," she answered without stopping as she ran blindly down a hall to the door leading to the garden. There were small lighted oil lamps all along the corridors. *Divali is a joyous holiday*, she thought, *a day to be happy*.

Instead, misery had caught up with her again.

At the gate of the garden wall she saw the guru in the distance garbed in a saffron robe standing motionless in front of his white beehive temple. She thought he looked a lonely figure. The meditative life must not be easy, drawn into oneself without the distractions of the world.

She sat for a long time under the banyan tree in the canedback steamer chair, trying to calm herself and decide what to do. The maharaja had died in this chair, too bad his powerful spirit wasn't here to help her. One thing was clear. She needed to pack up and get out of Gajpur as soon as possible.

It was probably time to leave India. Her research was complete and she could finish writing the book in New York. She'd file Ravi under *Life's Little Disasters & Pleasures*. She'd certainly miss the pleasure of Ravi.

Leaving India would be a pity for Niles who seemed content for the first time since she'd known him. He didn't confide in her about his affair with Vijay but dropped hints, watching her reaction as if fearing her disapproval of deviant sexuality. But Garnet didn't play that game. Happiness was too hard to get and she tried to show Niles she approved of joy, whatever the source. She was sure he'd freak out at the idea of returning to the States. If

only he could remain in India but she doubted anyone, even
Vijay, would take on responsibility for his life.

Now that her mind was made up it was best to leave as soon
as possible and avoid the lingering pain of pulling away from
Ravi. A quick, clean break. She'd start packing when she got
back to the palace, pick up everything from the floor and dump
it in her suitcases.

But first she'd walk to the beehive temple and say goodbye
to Sri Devanda, experience his presence and feel the inner peace
emanating from him. Even if it wasn't real, at least he would
psych up the illusion.

Blooms of hibiscus were scattered like scarlet flames on the
bushes along the garden wall. She picked off a cluster of blossoms and gathered them into a bouquet with the last of the
amaryllis lilies. A parting homage to Swami-ji.

She shut the gate behind her. *For the last time*, she thought
sadly, then resolved to put her impending departure out of her
mind.

When she neared the beehive temple the guru was sitting
cross-legged on the ground his eyes closed in meditation. There
were some scattered flowers around him on the blanket, signs
disciples had been to see him for the blessing of *Darshan*. Garnet kneeled, kissed the hem of his robe and laid the flowers
before him. The guru opened his eyes and looked at her in surprise. In Gajpur such veneration came from Indian disciples.

"I've come to say goodbye," Garnet said. "I'm leaving
Gajpur."

The guru nodded and waited for her to continue but Garnet
looked at him helplessly and said nothing.

The guru observed her for awhile, then spoke in a gentle
voice. "Be at peace, my child. Breathe, feel the air entering the
nostrils and departing. Together we'll chant *Oh-h-h-mmm* and
the sound will ripple through the heavens in ever-widening circles
like stones cast on the waters."

Garnet sat in the lotus position before the guru. Swami-ji

touched her head with both hands and gazed up into the heavens. The aroma from the flowers strewn around him intensified and rose up in the stillness until the scent of jasmine, hibiscus and frangipani filled her nostrils and a great calmness came over her. *Maybe there's no more good in life than this - the breath of flowers, stillness, the hope of God.*

She looked out at the parched, scrubby land beyond the temple and murmured. "Life is nothing but struggle."

"Live in the moment and let events pass away when they are over," the swami said softly. "Don't relive them in your mind."

"*I* don't relive them," Garnet sighed. "*They* replay themselves over and over like a bad movie."

"Force yourself back to the present no matter how bare it is," he urged. "Stay in the *now* and allow life to flow forward trusting events can move toward good without intervention."

Garnet rose and kneeled before the guru, bowing her head. Tears came into her eyes, splashing onto the flowers at his feet. "Please, Swami-ji, look after Ravi when I'm gone. Let him know I'll always love him."

Sri Devanda looked in her eyes with a tender expression. "There was a spiritual purpose in your coming to India. The soul senses where to overcome karma."

Garnet shook her head. "I can't stay. Quarrels and hostility are making me ill."

The guru placed a garland of jasmine around her neck, touched her forehead and blessed her.

"Go with God, and have faith," he said, his voice gentle and benevolent. "Your blessings will come, unexpectedly, like a flash of lightning on a hot summer day."

Garnet took his hands, wiped the tears away from her eyes with his fingers and kissed his palms. Then she leapt to her feet and without looking back ran toward the palace as fast as her legs could carry her.

viii

At the palace she surveyed the mess of the bedroom with dismay, clothes, toilet articles and trinkets scattered over the floor and piled on top of bureaus and tables. *There's no way to avoid cleaning this up*, she muttered, and crouched on the floor to sort things and fold her clothes into piles. She was tired but kept on working. *I've got to finish packing so I can get out of here.* When she finally straightened up she felt faint and queasy. *Lord, don't let me get sick again*, she prayed.

She sat down on the floor and leaned against the wall to rest when the door opened and Ravi came in. He was shocked to see her suitcases open on the bed, clothes piled up as if her departure were imminent. It occurred to him his mother may have played a part in the havoc he saw in the room and the hasty retreat she was obviously planning.

He'd been looking for Garnet since he returned from the village. On the way to his apartments he ran into his mother angrily stomping down the corridor, her heels clicking like the chattering of parrots on the marble floor. Ravi stopped her to ask if she'd seen Garnet but Khalili shook her head and refused to answer.

Ravi crouched down next to Garnet and kissed her on the cheek.

"I take it the maharani paid you a call."

"Queen to commoner!" she answered, feeling angry again. "The dynasty, the monarchy, the royal bullshit. Protecting the Precious Prince from the Witch of the West."

Ravi flushed, his face unsmiling and grim.

"Pay no attention to my mother. She has no power here."

"Tell *her*! It may come as a surprise."

Ravi slid down on the floor and stretched out his legs. He

took out a box of Gitanes, lit a cigarette and blew a cluster of smoke rings into the room before speaking.

"It's time the maharani retired from active palace life and assumed her rightful role as *Rajmata* of Gajpur."

Garnet rolled her eyes. *Another trip to la-la land!*

"Face reality, Ravi," she groaned. "Your mother will never leave me alone, and I can't tolerate her abuse. It will end with my fleeing. Better now than later. We'll both suffer less."

"Please, Garnet, give me a chance to straighten things out," he pleaded. "I'd like to follow you to America but my soul is chained here. My poor heart beats to India's sweltering climate, its dusty deserts, temple bells, muezzins chanting at sundown."

"India isn't the obstacle, Ravi, I love this country. But our worlds are light-years apart, planets from separate solar systems. Forget about me. It will never, never work."

"Come, Garnet," he said, pulling her up from the floor into his arms. "Let's drop this for tonight. We'll get a good rest and talk again in the morning."

"I'm sorry," Garnet whispered, trying to hold back her tears, "but I *am* leaving Gajpur, Ravi, as soon I can get ready."

She pulled her pillows and a coverlet off the bed, carried them into her study and dropped them onto the chaise longue. Ravi followed her.

"I need to be alone tonight," she said, avoiding his eyes.

Ravi looked stricken but Garnet bravely continued.

"How can I sleep with you knowing it's all about to end?" she said, trying to hold back the tears as she arranged the bedding on the chaise.

"Don't do this to me," Ravi pleaded. "Please, Garnet."

She looked at his face and began to weep. "I must, I must." He paused and stared at her in disbelief.

"You're breaking my heart, my darling," he cried. "But what does a penniless prince in a broken-down palace have to offer?"

As he turned slowly to leave the warm sienna of his eyes

faded and darkened. She could hardly bear it. *My heart's breaking, too.*

He closed the door behind him and another wave of nausea and dizziness swept over her. *Not again*, she thought. *My nerves are shot, or this is a relapse. I'd hate to get sick with Khalili breathing down my neck.*

She should have Dr. Karawalla examine her to be sure the cholera was out of her system before making the trip back to the States. Immigration might give her trouble returning to the States if she became ill on the plane, or thought she was still infected. She certainly didn't want to be quarantined in New York for weeks while they checked her out.

ix

She called the doctor's office in the morning. "I'm not feeling well. Maybe it's the aftermath of cholera but I should check it out with Dr. Karawalla before returning to the States."

The cheery nurse who helped care for her during her illness made an appointment, and Garnet asked Ravi if she could borrow the car to go into the village but without divulging her purpose.

"I'll drive you myself," he said.

But Garnet pleaded she needed to be alone and promised to return soon.

Dr. Karawalla rose from his chair when Garnet entered his office and came around the desk to clasp her hands. He felt a link with this young American, remembering the pleasure of his years in the States and the pretty girls at college who befriended an exotic foreigner.

Garnet explained her symptoms and Dr. Karawalla suggested a complete checkup including blood work, urinalysis, chest x-ray, cardiogram, etc. "There can be serious after-effects with cholera and it's wise to rule those out before you return to the

States. Cholera is a rarity there - unfortunately, we see too many cases, and your attack was severe. You were a very sick young lady and it was touch and go whether we could pull you through. Luckily, fate smiled on us. Actually, you're looking well, you've put on a few pounds."

"No wonder. Ravi tries to stuff me like a pig," she laughed. "Fat must be more prized in India than in New York."

"Not to worry. You could use a bit more. But let's check you out and see how we can make you feel better."

After preliminary tests, Dr. Karawalla gave her a thorough examination. He finished but said he wanted to check on a test in the lab and suggested she dress and meet in his office for the results. He arrived with a sheaf of papers in his hand. Garnet scanned his face to see if he were concerned but he wore the non-committal expression of a physician.

"Everything seems normal." He smiled at her. "You've recovered well from cholera and I don't find any problems there."

"What's wrong with me then?"

Dr. Karawalla reached over and patted her on the shoulder.

"My dear girl, dizziness and nausea are common in the early stages of pregnancy."

"What?" Garnet stared at him incredulously.

"You should feel relief soon as the pregnancy is well along, at least three months."

"But that's impossible," Garnet gasped. "A serious infection closed up my tubes after an abortion. Doctors said I'd never conceive again."

"How old were you when the abortion was performed?"

"Fifteen. Is that important?"

He knitted his fingers together and scrutinized her. "Sometimes if a girl is young the tubal condition reverses itself. Possible regeneration of cells. Or perhaps the tubes weren't closed, only narrowed. Have you missed any periods?"

"Yes, but I didn't think anything of it. You told me that could happen after my illness."

Garnet sat back, breathing heavily, trying to take in the news. "I find this hard to believe. Are you sure the *baby* isn't a tumor?"

"Positive," he assured her. This is confirmed not only by examination but lab test. The pregnancy seems well-seated and I don't foresee any problems in carrying the baby to term."

Garnet tried to speak but couldn't get the words out and began to laugh and sob. Dr. Karawalla put his arm around her shoulder to calm her but she wasn't able to stop. He waited a few moments, tried to give her a glass of water but she shook her head gasping for breath as the hysterics persisted. The doctor prepared a hypodermic and injected a sedative into her arm. He sat next to her, quietly waiting for the sedative to take effect, his fingers on her pulse. When he saw she was calm he asked if she were upset over the pregnancy and wanted him to arrange an abortion.

Garnet sat forward in the chair and protested. "No, no, of course not. It was just a shock. I've always wanted children but after the infection I was told there was no chance of my conceiving. This is a gift, a miracle from God."

Dr. Karawalla looked relieved. "I'll write out a prescription to help your symptoms. Don't worry, dizziness and nausea are natural reactions to hormones developing in your body. Come see me again before you return to the States but I don't anticipate any problems."

Garnet shook his hand. "Thank you, Dr. Karawalla. You can't imagine what this means to me. But please don't say anything to Ravi. I want to tell him myself, in my own time."

He smiled at her. "Of course. Even in India we adhere to the code of *patient confidentiality.*"

Garnet drove back to the palace slowly, trying to take in the news, hardly able to contain her joy. On the way, she stopped at a tiny hole-in-the-wall flower shop and overpaid the surprised owner many rupees to create an extravagant arrangement of blossoms for Ravi. A celebration and gift for a miracle. *But I won't tell him about the baby just yet. I must decide what to do first.*

She hoped Ravi wasn't worried about her. She'd spent nearly the whole day in the doctor's office after promising to return quickly.

x

Ravi was uneasy when Garnet left. He knew she was upset but hoped a respite from the palace would calm her and put her in a more receptive frame of mind. In the meantime, he had a serious task before him.

He confronted Khalili in the grand salon of the palace where he found her on the throne chair reading the gossip columns. Sitting on the carved throne, leaning into the softness of ruby velvet cushions comforted her. It was a reminder of her days as kumari when pilgrims and seekers bowed and knelt before her awaiting her slightest movement with trepidation as augurs of their future, and the years she reigned as maharani when Ashok was a monarch of wealth and power.

She relished receiving her friends in the salon, lording her past powers over them, hoping to see glints of envy in their eyes. Gilt chairs, all lower than the throne, were arranged in a circle around her so that she sat above her friends who had to raise their faces up to see her. *There was so much pleasure in power*, she gloated. *Only those who've experienced supremacy can understand its joy.*

Now Ravi stood before her insisting it was time for her to move on and leave the palace for a small house on the grounds.

"*Rajmata* is an honorable title," he said. "And the appropriate one."

"I refuse to be put out to pasture like one of your broken-down polo ponies," she responded indignantly.

"You pressured me to accept the role of maharaja, insisting it was my duty," Ravi said, emphasizing the words to make his point. "Now I claim my power. I've no intention of marrying any of the quasi-princesses you parade before me. We'll forget your disgraceful behavior toward Garnet in the past but disturb her again and you'll be exiled from Gajpur, sent to live in Simla."

The maharani narrowed her eyes and scrutinized him. He seemed a far cry from the pleasure-loving, careless prince she'd raised. He looked truly *formidable* and so much like Ashok when he was maharaja that she caught her breath. She thought it best to remain silent and decide what her options were in this new development.

"The next time you're tempted to interfere with Garnet or with my plans, think about Simla in the winter months. You know how you hate cold weather. Remember the icy mountains, the village streets covered in snow, the inadequate heating, and the loneliness of long winter months without your cronies to play cards and gossip with you. Take my advice, learn to get along with Garnet and accept my directives or you'll find yourself out in the cold, figuratively and literally."

Ravi turned and strode out of the salon. Khalili realized there was no way to fight him. He'd put her in a precarious position but one accepted by the culture, a father's death placed the son in charge of the family.

xi

Garnet returned to the palace in the late afternoon. Ravi was waiting at the great portal once gilded, now patched with bare spots, watching her as she drove the old Silver Ghost past the wrought iron gates and up the winding drive. He opened the door of the car and helped her out.

"Sorry I'm so late," she said, holding out the elaborate array of flowers like an offering.

"Wicked girl, I missed you. Are these beauties for me?" He

took the flowers and pulled her toward him, holding the bouquet behind her back as he leaned down and brushed his lips across her mouth.

She didn't mean to respond but the softness of his lips made her heart leap in her throat and she clung to him, kissing him back in a kind of desperate passion. *Control yourself*, she scolded, *this isn't about desire and obsession. You're mad for him, that's a given, but is it sensible to go with your bliss? Winslow would say yes, but maybe not if there was a Wicked Witch in the picture.*

She wrenched herself away and disengaged herself from his arms, embarrassed by such rash abandon. *Dangerous stuff if you're uncertain about staying. Avoid hooks until you decide.*

"I'm absolutely exhausted," she said, sighing to make the point.

"I accomplished quite a bit while you were gone and I'm tired myself," Ravi answered cheerfully, in a spirit more energetic than fatigued. "We need to talk about it."

"Not now, Ravi, please," she pleaded, kissing his cheek. "Let me have a bath and a rest first."

After bathing Garnet fell into a sleep so deep she woke wondering if she'd slept through the night. She was still half asleep when Ravi tiptoed in and sat on the edge of the bed.

"Mmmm," she murmured. "Is it morning already?"

"No, my darling," he answered, smoothing her hair back from her face. "You haven't slept that long."

She stared blankly at Ravi from a semi-dream state, not fully conscious of her surroundings. "Did you have dinner?"

"Of course not. You had a long nap and dinner is nearly ready to be served," he said, pointing to the tiny jade clock on the table. "Just time enough for our little talk."

His round cheeks were shining in the half-light and the brightness had come back into his eyes. He looked happy. *How handsome Ravi is. I hope the baby looks like him.* But she was confused. Perhaps she only dreamed the visit to Dr. Karawalla's office.

"I'm still not awake," she apologized. "Give me time to jump in the shower and revive myself."

Before getting into the shower she splashed her face with cold water and looked at herself in the mirror as she ran her hands over her naked stomach. It was unbelievable but true. *Grow strong and healthy*, she whispered, patting the little bulge over her womb. *Love is waiting for you here.*

She came back wrapped in a terry robe, still damp from the shower, her hair dripping from the towel wound around her head like a turban, her wet feet marking a trail of footprints along the wood floor. She stretched out on the bed and propped herself up against the pillows.

"Here I am. Awake and at your service."

"If only!" Ravi said, stubbing out his cigarette in a dish on the night table. "But I'm the bearer of good news. The maharani, henceforth known as the Rajmata, has capitulated and will soon be removed from the palace into a cozy house of her own. Furthermore, she's been warned under threat of banishment to Simla never to attack you again."

"I see," Garnet said, trying to take in his words and the implications.

Ravi filled her in on the details of his ultimatum to Khalili and reassured her of his protection. He would not allow her to be disturbed by his mother again.

"You mustn't think of returning to the States now," he said, kissing her damp forehead.

"I don't know what to do," she replied, feeling uncertain and confused. "I need to think things over. I should go away for awhile until everything is more clear in my mind."

He sat quietly for a moment, a little worried as he mulled over the idea of her going away. Then he clapped his hands. "Why not stay at the Lake Palace? No one will bother you there."

She was silent, thinking about the white palace and the maharaja.

"Not even you?"

"I promise," he swore, with his hand across his heart. "You'll have all the time you need for solitude and reflection."

After dinner, Garnet packed some clothes in a bag to take over to the Lake Palace in the morning and put away the rest of her things scattered around the room. Ravi tried to persuade her to spend the night with him but she insisted on sleeping on the chaise longue again.

She spent a restless night, shifting between euphoria and anxiety, thoughts jockeying back and forth like a ping pong ball. Her head whirled with indecision. Although Ravi assured her he'd keep the maharani in line she had her doubts whether anyone could control a woman so expert at trickery and treachery.

But despite her pregnancy she didn't have to stay in Gajpur with Ravi. If she wanted to remain in India she could live with Sushila in Agra, support the baby by writing articles or working for a magazine. Or she could leave India, raise the child vegetarian style in a commune in Taos, or go back to New York as a single mother in the Village. There'd be some *cachet* raising a child-prince in the snobbish, name-dropping city of New York and she could find work there if she couldn't live on the pittance offered by the poetry magazine.

In the morning, Veda came to help move her things. She decided to bring along the small writing desk as well as her books and files. In the end, she was so loaded down Veda had to send for one of the boy servants to help.

She directed them to put the desk and books in the maharaja's study and her clothes and personal things in his bedroom. Veda looked shocked but Garnet reassured him. "The maharaja would be happy knowing I'm here."

Veda nodded. The old monarch was fond of Garnet, cherishing her resemblance to Rani Elizabeth, as Veda himself did.

xii

Khalili paced back and forth in the Grand Salon. There was no hope of forcing Ravi into the advantageous marriage she planned for him. He was obsessed with the American and she had no choice but to accept it. But if he thought she was stupid enough to allow herself to be pushed out of the palace as a beggar he was sorely mistaken.

There must be some way she could hang on to the profitable offer she'd wangled. Perhaps she could find another bridegroom to present to the rich merchant and conclude a marriage arrangement where she'd be included in the deal.

First she approached Vijay, a legitimate if distant member of the Gajpur royal bloodline.

Vijay was aghast at her proposition. "Are you out of your mind? For god's sake, Khalili, you know what I am. I couldn't bring myself to go to bed with a normal girl, much less a retarded one."

The maharani stared at him coldly. There was no point in pursuing him. He was useless. He couldn't see beyond his ridiculous attachment to the homosexual life. But who else was there? She fixed her black eyes on Vijay while her mind raced. An absurd thought came full stop in her brain. A daring idea. But without risk there can be no gain. Could she pull it off? Why not? Her gift of cunning and the desperation of Princess Jali's family were on her side.

She sat up straight in the throne chair, a self-satisfied smirk on her face as she fanned herself with a peacock fan and addressed Vijay in an offhand manner.

"Ask Niles to come and see me."

"Niles? You must be crazy."

Khalili slapped the fan down on the table. "Do as I say, Vijay, if you ever want to step foot in the palace again."

Vijay salaamed. "At your service, Your Majesty. The one you labeled *wretched creature* shall appear before you. Just don't count on his cooperation."

"Stay out of this, Vijay, if you know what's good for you."

She breathed a sigh of relief and rested in the throne chair while she waited for Vijay to return. She could manipulate this one. Despite his affair with Vijay it was clear Niles had some desire for women. She'd seen his infatuation with Garnet, bisexual they called it today.

When Vijay returned with Niles the maharani dismissed him with a wave of her hand.

"Go, Vijay, go. I wish to speak to Niles alone."

After Vijay left the room she took a long, hard look at Niles. She had not seen such a pathetic creature since her days as kumari and the sight of this pale boy who looked as if he teetered on the edge of death was a reminder of her former powers. In her years as virgin goddess many piteous creatures passed before her in supplication and the power to heal was supposedly hers. Scrutinizing the boy before her made her feel empowered, infused with energy, alive.

She was clever enough not to broach the subject on her mind before she drew Niles under her spell. She began by telling him she could see the terrible suffering he endured in his life. This was a come-on which worked well with those who saw themselves as victims. Not only that, she continued, it was clear his wounds and scars were still there. But through secret knowledge gained as kumari in the temple at Kathmandu, she possessed healing powers to help him.

She told him the story of a young boy whose father brought him to her for healing. Half his face had been torn away by a tiger before his hunter father could shoot the beast. Khalili admitted she'd been a spoiled and selfish little kumari, indifferent to the plight of pilgrims who came before her but she was touched by this boy. The father explained his son was tormented by his disfigurement and refused to leave their hut, so deep was his shame and humiliation. The father had hidden his face under a bandanna and carried him over the mountain to make the pilgrimage to the virgin goddess.

'*Uncover his face!*' she ordered the father. The boy resisted but the father yanked the cloth away.

"For once, my cold little heart was moved by the sight of a boy's mangled face, a boy nearly my own age," Khalili confessed to Niles with a candor which impressed him. "I looked deep into his eyes, held his head in my hands and kissed the torn side of his face, praying that whatever mystical powers I possessed would come to my aid and heal him."

Khalili released him and the boy looked up, his eyes shining back at her, his childhood restored by the touch of her kiss and the love radiating from her eyes. His face was only partially healed but the boy had undergone a spiritual renewal. He accepted his disfigurement, forgot his mangled face. He left the temple smiling, stopping for a moment in the courtyard to wave goodbye to the beautiful kumari sitting in the window of the balcony garbed in scarlet. Months later, the father returned to give thanks to Khalili for the boy had gone back to school, played happily with other children and appeared not to notice his deformity. Strangest of all, the father said, children who once teased him no longer paid attention to his wounds. The father wept and pressed an offering into Khalili's hand. '*God's hand touched him through you.*'

"It was the only genuinely kind act of my life," Khalili conceded. "An altruistic stunt kept secret until now for I despised softness then, feared it would strip away my power."

She soon drew Niles under her spell using all the magic tricks and sorcery she remembered. He was mesmerized. No one had taken his sufferings seriously and he began his litany of whines and complaints. Khalili listened to him intently, nodding her head gravely and urging him on.

At the first session, she performed incantations over him in *Khas-Kura*, a dialect of the Nepalese language, and created her celebrated aura of mystical stillness. Her witchery relaxed and soothed Niles. Khalili was paying attention to his pain and it felt like healing to him.

She ordered him to return the following morning. When he arrived the salon was redolent with incense and the burning of scented candles. Khalili, seated on the throne, instructed Niles to kneel before her while she held his head and performed the rituals and chanting of blessings remembered from her childhood in the temple.

This went on for days. After each session Niles walked around in a daze feeling strangely calmed by Khalili and drawn to return for more. And she felt her old powers restored, stronger than ever. She was becoming attached to this strange boy. No one appreciated her mystical powers since she left Nepal but she'd discovered a disciple in Niles and the self-worth she felt in her childhood as a Living Goddess of rare beauty and occult knowledge, resurfaced and restored the confidence shaken by Ravi's threats to dispose of her.

When Khalili was sure Niles was under her power she subtly introduced the subject for which she had so patiently primed him. "Why go back to the States?" she said, leaning in close to his face, dizzying him with her perfume heavily scented with musk, as she fixed him with a piercing stare. "America is no place for you. What do you have there? Nothing. Stay in India and I can help you."

She painted an idyllic picture of the life she could provide if he remained in India. She was sympathetic to his needs, understood his relationship with Vijay and would not disturb their liaison, but protect them both. In fact, she'd been offered a proposition which could make everything possible.

"You've only to agree to marry a beautiful young princess. The girl is a bit simple but the family is rich and will provide every financial benefit including a villa on our land where Vijay can live with you and your bride. If you cooperate you'll have nothing to worry about for the rest of your life."

The maharani didn't tell Niles the deal included a cash settlement for her and money to keep up the palace. Niles talked it over with Vijay who laughed and said, "Why not? If you can take it and I'm included in the deal, our only worry will be how to enjoy the good life. At least, meet with the girl, see if you can stand her."

The maharani arranged a meeting with the family. She dressed Niles in an emerald satin tunic beaded with pearls, white silk pants, and matching satin turban pinned by a jewel at the center of his forehead. She insisted Vijay wear a similar outfit in blue and introduced them as cousins, whereupon she produced a document, a phoney family tree elaborately executed on parchment paper by her astrologer, costing a good many rupees to assuage his scruples, and passed Niles off as the aristocratic son of a cousin from an obscure branch of the late maharaja's family.

She excused Niles' pallid skin as a result of the mother's marriage to the grandson of an English lord, her royal Indian origins kept secret because of color barriers in the United States. The parents were impressed.

The deal of course, would not be quite as sweet without Ravi's princely title, but despite Niles' assumed identity Khalili didn't dare bestow a royal title on him. Still, luxuries would be provided in a lesser amount and a villa built for Princess Jali and her bridegroom with plenty of room for Vijay and the Rajmata.

Princess Jali was a sweet girl and both Niles and Vijay were impressed by her beauty and grace. Despite her limitations Jali was charming, grateful for Niles' attention and tolerant of his moods. Vijay set out to please her and she enjoyed herself immensely, laughing at his jokes and flattered by male attention. Vijay urged Niles to go ahead with the marriage. The father was satisfied, perhaps only too willing to settle his daughter, and the maharani reassured the mother that her daughter would be well looked after by her.

The next day Khalili negotiated the marriage contracts with the father, papers were signed and the wedding date set. The parents preferred the marriage to take place in Gajpur to avoid gossip about their daughter and Khalili agreed, happy to accommodate such good fortune. She breathed a sigh of relief. It was an ideal situation. The palace would be financed, her expenses assured, and as a quasi mother-in-law she'd have a certain amount of control and command respect from the young couple, if not from her princely son.

xiii

Veda and the servant boy unpacked the boxes and placed the small desk in the maharaja's study in the Lake Palace. After they left Garnet sat in a window seat and smiled as she gazed out at the blue waters of the artificial lake below. *It's only a paper moon, hanging over a cardboard sea . . .*

The maharaja's belongings were still in place waiting for Ravi to decide the disposition of objects and personal effects. He gave Garnet carte blanche to explore the Lake Palace including his father's personal papers.

"It will give you a bit of insight into Indian potentates. Not that our maharajas were in the same class as Mughal emperors but Gajpur had been a wealthy and influential state before our transition to a democracy."

Garnet persevered in finishing her work on Mumtaz Mahal. The rest of the time she concentrated on her dilemma. When overcome by indecision, she distracted herself from the anxieties plaguing her by exploring the minutia of the maharaja's past.

She felt strange at intruding despite Ravi's permission, putting away the maharaja's *x-rated* journals so despised by Khalili without reading them, respecting the old monarch's *angst* and cravings. The mass of political correspondence affirmed the significance of the state of Gajpur with boxes of medals including the *Légion d'honneur* awarded to him by the French government, for his devotion to France, and decorations presented by the British Raj in their efforts to keep peace with India's royal rulers who could be helpful in aborting rebellions.

She looked through his library, surprised by his books, Horace, Homer, Dante, shaking her head in disbelief. No wonder she loved him, a powerful king who esteemed the words of poets. There were also books on astronomy, mathematics, scientific technology and a superb collection of art books and biographies. Among the lives of the exalted she discovered the journal of Emperor Jahangir, father of Shah Jahan.

She was touched by Jahangir's tenderness on the death of his favorite princess, the five-year old daughter and firstborn of Mumtaz, an apparent victim of smallpox. The emperor was heartbroken, unashamedly displaying his affection and grief for the little princess.

Qwazini wrote in his Royal Court chronicles . . .

However much his Majesty Jahangir desired to control himself, his tears flowed. And for a long time at the mere hearing of some word reminding him of her death, His Majesty became agitated and could not control himself. Tears would drop from his eyes unrestrained, tearing the hearts of his faithful followers.

Sad to think the maharaja would never know Ravi's child. In his old age he would have been a doting grandfather. She unearthed a gold-tooled leather album filled with regal portraits and kissed Ravi's baby picture, a satin-garbed royal infant propped up on velvet cushions, smiling at photos of him as a toddler, then a schoolboy grinning in his Eton cap at the Doon School. She held up the book, patted her stomach and whispered to the *infante* to look at the daddy.

She was lonely and missed Ravi desperately but forced herself to stay alone until she decided the future for herself and the baby.

Ravi paced back and forth across the marble floor of the grand salon of the Gajpur palace.

"You'll make yourself ill, my prince," Veda admonished, from the corner of the room where he sat in meditation. "Divine power will prevail here."

"I can't lose her, Veda."

"We cannot lose what we do not own, nor own another human being," Veda counseled gently. "Such an idea is an illusion of the unenlightened who are veiled from reality. Have patience. Divinity works out our destiny."

The maharani interrupted their discussion by entering the salon and dismissing Veda with a wave of her hand. He rose, bowed and left the room shutting the door behind him.

Khalili sat in her throne chair and gave Ravi the news about the marriage contracts with Niles and the princess and her financial agreement. Ravi laughed uproariously as she described the meeting and recounted the details.

Khalili was indignant. "It's not funny. A marriage arrangement is a serious business."

"Not funny?" Ravi said, choking with laughter. "It's hilarious!" He took his mother's hand and kissed it. "What a woman you are, what a woman! Who taught you to survive like this?"

Khalili jerked her hand away. "Observing people in the real world since the age of five. Certainly not the decadent royals of Gajpur."

* * *

Ravi hurried to his rooms to record the amazing turn of events for Garnet and gave the note to Veda urging him to fly over to the Lake Palace and place it on her luncheon tray.

The Rajmata has worked a miracle and saved the deal with the rich merchant prince by passing off Niles as a quasi-prince. He's flattered by the adoring beauty of limited intellect who's awed at catching a bridegroom of such intelligence. As long as Niles can continue his affair with Vijay, he has no problem about his

*forthcoming marriage. Vijay is pleased and Khalili looks forward
to reigning over their ménage à trois of connubial bliss.*

Garnet read the note over and over again in disbelief, hardly
able to believe her eyes. Khalili's scheming maneuvers turned
out to be a blessing this time.

She spent the rest of the day on the upper terrace lounging
in the old British Raj rocker gazing out at the faux blue lake,
thinking about Ravi and wondering what to do next. She thought
about her life and Sailship Point, remembering the sun-tossed
waves of the sea on a summer morning and the green hills where
she loved to run, inhaling the sweet breath of trees, the maples,
magnolias, and weeping willows perfuming the air of her childhood. She might never see the beloved peninsula again if she
stayed in India. But Sailship Point held no life for her. Perhaps
not even America.

The sun began to burn the skin on her arms and she moved
back under the shaded overhang of the terrace to re-read Qwazini
on the betrothal of Mumtaz Mahal and Shah Jahan . . .

*"At a time when the ascendant star was favorable,
Their eyes deserved meeting each other."*

She'd envied Mumtaz Mahal and Shah Jahan but saw the
possibility she and Ravi could also have a deeply loving, intimate marriage. If the Rajmata would leave them alone. *Don't be
fooled by her,* she chided. *Shrews don't turn into saints.*

Her mind was dizzy with indecision. It was hard to think
rationally. If only Ravi weren't so appealing, if only the sight of
his blooming, radiant energy didn't make her want to cover him
with kisses, squeeze his cheeks and bite his soft lips, maybe she
could think more clearly.

It wasn't just his appeal. She had searched for healing and
found it with Ravi, restored by him in a way she never thought
possible. Ravi accepted and affirmed her despite her flaws and
for the first time she felt safe in the universe, cared for and loved,
able to exist as herself without effort. *Home is where you're prized*

*and respected, where your weaknesses are more loved than the
strengths of others.*

In the evening, she sat in the maharaja's rocking chair in the
dark, rocking back and forth trying to think, finally stumbling to
bed in her kurtah where she fell into a deep sleep.

She was awakened by murmurings and shadows moving
across the ceiling, and thought she heard Winslow whispering to
her. Was she dreaming? She recognized his warmhearted voice
and rich baritone laugh. She longed to see Winslow's face but
her eyes were glued shut so she waited, motionless and quiet, as
his voluptuous tones echoed down to her bed.

"I've been watching over you," Winslow said, the words pop-
ping into her head one at a time like a musical bouncing ball.
"Many prayers have been answered. My task is finished and I
must move on. Carry my love with you, and be gladdened."

Garnet tried to respond but the shadows moved away and
the murmurings stopped. She felt at peace. Winslow had seen
her safely through.

The message in his ghostly visit was clear. She'd longed for
India and she was here, had yearned for a deep and abiding love
and received it, no matter how fraught with difficulties. She'd
despaired at not being able to conceive a child and *unto her a
child would be born.*

India itself had been a path of healing with Ravi who nurtured her, Sushila who taught her not to be afraid of tender love,
the maharaja who cherished and trusted her, the wisdom of the
guru and the ordinary Indians who embraced her as one of them.
God had showered her with blessings. What difference if the
circumstances weren't what she had imagined?

In the morning Veda brought her breakfast and she sent him
back with a note asking Ravi to come to the Lake Palace. Ravi
arrived quickly, a bit tense as if he feared her news but his face
was plump and shining.

Garnet felt the pulse in her throat throb when she saw him.

Boom, bang, boom, faster and faster, pounding through her veins until she could hardly breathe.

Before she had a chance to speak, Ravi jumped in.

"Khalili has concocted a shrewd deal for herself," he announced, gleefully recounting the details of her intrigues leading to marriage contract between Niles and the princess.

"She and her *ménage à trois* will live like kings in a grand villa built by the merchant prince. The marriage settlement she conned out of *daddy* provides money to make repairs in the palace, helps us along, and pays the servants their wages."

Garnet shook her head in amazement at the maharani's manipulations. "India will be good for Niles. He needs a little happiness. He's wallowed in misery long enough."

Ravi handed her two blue velvet jewel boxes. "Open them up," he said. "They belonged to Rani Elizabeth."

She picked up the necklace in the larger box and held out the filigreed gold chains interspersed with pearls and small emeralds. In the other box she found an emerald ring encircled with tiny diamonds.

"These are family heirlooms," she protested.

"Sentimental value," Ravi assured her. "My grandfather gave them to Granny when they had to meet secretly. She loved to show them off and boast of two lovers who couldn't be parted."

Tears came to Garnet's eyes. He didn't know that she often sensed Elizabeth's ghostly presence and felt close to her. Ravi kneeled down and placed the emerald ring on her finger.

"Stay, Garnet," he implored her. "I'd be lost without your feistiness, your crazy mix of tough boy, tender girl, stubborn intellectual and now a surprisingly wild, hot-blooded lover."

Garnet rolled her eyes. "I wouldn't talk about hot blood if I were you - a descendant of royal seducers for centuries!"

"Then we're two icons of passion. So much the better." Garnet held up her hand up to admire the ring. "How precious this is," she said, taking his hand and kissing his fingers.

Ravi took a deep breath and rushed on. "Don't worry about

the Rajmata. She's in her element. She'll patronize the simple-minded princess, enjoy the sexual byplay of Niles and Vijay and harass the servants who'll kowtow but make fun of her behind her back. She'll be far too busy with her intrigues to bother us."

Ravi paused and sat down in a chair.

"You've nothing more to fear from my mother," he reassured her. "I will assert my authority as *maharaja* and protect you like a fierce lion."

Garnet felt shy to blurt out her news so began by saying she'd been feeling ill and dizzy and had made an appointment with Dr. Karawalla to be sure she'd recovered from cholera.

Ravi looked worried.

"It turned out to be something quite different," she said, trying to hide her pleasure.

Now he was puzzled. But she could no longer stand the suspense. She got up from her chair, sat on the floor next to him and pressed her head against his knees. "The miracle has happened," she whispered.

He looked disbelieving. "But I thought . . ."

"It turns out the doctors were wrong. Or the angels came in on my case."

Ravi laughed in delight and pulled her up on his lap, kissing her all over her face, her eyelids, nose, forehead, chin. "Didn't I tell you to light the incense and pray at the shrine of fertility? You called it nonsense. Now maybe you'll believe in the magic of India."

"I believe in the miraculous, wherever it comes from," she vowed, ruffling his hair and burying her lips in his soft neck.

"Now you have to marry me!" Ravi chortled triumphantly.

"Oh, I'll have to think about that," she said, and got up from his lap. She stretched out on the bed and gazed up at the ceiling as if mulling it over.

But there was no turning back. She had not intended this, had not considered spending the rest of her life in India but fate had landed her here and she was not in charge of where her desires and longings would be fulfilled. *Answered prayers*. Still the best kind.

Ravi was watching her, his brown eyes expectant and wishful. "I have a confession to make," she murmured, smiling to herself.

She sat up, pulled Ravi toward her and wrapped her arms around his neck.

"I've been madly in love with you since the day we met," she confessed.

Ravi gave a sigh of relief and smiled at her. "You may find captivity seductive. We're tender conquerors."

"I find *you* seductive," she said, kissing his ear. "Be prepared."

"Don't worry," he said, holding her tight. "I intend to make up for lost time."

Yes! Carpe Diem! Garnet thought, as she looked at Ravi's happy face. Grab what you love while you can. This was *their* time, like Mumtaz and Shah Jahan. *Their eyes deserved meeting each other. For perfect wisdom demanded that each happy Jupiter should seek union with a Venus-faced one.*

She'd never have believed contentment could be found in a broken-down palace in an arid desert. Or that she'd feel so glad to be alive in the universe.

The world was full of surprises, often tied up in strange packages. God's gifts were meant to be unwrapped carefully and embraced with love.

* * *

BOSTON
PUBLIC
LIBRARY

BEYOND
CONFLICT

PETER R. BREGGIN, M.D.

BEYOND
CONFLICT

▼▼▼▼▼▼▼▼▼▼▼▼▼▼▼▼▼▼▼▼▼▼▼▼▼▼▼▼▼▼▼▼

From Self-Help
and Psychotherapy
to Peacemaking

ST. MARTIN'S PRESS
NEW YORK

First published in the United States of America in 1992

Printed in the United States of America

ISBN 0-312-07654-1

Library of Congress Cataloging-in-Publication Data

Breggin, Peter Roger, 1936–
    Beyond conflict : from psychotherapy to peacemaking / Peter R.
  Breggin.
      p.   cm.
    ISBN 0-312-07654-1
    1. Interpersonal conflict.   2. Social conflict.   3. Conflict
  (Psychology)   4. Love.   I. Title.
  BF637.I48B74   1992
  303.6'9—dc20   92-4959
                                                          CIP

DESIGN BY SNAP-HAUS GRAPHICS
First Edition: September 1992

For my wife, Ginger Ross-Breggin,
who continues to inspire and enlighten me
with love in every sphere of life.

CONTENTS

▼ ▼

ACKNOWLEDGMENTS
AND RESOURCES

▼ ▼

As in all my work, my wife Ginger Ross-Breggin is the single most important and beneficial influence. She continues to inspire me to write in a more easily understandable manner and adds immeasurably to my awareness of the human condition. While I held my beliefs about love long before I met her, I genuinely doubt if I could have sustained them much longer without her. Love is a powerful idea; but so many forces in life, and too many within ourselves, act to discourage it. This book is a hymn to our "shared values," Ginger's concept that enriches the final chapter.

I am deeply grateful to my friends Leonard Roy Frank and Pam Clay, both of whom read the manuscript with great care and made many useful suggestions and necessary corrections. My neighbor, David Whitford, also carefully read the manuscript and made significant contributions.

Richard Rubenstein, my colleague at George Mason University in the Institute for Conflict Analysis and Resolution, offered important insights and much-needed encouragement as well. Without his original invitation to join the Institute, it's possible that I would not have been inspired to write this book. Another George Mason colleague, Frank Blechman, also made useful criticisms. In general, I want to thank all the members of the Institute and, in particular, Mary Lynn Boland, for making it all run smoothly.

Sharon Presley was especially helpful in directing me toward recent research in social psychology. Keith Hoeller also went through the book from beginning to end and found many ideas that needed clarification and elaboration. Emilio Viano and Robert Morgan not only helped with the manuscript, they provided lengthy, encouraging evaluations that helped inspire the finishing touches. In addition, I received a combination of moral support and/or criticism from David Cohen, David K. Hart, Larry Tirnauer, Craig Blaner, Yvette Ogle, Joann Robertson, Gerald Dubin, and Jean Ross.

Claudia Delgado has helped with innumerable office tasks surrounding the manuscript and Marilyn Cramer has come through as a consultant every time I've created a computer disaster for myself.

My agent for my recent books is Richard Curtis. He and his staff have done everything an author could hope for.

As I describe in the Preface, this book was completed only a few months after *Toxic Psychiatry*. St. Martin's is the publisher of both books, and I have been enormously pleased with the company and *all* its staff members. In the acknowledgments to *Toxic Psychiatry* I have already thanked senior editor Jared Kieling for his work on that book, which became an important step toward the publication of this one. Thanks again, Jared. Now I also want to thank his assistant, Ensley Eikenberg.

Simon Winder is the St. Martin's senior editor for *Beyond Conflict*, and it would be hard to imagine a more enthusiastic and appreciative supporter. Finally, authors do not usually get to thank their publicists in print because they don't know whether they want to thank them until several months after publication. Well, I have reason to thank the entire promotions office at St. Martin's, and especially Kate Kahn, for their efforts on behalf of *Toxic Psychiatry*.

For anyone who wishes to learn more about the burgeoning field of conflict analysis and resolution, many resources can be found at the Institute for Conflict Analysis and Resolution (ICAR), George Mason University, Fairfax, Virginia 22030-4444. ICAR offers masters degrees and doctorates in conflict analysis and resolution. It also houses two important national organizations in the field—COPRED (Consortium on Peace Research, Education and Development) and NCPCR (National Conference on Peacemaking and Conflict Resolution).

For people who wish to learn more about psychiatric reform, *Toxic Psychiatry* provides an appendix on resources.

I would also like to acknowledge Kenneth Boulding (1970, 1978) who has suggested a somewhat similar three dynamic analysis limited to the societal level, but with rather marked differences that do not so readily lend it to personal growth and conflict resolution theory. Boulding used the term dynamics or social organizers in his theory of human relationships and specifically described them as the threat system, the exchange system, and the integrative system. His theory helped to clarify the development of my own, but there are important differences. As one example, Boulding sees the integrative or love system as a form of exchange, while I envision it as unconditional love or gifting. This leads to both a different analysis and a different social ideal. Boulding does not relate the concept of dynamics or social organizers to basic human needs and does not apply his theory to self-development or interpersonal conflict resolution.

In addition, a variety of humanistic psychologists and psychiatrists have contributed to my thinking, as well as to basic needs theory in general. They include Erich Fromm (1956, 1976), Erik Erikson (1963), Gordon Allport (1955), Karen Horney (1945, 1950), Alfred Adler (1969), Ansbacher and Ansbacher (1956), and Abraham Maslow (1971).

PREFACE: FROM *TOXIC PSYCHIATRY* TO *BEYOND CONFLICT*

▼ ▼

Surprisingly, the two books that most fully present the twin aspects of my work have been published within less than a year of each other. First came *Toxic Psychiatry: Why Therapy, Empathy and Love Must Replace the Drugs, Electroshock and Biochemical Theories of the New Psychiatry* (1991), and now this book, *Beyond Conflict: From Self-Help and Psychotherapy to Peacemaking*.

While *Toxic Psychiatry* does describe caring, human service alternatives to conventional psychiatry, it is mainly a sweeping criticism of modern biologically oriented psychiatry. It exposes the politics of psychiatry and the damaging effects of drugs and electroshock. *Beyond Conflict* has a more positive thrust. It presents my approach to life as a practicing psychiatrist and psychotherapist, and a professor of conflict analysis and resolution. It is, in the words of one of my friends, a much more "uplifting" book.

Yet the themes of my life and work, as reflected in the separate books, are really inseparable. *Toxic Psychiatry* is an aggressive attack on the destructive principles, fraudulent claims, and dangerous technologies of modern psychiatry; but the spiritual energy behind it derives from the principles of liberty and love—my belief in human rights, the inviolability of every single human being, and the healing power of human caring. *Beyond Conflict* more fully articulates that spiritual energy. It proposes that love must become the guiding principle of human relationships in general, as well as the ultimate solution to the most severe personal, societal, and political conflicts.

The aim of both books has been to present scientific and philosophical ideas in a form available to any interested reader. They reflect my commitment to more holistic writing, accessible to any thoughtful person, and based on equal parts of thinking and feeling, scholarship and real-life experience. People need books that offer better principles through which to guide their lives. Toward that end, writing should be comprehensive *and* comprehensible. I have tried to meet that standard.

Part I

▼ ▼

Understanding the Three Dynamics: Love, Liberty, and Coercion

CHAPTER 1

▼ ▼

From Self-Help and Psychotherapy to Peacemaking

Human values must be universal. In the past, narrow values have led to tragedy. As the twentieth century draws to a close, our values must be broad and deep. The question of the kind of life human beings ought to lead cannot be solved within the framework of accepted social commonplaces and mere common sense. This is true because man himself is not limited to a single society in a single country but is part of a chain connecting humanity, the natural phenomena of the whole earth, and the cosmos.
Daisaku Ikeda, **Choose Life** *(1976)*

We are the aware generation. Modern psychology and modern communications have enabled us to see conflict everywhere: within ourselves, between ourselves and others, on the world scene, and with nature. But we have not become so successful at seeing solutions—at finding ways of easing and resolving conflict within ourselves and our society.

In every aspect of life—from self-help and psychotherapy to peacemaking—we need better principles for resolving conflict and promoting harmony within ourselves and others. We need approaches that make personal *and* political sense, that connect us in a rational and caring manner to ourselves as individuals and to the world around us, including other people and nature. We need a viewpoint that helps us understand and heal the pain of human conflict.

A good set of healing principles should be useful in every aspect of living. Inner peace and world peace are, at root, one and the same. Complexity of course increases as we move from issues of personal growth to those of world community; but the principles, I believe, remain basically the same. This means we can deepen and fine-tune our understanding of life through self-examination and through studying society. We can apply one basic approach to self-help and to helping others, to resolving personal conflict and to ending social strife. This book attempts to provide such a holistic approach.

THE IMPORTANCE OF BASIC NEEDS

If we can understand basic human needs and how they become frustrated or satisfied, we will have made a critical step toward finding better ways of resolving all kinds of conflicts. The most severe conflicts often have to do with psychological and social needs, rather than physical or material ones. They can be resolved through improving human relations and, especially, through the collaborative satisfaction of each other's basic needs.

Human needs can be divided into three categories: love, liberty, and coercion. *Love* includes the whole range of motivation related to human bonding, from the infant's desire for holding to the adult's dependence on close friends, family, and community. *Liberty* includes needs associated with autonomy, independence, self-determination and freedom, such as the infant's first efforts to walk and the adult's later efforts to take charge of his or her own life. *Coercion* encompasses the need to use force, violence, and intimidation. It rears up in a small child's frustrated rage, in a man or woman's attempts to control a spouse, or in a politician's call to arms. Whether coercion and even violence are *basic* needs or purely learned responses remain controversial.

Human needs do not exist in a social vacuum. They develop and find expression through human relationships. A baby's smile at the sight of its mother is inseparable from the presence of a mother, and both mother and child interact to increase each other's tendency to smile. The desire for romantic love requires feeling passion toward another person, and it cannot fully mature without reciprocity. The development of feelings of esteem in a child depends upon those who encourage or undermine it, and even the most autonomous adults continue to respond to how others feel about them.

From infancy on, individual human needs cannot be teased out from the fabric of social relationships that satisfy or frustrate them. Indeed, it is impossible to conceive of an infant becoming a normal human in the absence of nurturing relationships. Babies don't learn to smile frequently without reciprocal responses from adults, and abandoned or neglected infants cannot by themselves grow into effectively functioning adults (see chapter 2).

THE PSYCHOSOCIAL NATURE OF BASIC NEEDS

Biological needs, such as sex or hunger, do not by themselves produce conflict. Conflict results from unfulfilled psychosocial needs, such as the desire for self-esteem, autonomy, or love. Both human beings and chimpanzees have needs for touching, nurturing, and companionship. Both humans and chimps compete for love in their communities and families, creating conflict among themselves, and both use loving gestures and overtures as a method of conflict resolution (see chapter 2).

Biological needs, such as sex, become sources of conflict through the psychosocial meanings or values attached to them. The rapist is no more out for "sexual gratification" by itself than is the lover. The one seeks power or revenge, the other tenderness or intimacy. The needs for power and for intimacy are the motivating forces, not physical sex.

Similarly, in typical marital disputes in my therapy practice, the man desires sex in order to feel respected or loved while the woman desires respect and love before she wants sex. Often sex becomes little more than the focal point for conflict over autonomy and control.

Some men and women suppress their sexual desires out of religious conviction, and still others seek sexual release without help from other people. In every case, the biological need for sexual pleasure or release is much less important than the psychosocial needs surrounding it, such as autonomy, self-esteem, or love.

The same is true of hunger or thirst. People are motivated by these instinctual drives to seek food or water, but are not necessarily driven into conflict with other people, even when they are starving to death or dying of thirst. For example, the social prohibition against killing people for food is rarely broken even under extreme circumstances. But when people associate hunger with injustice or other psychosocial or community issues, then it becomes a major source of personal and political conflict.

PSYCHOSOCIAL DYNAMICS

The word "dynamic" connotes energy, force, change, and progress. It suggests the capacity of human beings to overcome at least some of their biological constraints and cultural experiences to achieve a higher level of functioning based on rational values and loving principles.

Dynamic is most familiar through the term psychodynamic, a loosely defined concept indicating the internal forces and processes of the mind. Dynamic in this book refers to *psychosocial* experiences—interactions between an individual's needs and the social relationships that satisfy them. The love dynamic, for example, encompasses both the person's need for love and the kinds of relationships that stimulate and satisfy it. The liberty dynamic includes the individual's desire for autonomy and independence and how that is expressed or frustrated through relationships.

THE THREE DYNAMICS

The three psychosocial dynamics correspond to the three basic needs: love, liberty, and coercion. Each of the dynamics—love, liberty, and coercion—produces a very different kind of psychological and social experience. The feelings, thoughts, and actions that occur along each dynamic are different, and the outcomes for everyone involved are different as well. From each dynamic, we can identify a consistent set of unique principles to guide our actions and our lives.

Once we learn to identify each dynamic, we can more quickly and thoroughly grasp the implications of what is taking place within and among the participants. We can influence the quality and the result of a relationship or conflict depending on which approach we take toward others, and which approach we encourage them to take toward us. We can decide which principles to implement and to live by.

If a father, for example, has a conflict with a son, he has three basic options. He can force a solution on his child (coercion), he can create an environment in which his son has as much choice as possible (liberty), or he can solve the problem in a loving manner aimed at satisfying his son's basic needs (love). Or the father may try a mixture of all three approaches.

Similarly, if a nation is planning strategy for handling an international conflict, it again has three basic options—love, liberty, or coercion—and again, the outcome will be greatly affected by its choices. The nation can threaten war (coercion), seek to negotiate through diplomatic channels (liberty), or offer to collaborate with the adversary toward the mutual satisfaction of each side's basic needs (love).

People prosper psychologically and socially when they reject coercion and promote liberty and especially love in their lives. *People can improve their personal well-being and promote conflict resolution by identifying the three dynamics and by taking actions that limit coercion and promote liberty and love. This is true in personal as well as political activities.*

UNDERSTANDING THE THREE DYNAMICS

The following is a brief summary of the essential principles of each of the three dynamics:

LOVE (DYNAMIC I):

1. Nurturing, sharing, and giving gifts

2. Cooperative relationships

3. The generation of feelings of empathy, caring, and love

4. The abhorrence and rejection of force

LIBERTY (DYNAMIC II):

1. Bargaining, negotiating, or making voluntary exchanges

2. Competitive relationships

3. The generation of feelings of respect or esteem

4. Force limited to self-defense

COERCION (DYNAMIC III):

1. Forcing, threatening, bullying, and manipulating

2. Involuntary or oppressive relationships

3. The generation of negative feelings, such as hate, guilt, shame, anxiety, numbing, and chronic anger (These feelings will be identified as expressions of psychological helplessness.)

4. The arbitrary use of force

Attitudes toward force can be critical in identifying each dynamic and in understanding their outcomes. In love, force is abhorred. We do not wish to injure our loved ones even in self-defense. In liberty, we exercise the right to use force in self-defense, but we never initiate force. In coercion, we initiate force to satisfy our needs.

Love creates bonding on a personal and societal level. It is fulfilled through both caring personal relationships and through community. It encourages mutuality, sharing, and the equal worth of all people. Liberty encourages or produces independence in personal relationships and the free market in society. It encourages competition and ranking people according to a hierarchy of achievement or success. Coercion suppresses and injures people in authoritarian relationships and in the extreme produces totalitarianism in society. It fosters power and control on the part of the perpetrator and submission and helplessness on the part of the victim.

Notice that each dynamic has a both a personal and a political parallel:

Love generates personal bonding and human community.

Liberty generates personal autonomy and the free market.

Coercion generates personal oppression and totalitarianism.

Unhappily, coercion is too easily resorted to, especially in the handling of our most difficult personal and political problems. Too much of life is made up of dominators and dominated. Meanwhile, the competition generated by liberty too easily deteriorates into winners overpowering losers. Love is required to reject coercion and to soften the competition of liberty. But love itself can become as elusive as a mirage in a desert, a distant vision maintained only by our sheer thirst for it. We frequently seem unable to love our immediate family and friends, let alone other members of our society, foreigners, nature, and the earth.

The three-dynamic approach encompasses all the ways human beings try to resolve their conflicts. In a broader sense, it also encompasses the whole range of human relationships. Thus it provides guidelines not only for resolving conflict but for personal growth and human progress in general.

Progress, however, is no longer a concept that can be glibly used. It cannot uncritically be identified with industrial or techno-logical development, with an increasing gross national product, or a higher material standard of living. In our personal lives and within society, progress must take into account the *quality* of life, including the quality of our inner life, our relationships with other human beings, nature, and the earth itself. Human beings must learn to value nature and the earth as they would ideally value each other—with unconditional love.

NEEDS AND VALUES

All individuals probably begin with somewhat similar "human na-ture" or biological capacities to feel. How these capacities are in-hibited or channeled into psychosocial needs will depend upon individual personality, varying social roles and culture.

When needs are assigned negative or positive worth, we call them *values*. Love begins as a biologically based potential for hav-ing feelings toward other people, becomes expressed as a psycho-social need, and then, with the aid of human consciousness, it is recognized as a positive or negative value.

INSTITUTIONS AND IDEOLOGIES

Needs become values, and then values become further elaborated into philosophies, religions, and ideologies; and these in turn be-come embedded in social institutions, such as the family, schools, churches, or governments. Love, for example, is transformed by culture into love of school, country, or God. It may even become corrupted by coercion in religious or patriotic wars.

Even among chimpanzees, love is embodied in an institution, the chimpanzee family consisting of the mother and her offspring, and their extended relationships within the group. Like human children, young chimps learn to love, or fail to do so, depending upon their upbringing. An elderly, failing mother chimp may pro-duce an offspring who is "spoiled," lacking in both self-control and a sense of being loved. Similarly, both humans and chimps learn, or fail to learn, loving conflict resolution through their familial and social experiences (Goodall, 1986; de Waal, 1989; [see also chapter 2]).

We will at different times focus on feelings, needs, values, ideologies, and their institutional and societal embodiments, such as religion and the state. It is important to remember that they are one package seen from different perspectives, and that basic human needs are at the root of it all.

THE ALIENATION OF VALUES FROM THEIR ORIGINAL NEEDS

Unfortunately, values and ideologies can easily become divorced from the underlying basic needs. People end up competing and fighting over values and ideologies that have taken on a life of their own. The conflict cannot be resolved because all involved have lost sight of their underlying needs.

A married couple quarrels over money with no awareness that the struggle originated over feelings of financial insecurity or the need for power and control. Or they fight over sex without discussing the underlying issues of love and self-respect. A parent and child struggle over bedtime or homework without recognizing and resolving conflicts between the child's need for autonomy and the parent's need to fulfill a parental role.

Cultures and nations similarly go to war and slaughter each other over slogans and ideologies that have long ago become estranged from their underlying basic needs. Political leaders often take advantage and generate "patriotic" wars to distract citizens from their frustrated needs for economic security or cultural identity. They foment outrage over fabricated atrocities in order to motivate people to support violent solutions to conflict. For conflict resolution to take place, people must be redirected to their basic needs and to principles and methods of satisfying them, often in collaboration with their supposed enemies.

THE CHILDHOOD ORIGINS OF CONFLICT

More confusing, the origins of the conflict may extend back into the childhood of one or more of the participants without their being aware of it. A woman may persistently ridicule her girl-friends without realizing that she is compulsively reacting against the humiliation she received as a small child from her older sister. A man may feel compelled to dominate a woman without knowing that he is responding to the shame and "unmanliness" he feels over being sexually abused as a child. In both instances, resolution of the earlier conflict can ameliorate the more recent ones.

The childhood origins of the harmful behavior should not be used to excuse or condone it; but understanding the origins can help the perpetrator control the impulses (see chapters 4 and 5). In the meanwhile, the oppressive conduct should be controlled by the individual, and if necessary by others, regardless of the compulsion behind it.

A SUMMARY CHART OF THE THREE DYNAMICS

The essential qualities of the three dynamics are summarized in the following chart. It focuses on the differences among the three dynamics in regard to eight important factors:

1. How people are viewed;

2. How people obtain value;

3. How force can and should be used;

4. The nature of relationships;

5. The nature of attachment;

6. The degree of honesty;

7. The kind or quality of emotions, and

8. The effect on conflict resolution.

Remember that each dynamic represents a group of psychosocial needs and their method of expression through other people. The chart should become increasingly meaningful as the reader progresses through the book.

The Three Dynamics

	I. LOVE	II. LIBERTY	III. COERCION
1. PEOPLE:	persons, beings	agents, doers	objects, subhuman
2. VALUE:	unconditional	earned, acquired	assigned
3. FORCE:	abhorred, rejected	in self-defense	arbitrary
4. RELATION-SHIP:	gifting, sharing	voluntary, competitive	involuntary, coercive
5. ATTACH-MENT:	interdependent	independent	detached
6. HONESTY:	maximized	contractual	restricted
7. EMOTIONS:	love, joy	esteem, respect	helplessness, emotional pain
8. CONFLICT:	prevented, resolved	barely controlled	suppressed, exacerbated

   Three dynamics typically occur in combination within both individuals and institutions. A person or a religion, for example, may express a mix of themes based on love, liberty, and coercion all at once. The goal is to identify the dynamics, to understand their characteristics and consequences, and, if possible, to encourage shifts toward liberty and ultimately toward love.

THE THREE DYNAMICS AND CONFLICT RESOLUTION

Love, with its abhorrence of force and inherent valuing of the other, is the ultimate route to conflict resolution. The deepest conflicts can rarely be prevented or resolved without empathic love for those with whom we are in conflict. Only when people treasure each other and care about *each other's* basic needs can conflict be turned into mutual cooperation with lasting peace or harmony.

Love is the ultimate source of conflict resolution in every aspect of our lives. To resolve inner or psychological conflict, we must learn to love ourselves; to resolve interpersonal conflict we must learn to love ourselves *and* those with whom we are in conflict; to resolve global conflict we must learn to love ourselves *and* all other human beings; to end our abuse of nature, we must learn to love ourselves and the earth as well.

Liberty, with the use of force limited to self-defense, is an important stage in conflict resolution. The principle of equal rights provides the safety people often require before they will dare to become intimate and loving. The principles of reason, self-determination, and equal rights encourage bargaining and mediation. Too often, conflict resolution is based on these Dynamic II concepts of liberty without aiming at the more profound level of mutuality and love.

Liberty without love results in more superficial and temporary solutions, with the regeneration or recycling of conflict at a later date. A married couple bargains over where to go on vacations, and each year one of them is less satisfied with the choice than the other. Annually they must go through tense and competitive negotiations over how to spend their two weeks together. Conflict resolution occurs when they love each other sufficiently to take joy in each other's happiness. They become as delighted with their partner's pleasure as with their own, and now help each other find their ideal vacation spot. When people in conflict work together to identify and to fulfill each other's needs, the result is always a more lasting and profound conflict resolution.

The same is true on an international level (see chapters 9–11). To create a war, a leader must stir up hatred for the enemy. To bring lasting peace, as between the United States and Canada, people must feel affinity for each other. They must seem so alike to each other in terms of their common humanity that they would not dream of resorting to violence to solve their problems.

The most successful policies of the United States—for example, the Marshall Plan that helped reconstruct postwar Western Europe or Douglas MacArthur's successful efforts to bring democracy to Japan—have been based on the principle of empathic caring. In each case, the United States helped other nations fulfill their basic needs in ways they could not have done alone. Having been joined together in this mutual effort, the possibility of war between the United States and its old enemies now seems remote.

Coercion all too often seems the preferred method of conflict resolution, but it only leads to suppression, and ultimately to the creation of more severe, long-lasting conflicts. Coercion, as we shall see, has negative consequences for the perpetrator as well as the victim in both the personal and the political arena (see chapter 4).

REJECTING OUR COMMON HUMANITY

Nothing causes and perpetuates conflict more than the notion that our adversaries are by their very nature different from us and from other more valued human beings. This rejection of the equal humanity of our adversary is among the greatest impediments to conflict resolution. It justifies and intensifies conflicts between parents and children, husbands and wives, different races, conflicting cultures, and hostile nations. In each case, at least one party to the conflict has decided that the other is "inferior," "less worthy," "more dangerous," "basically untrustworthy," or otherwise alien to the human race. Too often, *all* parties to the conflict think this way about each other. To grasp this problem, and the road to its solution, it is useful to envision "the conflict tree."

THE BASIC NEEDS CONFLICT TREE

The metaphor I call the Conflict Tree describes how we lose track of our ties to each other as human beings as we become separated by our values, cultural views, special interests, and the ideological commitments of our groups and leaders.

The common root of the tree is our human nature with its basic needs. This reflects the fact that our brains and bodies do not significantly differ on a racial, national, cultural, or other basis. Unfortunately, this single human root lies below ground and takes imagination to envision.

Immediately above ground, the trunk quickly begins to divide into the varying *expressions* of our basic needs. While all people have more or less the same underlying needs, the needs are manifested and satisfied somewhat differently from individual to individual and culture to culture.

Above the already diverging basic needs, the trunk further divides into branches called values—the conscious awareness and expression of the basic needs. These vary according to temperament and upbringing. Special interests and ideologies are next on the now broadly diverging canopy of the tree. Some of these are personal: my family, my job, my gender, my money, my property. Some are more societal: my country, my religion, my political party, my ethnic group, my race. The differences and potential sources of alienation and conflict are becoming infinite.

As the tree spreads, leaving our common root of human nature further and further below, values and interests tend to become rigidly embodied in social institutions, political ideologies, and the leaders of contending groups and viewpoints. In the last stages of alienation, the conflicts become directed by leaders with their own special interests, ideologies, and institutional commitments.

In order to drive a greater wedge between their peoples, the leaders often hurl epithets at each other. George Bush is the devil; Saddam Hussein, the madman. For the Iraqi, the ultimate insult is a religious condemnation; for the Americans, it's a psychiatric label. That tells us something about which institution has the greatest moral authority in each of the societies: religion in Iraq, psychiatry in America (see chapter 7). Either way, devil or madman, the citizens of Iraq and America are encouraged to reject their common heritage as members of the human race.

The Conflict Tree metaphor dramatizes how human beings start with much in common—their human nature and basic needs—and too often end up locked in mortal conflict with adversaries whom they see as wholly alien from themselves. Consider the tragic image of the spreading branches and dividing trunks flailing about in violent clashes with each other, with no realization that they come from the same root.

Conflict resolution attempts to help people "climb back down" the Conflict Tree to reach and recognize their common origin. There, at the foot of the tree, they can meet on common ground— their shared human nature and basic needs—while appreciating the tree of their cultural differences.

When people realize that their inherent differences as humans are negligible, the conflict tree can blossom into an appreciation of cultural differences. Its canopy of branches with its leaves, flowers, and fruit becomes a source of inspiration instead of mortal conflict. This is true whether we are attempting to "climb back down" the tree with someone we love, or whether we are trying to grasp the common humanity of all human beings. When we become aware that all people are made of the same biological and psychospiritual stuff, we have begun to love humanity.

The metaphor may be extended to the whole of existence—the entire animate and inanimate universe that supports and interrelates with this human tree. The tree exists in relation to the earth, air, and water, and all its inhabitants. The roots draw life from the earth and the leaves draw it from the sun and the air. Life becomes our tree; our tree becomes life.

THE THREE DYNAMICS TABLE

The Three Dynamics Table (see p. 12) expands on the summary chart (see p. 11) and provides a more extensive overview of the theory. The reader might wish to glance at it now and perhaps on occasion later in the book as the concepts are further developed. The table is, to say the least, a simplification. The catchwords and phrases are intended to help the reader to scan the salient points, especially the principles and qualities of relationship and life associated with each of the three dynamics. The table is not presented as a philosophic blueprint or final word on the subject of the three dynamics.

PROCESS VERSUS SOLUTIONS

Keep in mind that the principles of conflict analysis and resolution, as well as those of self-help and psychotherapy, do not prescribe specific outcomes for individuals, institutions, or societies. Instead they suggest ideal approaches for resolving conflict through actions based on liberty and love.

There are several generally accepted principles that are characteristic of modern conflict resolution as a growing discipline (Burton 1987, 1990a, 1990b; Coate and Rosati, 1988).

1. The process is voluntary.

2. The parties do not resort to power.

3. Basic needs and vital interests are identified and addressed.

4. The benefits of ending the conflict are weighed against the negative costs of continuing it.

5. Collaborative analysis and problem solving are encouraged toward the development of mutually satisfying solutions, including those that benefit both parties. Win–lose conflicts are redefined, when possible, into win–win conflicts. Competition is replaced by cooperation.

6. Alternative options are generated that satisfy the basic needs of all the participants.

It is frequently thought in the field of conflict resolution that the facilitator or conflict resolver should be neutral (Burton, 1990a). Instead of neutrality, I favor a strong, personal, caring commitment to the interests of both parties (see chapter 6). It is more realistic to try to care about both parties than to try to be neutral about them. Similarly, I believe that the therapist or conflict resolver should be loving rather than merely objective and analytic. Ultimately, he or she should facilitate empathy for each other among the adversaries. While love is the key to thoroughgoing conflict resolution, it is rarely discussed as a principle in the practice of psychotherapy and conflict resolution.

When individuals relate freely and lovingly, they function creatively and will bring forth new and often unexpected approaches and solutions to life's problems. While no one can predict the specific outcome of these efforts, certain trends can be expected. These are reflected in the scheme of values in the Three Dynamic Table. The principles of liberty and love enable people to satisfy their basic needs and to develop their human potentials *from their own viewpoint* and *to the best of their ability*. When people combine liberty with love, conflict will be more easily prevented and resolved *to everyone's satisfaction*.

In helping individuals, groups, and societies live by the principles of liberty and love—we can anticipate the best for them, without knowing what their best will be. We cannot predict the exact results of living by better principles—other than that they will be better from the viewpoint of the participants.

At present there are few state or community resources for conflict resolution. There are few institutional mechanisms for effectively addressing basic needs within the family and society. Can social and governmental institutions be developed for the purpose of satisfying basic needs and resolving conflict within the family and community? In the words of Richard Rubenstein, "Can the state become a conflict resolver instead of a power broker?" Can governments and other social institutions assist conflicted parties in identifying and satisfying their basic needs through cooperative activities without the coercive use of power?

The flow of the book will take us through love, liberty, and coercion, in that order, in the next three chapters. Then we will look at psychological or inner conflict, interpersonal and family conflict, the role of psychiatry in conflict resolution, and liberty and love within business corporations. In the final three chapters, the perspective is further broadened to include societal conflict as illustrated by recent events in the former USSR and Eastern Bloc nations, and international conflict as exemplified by recent events in the Middle East. Finally, the book concludes with basic principles for building a more loving personal and community life, including an emerging group of "shared values" within contemporary reform movements.

Because it is so key to conflict resolution, we now turn to the subject of love.

CHAPTER 2

▼ ▼

Understanding Love

I am ready to say to every human being "thou art my brother"
and to offer him the hand of concord and amity.
                            Thomas Jefferson, letter (1819)

I can never be what I ought to be until you are what you ought
to be, and you can never be what you ought to be until I am
what I ought to be. This is the interrelated structure of reality.
                    Martin Luther King, Jr., Strength to Love (1963)

We are members one of another; so that you cannot injure or
help your neighbor without injuring or helping yourself.
George Bernard Shaw, "Why Not Give Christianity a Trial?"
                        Preface to Androcles and the Lion (1912)

But whatever may be the cause of sympathy, or however it may
be excited, nothing pleases us more than to observe in other men
a fellow-feeling with all the emotions of our own breast.
            Adam Smith, The Theory of Moral Sentiments (1759)

Many people believe that love can prevent or resolve *personal* conflicts, but few seem to believe it can do the same for *societal* or
political disputes. The premise of this book is that love is the best
and most effective approach to conflict resolution on every level
from the personal to the political.

LOVE IN THE JUDEO-CHRISTIAN TRADITION

While rarely invoked within the academic community, love holds
an honored place in the Judeo-Christian and Western tradition and
in the spiritual life of millions of people throughout the world. In
Leviticus the Hebrews are instructed, "Thou shalt love thy neighbor as thy self (Hertz, 1960)." Drawing on ancient Hebrew

wisdom, in the New Testament Jesus makes clear that love is the central theme of his teachings, and he reaffirms the Golden Rule as "Do unto others as you would have others do unto you."

In *The Good Society* (1937), Walter Lippmann notes that the Golden Rule, in its positive or negative form, has been "enunciated among many peoples widely separated in time and space," (p. 376):

> *In the Upanishads of Indian Brahmanism it is said: "Let no man do to another that which would be repugnant to himself. . . . In refusing, in bestowing, in regard to pleasure and to pain, to what is agreeable and disagreeable, a man obtains the proper rule by regarding the case as like his own." "My doctrine," says Gautama Buddha, "makes no distinction between high and low, rich and poor. It is like the sky. It has room for all, and like waves it washes all alike. . . . to him in whom love dwells, the whole world is but one family." The rule appears again and again in Confucius: "When one cultivates to the utmost the capabilities of his nature and exercises them on the principle of reciprocity, he is not far from the path. What you do not want done to yourself, do not do unto others." (pp. 376–377)* [Ellipses in original.]

To exclude these religious teachings from our analysis on the grounds that they are not "scientific" is to ignore how profoundly they influence Western thought. Such an exclusion also ignores the reality that the psychosocial sciences themselves are fundamentally ethical in nature. Neither their methods nor their aims can be divorced from values.

That religious institutions too often fail by their own standards and frequently foment hatred is not the issue at hand (see chapter 11). What matters at this point is the ideal—that many religions recognize love as the guiding principle of life.

THE NATURE OF LOVE

Before examining relevant scientific research involving animals and humans, I'll first discuss the concept of love in general. The time-honored word "love" will be used to describe all of the

Dynamic I psychosocial needs, variously described in the conflict resolution literature as nurturing, caring, bonding, affiliation, recognition, and valued or meaningful relationships. Love is the more generic word, and it grounds us in everyday life and language.

Love encompasses two related phenomena—human *bonding* in general and, more specifically, a *joyful awareness and treasuring* of other people, personal activities (such as work and play), nature, or life. Bonding and joyful awareness are inextricable. A well-loved infant experiences joy in the bonding or strong connectedness it shares with its parents. Within weeks after birth, smiling, body wriggling, and other signs indicate the child's joyful recognition of other human beings. With growing maturity, these feelings can become a way of life.

Conversely, when bonding fails to occur between infant and parent, the social capacities of the growing child are hampered. A joyless attitude toward all of life, and even withdrawal and death, may result (see p. 44).

The concept of love is not rarified and abstract. Love is a biological and social phenomenon—a dynamic. It emanates from the whole human organism as a basic need and finds its expression through other people, nature, and an infinite variety of creative activities.

The capacity for love is present in all at birth. As children and adults with developmental retardation exemplify, love is more deeply ingrained in us than intelligence and can flourish in people who function intellectually below normal. Love also plays an important role in the life of animals, and in relationships involving humans and animals. Many people experience the high point of love in their daily lives when they return home to be greeted by a dog that wildly wags its tail, barks in ecstasy, jumps and whirls about, and otherwise communicates a joyful greeting. Chimpanzees routinely hug, kiss, and display other signs of affection for each other when they get together or settle conflicts.

Love is an attitude and feeling that can be found to some extent in every human being. Few people are wholly devoid of positive connections to people or other aspects of life. Clinically, a person with no experience of joyful awareness would be withdrawn, living in a lifeless world of objects. Psychosis often reflects the breakdown of all connectedness to other human beings, and a loving relationship is the most therapeutic intervention (Breggin, 1980, 1991).

Love can be viewed as the experience, conscious or unconscious, of being drawn toward and valuing others. It is a connection to others that is fundamental to our social life, an essential connection. It binds mothers and fathers to their offspring and to each other. It binds friends, family, and society.

In spiritual terms, we would say love reaches from essence to essence, from soul to soul. In psychological terms, we would say it reaches from person to person. In more social terms, love is the evolutionary force that nourishes the psychosocial growth of the infant and creates community and culture. It is Dynamic I, the primary motivator of social life.

Love exists along a continuum of intensity and of specificity for particular individuals (Schneider, 1964). In the most general sense, it designates the need people have for human contact of any kind. This is a profound aspect of ourselves. Not only are we literally formed as infants and children by our contacts with other people, as adults we tend to unravel without them. The worst punishment of all is solitary confinement. People in isolation can become psychotic—their very minds coming apart in the absence of social contact. As a patient of mine said, "When I get too isolated, I start to hallucinate."

Love can also focus on specific persons. In romantic love, it can become an intense desire for sexual merger with one particular human being, to the exclusion of all others. The underlying experience is the same—a fundamental valuing of other people (Breggin, 1987; Ellis, 1937). What varies is the intensity and the specificity for one or another particular individual.

Love is at root a happy feeling. The radiant connection between mother and child is pleasurable, as is the warmth we feel in good company. It feels good to be with other people, to openly love them, and to express passion for them. But because human beings are so vulnerable to each other, and so often have a history of severe injury at each other's hands, love can become chronically associated with pain. Because people need each other so much, they can become afraid of the potential loss associated with love. Yet love itself is a positive, joyful feeling.

Love, as noted, involves the placement of value on others. At times, their value to us may approximate or even exceed our own.

A parent, for example, may sacrifice his or her life for a child. Similarly, a lover may willingly die in defense of his or her loved one. I have known people who have risked their lives for beloved pets. I recall a young boy who drove a large, vicious dog out of his yard when it was threatening his crippled cocker spaniel.

There can be less noble motives, such as guilt and fear, that cause people to "sacrifice" for each other. But in loving relationships, people do not experience altruistic actions as sacrifices. It is no sacrifice to risk one's life for another life of equal or greater value.

LOVE AND EMPATHY

Mutuality, sharing, and sacrifice depend upon empathy—a caring awareness of the viewpoint and condition of another or others. Empathy is essential to love and in many ways epitomizes it.

Empathy first appears in an undeveloped form in infants and in more mature forms in small children. It is a part of human social life from the start. There is even some evidence that infants *in utero* respond selectively to their mothers' voice.

Even though love is fundamentally a joyful feeling, empathic love can end up eliciting emotional pain. But if people experience the same intensity of pain as their injured loved ones, they may become helpless and lose their effectiveness as helpers. In psychotherapy or surgery, in coming to the aid of a pet or friend, in helping to resolve painful marital conflicts, individuals must not become overwhelmed with the suffering of others.

If caregivers do become overcome by empathic pain, they can worsen the situation. They can lose their rationality and self-control. They can end up resenting the sufferer for inducing pain in them as well. To protect themselves from further pain, caregivers may withdraw from those who are suffering or even deny that they are in pain.

If the person offering help shows signs of becoming overwhelmed, the original sufferer may be made to feel more helpless. If a the potential helper cannot handle the suffering of the victim, how can the victim expect to survive it? The victims may also end up feeling guilty about the suffering they are causing. This can lead them to hide their pain or to avoid seeking help.

EMPATHY AND CONFLICT RESOLUTION

Empathy is an essential ingredient to conflict resolution in children and adults. It is the most powerful force in leading us to care about the basic needs of others and to seek ways of satisfying them. Thus empathy can be viewed as the essential element or principle of love that most directly affects conflict resolution.

Love, with its special empathic quality, tends to render meaningless the distinctions between self-interest and the interests of loved ones. When a parent loves a child, or a lover her loved one, the other's needs, well-being, and happiness become of great importance. The parent wants the infant to thrive, even at the parent's expense. On the other hand, she knows that she must thrive in order to help her infant do so. Needs become mutual rather than individual. Instead of being in competition, the other's needs approximate and dovetail with one's own.

Thus empathy transforms self-interests into joint interests, individual needs into mutual ones. This is why love is the ultimate avenue to conflict resolution. Love transforms conflict into cooperation and mutual aid.

Adam Smith is best known as the leading Eighteenth-century advocate of competition and the free market; but in his 1759 book, *The Theory of Moral Sentiments* (1976), he provides one of the most thorough arguments for the necessity of empathy in the good society. For Smith, "fellow-feeling" ameliorates bitterness and competition, and cements loving community. He declares, "The bitter and painful emotions of grief and resentment more strongly require the healing consolation of sympathy," (p. 87).

Smith considered empathic, unconditional love to be an essential principle in human beings:

How selfish soever man may be supposed, there are evidently some principles in his nature, which interest him in the fortune of others, and render their happiness necessary to him, though he derives nothing from it, except the pleasure of seeing it. (p. 47.)

Love can play a key role in resolving conflict even when those in conflict do not feel love for each other. Adversaries can find a common interest through their love for *other* people or things.

Couples who are separated or divorced can be motivated by love for their children to resolve their conflicts. People who feel little for each other may join together in their love for animals, the environment, or the whole earth. Even the love of liberty can bind people into common action. Indeed, the love of seeming "abstractions" such as God, country, or liberty frequently brings people together to make a common cause.

LOVE AND THE ABHORRENCE OF VIOLENCE

Because empathy and love encourages people to feel one-and-the-same with those whom they love, the use of force within a loving relationship becomes abhorrent. The pain they might cause their loved one afflicts them as well. There is a reluctance to use force in self-defense if it means hurting a loved one. Thus the principle of self-defense, which is so critical to liberty (see chapter 3), may be rejected in a caring relationship.

Love does not lead to a masochistic way of life in which people seek out or luxuriate in suffering. However, when people love, they wish to protect and nurture their loved ones even if it means accepting some increased risk of personal harm or suffering. Nonetheless, loving people can exercise judgment about whether or not to remain in a chronically conflicted or threatening relationship.

When people are loving, they will in fact be more aware of when others are oppressing them. The ability to love makes people more aware of when their own needs are not being met or are being thwarted by coercion and rejection. The more loving an individual is, the more likely he or she will be sensitive to the lack of it in others. The loving person will more easily recognize and seek similar companions.

The salutary effect of love on violence is extremely important for conflict resolution and provention. Caring relationships produce an environment in which violence is abhorred and sometimes totally rejected. When touched by love, people feel motivated to resolve conflicts through cooperation and mutual aid, and by actions that, in the absence of love, might be labeled self-sacrifice.

THE LIMITS OF SELF-LOVE

In modern popular psychology there is an axiom that one must love oneself first and foremost. In reality, people who attempt to live by this principle are likely to be profoundly unhappy and socially incapacitated.

Human beings are born into a world in which people are designed by genetic and cultural evolution to take care of and value each other, and especially to lavish attention on infants. Ideally, the wholly dependent, helpless infant is nurtured by a parent who in many ways may value the life of the infant above his or her own. A typical mother will feed her infant ahead of herself and defend it at the cost of her own life. A father and mother will often sacrifice sleep for months to comfort a colicky infant. In a similar vein, modern parents may work hard to put their children through school and provide for them as they grow, and if necessary may defend them with their lives.

Humans often take action to help others outside their immediate family. Most disasters produce stories of individual heroism. Many people choose occupations or volunteer jobs that pay little or nothing financially but which greatly benefit society. To live a happy, full life usually means daily decisions that constantly put other people and values ahead of our immediate interests and needs, and sometimes ahead of our long-term ones as well.

As we have seen, the human being is a fundamentally social creature who, starting from infancy, learns to love through being loved. The infant has the inborn capacity to love, much as it has the innate capacity to experience itself as a unique individual; but love and self-awareness are developed through the infant's and child's relationships with others. The infant does not learn to "love itself" first. The infant experiences *being loved*. Without that, the infant may not thrive at all. He or she may not survive.

Out of the experience of being loved develops our social capacity, including our later ability to relate and to love. People feel loved and loveable, and in the process they learn to love. We learn to feel loved and loveable through the gift of love from other people.

In my clinical practice, I frequently find that people can love others despite grave deficits in loving themselves. Often we love our children more than ourselves, devoting ourselves more to their happiness than to our own. I do not advocate this, but note it.

Can the isolated, unloved person learn to love himself or herself? Despite modern notions of "self-sufficiency," I doubt it. The nearest example might be that of reclusive mystical ascetics who learn to love themselves through God's love for them; but again the source is envisioned as coming from outside oneself.

Perhaps the emphasis on the primacy of self-love is the product of a hierarchical male society in which men—having alienated themselves from each other, from women, and from children—turn to their "inner self" for love. Whatever sense of power this apparent self-sufficiency endows us with, it does not give us a feeling of being truly loved.

A feeling of being loved is not something one can give to oneself. Efforts to do so result in tragic aberrations such as autistic withdrawal or mania. A rejected, abused child—rocking and stroking himself or herself in the corner of an institution—exemplifies a last ditch effort at self-love. It is self-destructive to turn our social nature on its head, claiming that we must love ourselves before we can love others.

Once we have learned to love, we can then become capable of maintaining the feeling toward others in an independent, self-sustaining manner. We can generate unconditional love—a joyful, positive valuing of another that can withstand the vicissitudes of relationship, including rejection and betrayal. In most of our roles in life—as parents, spouses, friends, colleagues, and contributing members of society—we are likely to undergo rejection, betrayal, and other threatening experiences. We sustain ourselves and sometimes our relationships by maintaining our ability to love through the ups and downs. Deep-rooted conflict resolution often requires unconditional love on the part of all those involved.

LOVE, REVERENCE, AND BEINGNESS

Reverence reflects respect for the intrinsic worth of another. It has a spiritual connotation that suggests a holiness to the value placed upon the individual. After years of searching within the traditions of the East and the West, Albert Schweitzer finally summed up the essence of his philosophy in the phrase "reverence for life." (See chapter 11 for further discussion of Schweitzer's views.) In *My Life and Thought* (1933), he declared:

The ethic of Reverence for Life is the ethic of Love widened into universality. It is the ethic of Jesus, now recognized as a necessity of thought.

For Schweitzer, reverence for life was divinely inspired, and extended itself to all life forms, to the "mysterious value" of life itself. Anecdotes about Schweitzer abound concerning the sincerity of his devotion to all life. He would turn down his reading lamp at night rather than singe an occasional flying insect; he would not dip fence posts into insecticides for fear of harming individual termites.

In *I and Thou* (1923), theologian Martin Buber, whose work influenced interpersonal psychology and psychiatry, infused all human relationship with sacred meaning. He distinguishes "I–Thou" relating from "I–It." In I–Thou relating "the whole being" of the individual is in the relationship. I–Thou relating involves "revealing" the divine in each other, a standing in the presence of that divine, rather than a simple feeling between people. I–It relating separates us from the other and his or her spiritual worth. It enables us to reject or coerce the other.

Humanists often view love for humanity as central to their philosophy and their words communicate a secular holiness. In the *Philosophy of Humanism* (1949), atheist Corliss Lamont rejects "brute egoism" as well as one-dimensional motivational systems based on economic self-interest, sexual pleasure-seeking, or self-interest in general. He states:

On the ethical and social side Humanism sets up service to one's fellowmen as the ultimate moral ideal. It holds that the individual can find his own highest good by working for the good of all, which of course includes himself and his family. . . . It insists on the reality of genuine altruism as one of the moving forces in the affairs of men.

There is a reverent ring to Lamont's discourse on how humans should be guided by altruism as a moral imperative. I can find no satisfying logical argument for this view within his writing. Love inevitably remains something of a mystery. It is so deeply and completely rooted in our nature that we stumble over analyzing it as something separate from ourselves. We try to make an abstraction or principle out of that which simply *is*.

Erich Fromm places love at the center of his secular philosophy. In *The Art of Loving* (1956), he sees love as "the answer to the problem of human existence":

The awareness of human separation, without reunion by love—is the source of shame. It is at the same time the source of guilt and anxiety.
The deepest need of man, then, is the need to overcome his separateness, to leave his prison of his aloneness. The **absolute** *failure to achieve this aim means insanity. . . .*

From the theologian Buber to the secular psychoanalyst Fromm, there is an attitude toward the human as a *being* rather than a thing or an "it." To say people are beings is to invest them with sacred meaning—with special, *inviolable* importance.

There is a growing tendency among environmentalists and ecologists to view the earth itself as a living being, sometimes called Gaia. What some people would call a thing becomes invested with an aura of inviolability.

UNCONDITIONAL LOVE AND INTRINSIC WORTH

To love humans—to experience them as beings—means recognizing their intrinsic worth. Love, as I am defining it, is therefore *unconditional*—not contingent on anything particular about the individual who is loved. Rather, love reaches to the essence of the individual, the beingness, and sees the inherent value.

Since this value is inherent, it is not earned. Rather, it is made visible by the individual or recognized by someone else. Thus, love differs drastically from respect and esteem, which are barometers of how we judge or evaluate another's ethics or accomplishments. Esteem plays a necessary role in human relationships, but it should not be confused with the much more fundamental experience of love (see chapter 3). Lacking the more basic sense of feeling love-able and loved, many people compulsively seek to be esteemed and respected, while finding little or no peace in the process.

The concepts of intrinsic worth and unconditional love are at the center of this book. They extend not only to people, but to all life forms, and to life itself. The concepts of intrinsic worth and un-conditional love must reach toward the physical earth as well and may be required for the survival of life on the planet.

The question of the intrinsic worth of people is a very important one in everyday living and therefore in self-help, psychotherapy, and conflict resolution in general. When we accept that people have intrinsic worth, then our conflicts with them take on a rev-erential, caring aura. We cherish or treasure the people with whom we are dealing and find their well-being inviolable, even as we seem locked in deep-rooted, severe conflict with them.

FALLING INTO FEAR AS WELL AS LOVE

Sometimes we find it easier to recognize the intrinsic worth of animals. We may love a dog or cat, for example, who has little practical value to us and who has done little to earn our respect or esteem. Instead we feel a connection to the "life force" or "being" within the pet. We become happy feeling love for and feeling loved by our pet. In my home, a small Eastern-Painted turtle is often the center of attention and genuine love.

I am reminded of a patriarchal male, a high-ranking military officer, who always severely judged the women he had known, including his current wife. He seldom praised them and always tried to make them over into his compliant ideal. In couples ther-apy, he acknowledged only one regular experience of sheer, un-adulterated, nonjudgmental delight in a being. It was felt toward his now-deceased cat for whom he felt a special love.

Similarly, we feel love for infants before we can claim to respect their individuality or to admire their unique properties. People who wish to adopt newborn infants, for example, are sometimes advised not to let their natural mothers see them, even for an instant, for in mothers, as well as lovers, there can be an element of "love at first sight."

Love for plants or for nature also indicates an impulse toward something essential and inherent in that which we love. We may feel peace in being "at one with nature" and we may feel joy at the sight of a lovely bird or a beautiful sunset. Sometimes apparently mundane aspects of nature—a pebble or a cloud—may evoke delight in us. This delight or joy in awareness is the essence of love. I sometimes define love as nothing more nor less than *joyful awareness and treasuring*.

Why can we more easily express unconditional love for infants, pets, or natural phenomena? Because it feels more threatening to love adult people than to love infants, animals, or nature. None of us are tough when it comes to our innermost selves and innermost yearnings for closeness or oneness with other people. Our souls are wrapped in tenderness.

It would fill volumes to survey the ways in which people fear being hurt by other people, from accidental loss through death to willful betrayal. I tend to doubt if someone is falling in love if they are not falling into fear as well.

THE SELECTIVITY OF LOVE

If love reaches toward essences, and if all people are equally valuable, then why do we love one person more than another? I am tempted at this moment to fall back on the notion that love is a mystery. But there's more to say than that. Love is a blessing, a form of "gifting"—of giving that which no one feels they really or wholly deserve. When a person feels truly loved that person feels grateful. We often doubt that our true value can match the value assigned to us by those who love us most profoundly.

It is often difficult to understand why people single out each other to love, but to some extent it has to do with visibility, with how easily we can see the "essential humanity," the spirit, being-ness, or inherent worth of another. Some people are more visible or psychologically available to us, and we love them more easily. They may be more available because of their own traits: they are more open, communicative, or loving. We can also esteem them for the work it takes to reach such a spiritual state. Or they may seem to meet some standard of beauty or status that then allows us to overcome the fear or shame surrounding love. We may even think we love them because of their beauty or status, when in reality those qualities have merely provided us the "window to the soul." The socially approved qualities have given us permission to love.

Often we allow ourselves to love others because of their weaknesses or negative traits. More precisely, their vulnerabilities or personal problems enable us to love them. Many people, for example, are drawn to love members of the opposite sex who seem weak or ineffectual. This often puzzles those who view the relationship from the outside. Because of their own fears, people often feel safer in the presence of weakness in another person. They may feel the other person less likely to hurt or reject them. They may hope that the other person will be more in need of them. Even though its expression depends upon the vulnerability of the other, the love can be genuine. The nature of the pairing, based in part on emotionally injured aspects of the partners, may become an increasing problem in the relationship, and may even doom it; but it does not necessarily render the love less real. The need and desire to love is no less pure because the individual can only express it within the confines of a seemingly safe relationship.

If love reaches toward intrinsic values, then can we love all people—and perhaps even love all people *equally?* Is that absurd or utopian? I believe it is *impractical,* given the limitations we have as human beings and the constraints under which we live. To love all people equally, an ideal maintained by some mystics and encouraged by Jesus, also deprives us of the special joy of focusing our attention and deepening our knowledge of one single person or family. To *pretend* to love all people equally can even become a defense against loving one person or one family fully, with all the fears and responsibilities entailed in personal relationships and domestic life. Mystical love for humanity may indeed reflect escapism from the realistic needs of the people in their lives, including husbands, wives, and children. Women, needless to say, have not generally been permitted this luxury, nor would they tend to choose it at the expense of their dependent children. Some women end up choosing a professional career over marriage and family because they cannot find a husband to share homemaking with them.

Despite these caveats, psychotherapists and others in helping professions need to empathize with and even to love each of their clients, or else they are likely to fail in their healing work. As I will discuss in chapter 6, a deeper understanding of love can help the therapist open his or her heart to increasing numbers of people.

While we may not be personally or practically capable of loving all people, recognizing the possibility—confirming the inherent worth of all people—remains an important concept for guiding our actions. Only through the growing extension of our love to all people will we eventually end deep-rooted, murderous conflict on earth. Only by extending love to the whole earth are we likely to prevent its demise as a liveable planet.

ROMANTIC LOVE

Some authors have linked romantic love directly to liberty and have claimed that it could not truly exist until the flowering of individualism in Western Europe (Branden, 1969). While the widespread cultural acceptance of romantic love does seem to be a relatively modern phenomenon, examples of it can be found in ancient mythology and religious literature, including the Hebrew Bible (see Breggin, 1987).

Romantic love is among the most intense expressions of love experienced by most people. It is a realm in which mystery and spirituality truly abound, and in which cynicism and skepticism often set in. In the story of Cupid and Psyche, a god, Cupid, falls in love with a mortal, Psyche, whose name means butterfly . . . or soul. Eventually, Cupid and Psyche are married, but first Psyche is made an immortal. In this great love story, the model for many others, including Shakespeare's *Romeo and Juliet,* the romantic and the spiritual are wholly intertwined, and love ultimately endows a human with divine qualities (see Breggin, 1987).

Not everyone accepts the mystery that shrouds romantic love. Not everyone believes in romantic love as a viable way of relating. The great American psychologist William James, in *The Principles of Psychology* (1890), diagnosed romantic love as a form of insanity or "monomania":

The passion of love may be called a monomania to which all of us are subject, however otherwise sane. It can coexist with contempt and even hatred for the "object" which inspires it, and whilst it lasts the whole life of the man is altered by its presence.

To confirm his viewpoint, he presented the case history of man driven to "frenzy" and "melancholy" by a humiliating attachment to a woman.

James's viewpoint seems rooted in a misogynous fear of women. The lover in his vignette struggles to possess the *object* of his desires, a woman deemed inferior to him, and suffers the humiliation of failing to have his way.

Ironically, James invested mystical union with God with the intense romanticism that he denied to human relationships. In *The Varieties of Religious Experience* (1929) he criticized "medical materialism" in regard to religious devotion to God, but not in regard to love for human beings. He promotes a deep, mystical connection to God as a route to the fulfillment of our innermost personal need for completion. His descriptions parallel closely that of romantic love.

James, like so many other men, rejected passionate down-to-earth relating to women in favor of something else—in this case, the mystical experience. His philosophy embodies what many feminists, including Marilyn French in *Beyond Power* (1985) and Kate Millett in *Sexual Politics* (1978), have described as a hierarchical attempt to transcend relationships with women. This transcendence involves the rejection of love between equals in favor of "power over" and control, or escapism.

In many ways Freud's position paralleled James's, especially in its rejection of love for women. Like James, he viewed love as a form of insanity, a "narcissistic" derangement. However, instead of directing his passionate, spiritual desires toward God, Freud utterly rejected the validity or worth of these feelings. As many critics have confirmed, he denigrated women in the process.

Freud's disciple, Alfred Adler, who later broke with him, had a wholly different vision. He found human beings motivated by "social interest" and the desire to have meaningful relationships with each other.

LOVE THAT LEADS TO BAD OUTCOMES

Love can be misdirected or manipulated toward bad ends. This is perhaps most obvious within the family. As Susan Moller Okin has documented in *Justice, Gender and the Family* (1987), patriarchal philosophers have long argued that love, rather than justice, should be primary in family life. They have done so in the interest of maintaining male dominance and the subservience of women to the needs of others. On a more personal level, men who batter women almost always state that their attempts to control their victims are motivated by love; and adults who sexually abuse children frequently profess love for them.

Whether or not abusers actually feel the love they profess, their oppressive actions are typically motivated by their own personal feelings of helplessness and inferiority, expressed through culturally sanctioned attempts to overpower women and children. Furthermore, their actions actually suffocate love. Coercive relationships breed dishonesty and manipulation in both the perpetrator and the victim, and tend to be incompatible with love (see chapter 4).

Love is also used outside the family to justify the abuse and control of other human beings. Dictators give speeches about how much they love the victims of their totalitarianism; slave owners profess love for their chattel; and institutional psychiatrists claim to care about the inmates they confine and otherwise abuse.

The need for love can motivate a person to submit to coercion. The German people, for example, were motivated in part by "love for the Fatherland" in joining the Nazi party. Hitler became a beloved father figure for many of them. Similarly, love for a cult leader or fellow members of the cult sometimes helps to motivate destructive activities. There may even be meaningful and sometimes joyful bonding among the participants or conspirators, despite the other disastrous consequences. Often there is a sense of purpose, identity, or recognition as well. Thus love can resolve conflicts within a group while nonetheless bringing forth hideous consequences for others outside the group.

Because of the potential victimization of women, romantic love as a principle has been criticized by some feminists as a snare for women. The trap may be subtle, as in the submissiveness inherent in what Betty Friedan has called "the feminine mystique," or it may be more brutal for women who remain in battering and abusive relationships. While it is true that many other forces, including male domination and control, influence women to stay in these relationships, many women feel that love for the man plays a significant role.

Love should not be used as excuse or rationalization for infringements on liberty. While love can surmount almost any obstacle, it is most easily achieved and expressed within a context of liberty. Liberty and love, properly understood, supplement and support each other. Love finds inherent worth in whomever is loved; the principle of inherent worth leads logically to equal rights, justice, and liberty. Dr. Martin Luther King, Jr. was especially adept in politics at making the connection between the Christian ideal of the equality of all souls and the Western ideal of equal rights (see chapter 10). Indeed, the Declaration of Independence connects the ideal that all people are "created equal" to the principle that they are "endowed by their Creator with certain inalienable rights."

Love *requires* liberty as a context or it risks becoming an excuse for oppression. The interaction between liberty and love, as complex as it is, remains critical to human well-being on both a personal and political level. Liberty—addressed more thoroughly in chapter 3—remains primary in establishing a just (and hence, safe) context for the expression of love.

The reader might wish to take a moment once again to review the Three Dynamics Table (see p. 261) that compares the attributes of Dynamic I: love and Dynamic II: liberty. It is discussed in chapter 1.

LOVE IN SOCIETY AND POLITICS

Throughout Western philosophy and even political theory, love has frequently reappeared as a guiding principle. In recent centuries it can be found in one form or another in such diverse sources as Adam Smith's *The Theory of Moral Sentiments* (1759) (see p. 24) and in Karl Marx's *The Economic and Philosophic Manuscripts of 1844*, where "alienation" from work and ultimately from society is seen as the unacceptable cost of capitalism. Citing Leo Tolstoy's *The Kingdom of God Is within You* (1894) and John Ruskin's *Unto This Last* (1860), Mohandas Gandhi saw love as the ultimate source of truth and of power. Later, Martin Luther King, Jr. would follow in his footsteps (see chapter 11 for a discussion of Gandhi and King).

In modern times, economists have begun to emphasize that something more than self-interest fuels human society. In *Ecodynamics* (1978) Kenneth Boulding has described affiliation or love as one of three moving forces or social organizers in our socioeconomic life. Drawing on John Kenneth Galbraith's *The Affluent Society* (1958), as well as on Boulding and others, modern writers have increasingly tried to escape the confines of economics based solely on self-interest.

Amitai Etzioni, in *The Moral Dimension: Toward a New Economics* (1988), has proposed that individuals, operating in the economic and political realm, are motivated by two sometimes-conflicting paradigms. One is the "utilitarian, rationalist, and individualist paradigm" of self-interest and competition. The other is unselfish morality—"a sense of *shared* identity, and commitment to values, a sense that 'We are members of one another.' " He believes that individuals are motivated in part by a spirit of cooperation based on an altruistic concern for others.

LOVE IN PSYCHOLOGY AND PSYCHIATRY

As a principle in personal living, love dominates popular music, romantic novels, and some popular psychology. It has only occasionally been addressed as a guiding principle by more academic psychologists. There's no mention of love as a healing principle in the commonly used textbooks of psychiatry, and there is merely passing mention of it in reference to "rapport" or "positive reinforcement" in most psychology textbooks (see Breggin, 1991).

However, two psychiatrists have made love the central theme of their work, and each resonated sufficiently with the public to attain substantial popularity. Both have drawn on a combination of psychotherapeutic and religious insights.

Psychiatrist Smiley Blanton was a close associate of Norman Vincent Peale, and Blanton's own book, *Love or Perish* (1956) clearly draws on Peale's somewhat simplistic concept of "the power of positive thinking." Blanton's psychoanalytic and religious background leads him to conclude that all human beings must struggle within themselves between love and hate. In religious terms, it is the conflict between good and evil; in Freudian, eros (the life instinct) and thanatos (the death instinct). Much more idealistic and optimistic than Freud, Blanton declares:

Love has reached across the ages to bind men together in an ever-widening circle of humanity. It has served to construct the essential fabric of most the world's great religious and ethical teachings. (p.12.)

Consistent with my own views, Blanton sees love as a "universal need," (p. 3) that is expressed through all of human life:

Love is born when the child rests in its mother's arms. From this beginning, love grows until it includes the love of family and friends, of school and country, and ultimately of all the world. . . . Love is all of one piece—from the love of mother and child to the love of sweethearts, husbands and wives, and friends. It is present, too, in the laborer's devotion to his work, in the teacher's solicitude for her pupils, in the physician's dedication to his art. All that heals, cultivates, protects, and inspires—all this is part of love. (p. 2.)

More recently, psychiatrist M. Scott Peck has written an enormously popular book, *The Road Less Traveled: A New Psychology of Love, Traditional Values and Spiritual Growth* (1978). Again drawing on both psychotherapy and religion, Peck declares "Love is too large, too deep ever to be truly understood or measured or limited within the framework of words," (p. 81). His own attempted definition of love is "The will to extend one's self for the purpose of nurturing one's own or another's spiritual growth," (p. 81). Love, for Peck, is key to normal child development and to psychotherapy:

For the most part, mental illness is caused by an absence of or defect in the love that a particular child required from its particular parents for successful maturation and spiritual growth. It is

obvious, then, that in order to be healed through psychotherapy
the patient must receive at least a portion of the genuine love of
which the patient was deprived. (p. 175.)

LOVE AND EMPATHY IN EVOLUTION

Is there an inborn capacity for love, cooperation, or some other
closely related social instinct? Behavioral scientists steeped in the
theory of evolution, including Herbert Spencer (1916) and contemporary sociobiologists, such as Edward O. Wilson (1978), believe in
an inborn drive toward the pursuit of self-interest that leads us to
compete *against* others. But as early as 1902 in *Mutual Aid* and then
in *Ethics: Origin and Development* (1924), Petr Kropotkin analyzed
the tension between individual striving (liberty) and mutual aid
(love). He demolished the attempt of the social Darwinists to impose on human society a constant struggle for supremacy and the
survival of the fittest. Kropotkin found that human beings and
animals alike survive and thrive through mutual aid—benevolent
sharing. He cited many examples of animal and human society in
which social cooperation is the most pro-survival activity of all.

Empathy, as we shall see, is closely related to human relations in
general and more specifically to love. Robert Plutchik has reviewed
the "evolutionary basis of empathy," (1987). He believes that empathy is a "widespread phenomenon in the animal world" as im-
plied in a wide variety of behaviors, including "schooling behavior
of fish, flocking and mobbing behavior of birds, and herding behavior of mammals." He cites alarm calls as an example of empathic behavior, "the communication of an emotional state from
one organism to another." He also finds empathic behavior in
animal play that requires "mutual affective signaling" to make clear
that no real hostility is intended. He lists a variety of display behaviors that are both social and empathic in animals. These displays are found in greeting or recognition, courtship, mating,
dominance, submission, alarm, challenge, distress, feeding, and
food-begging.

Courtship displays, Plutchik points out, are "designed to overcome aggressive and fearful barriers that might normally exist between males and females." This pertains to an issue we shall
examine further—the tension between liberty (self-defense) and

love. Even in the animal kingdom, love in the form of mating must overcome aggressive tendencies to defend oneself. Most or even all social animals have built-in protective mechanisms to separate and protect themselves not only from outsiders but from members of their family and species. Thus our two Shetland sheepdogs will at times nip at each other to maintain their own "space" when one or the other doesn't feel like playing.

Plutchik summarizes:

Empathy may also be thought of as a component of affective communication and is triggered by the large number of display behaviors seen in animals. The available evidence suggests that empathy can be inferred in both young and mature animals and that it is probably based on innate schemata that are genetically determined. As with all behaviors that have genetic components, there is reason to believe that experience and learning may also influence the intensity and frequency of empathic behaviors.

From an evolutionary point of view, empathy has important survival value. . . . It assists individuals in gathering and hunting for food, detecting predators, courtships, and ensuring reproductive success. (pp. 44–45.)

The potential for love is innate. Aspects of love are apparent in the infant from birth, and without love, the individual cannot develop into a social being capable of autonomous activity or mutuality and cooperation.

INFANT SOCIALIZATION AND EMPATHY

Research has begun to confirm what mothers have always known—that the infant is a social being from birth. Ross Thompson (1987) reviews research indicating that infants react by crying in response to the crying of other infants as early as one to four days after birth. This may well reflect the rudiments of empathy. According to Thompson:

First, it is clear that from early in the first year, infants are capable of emotional resonance or contagion—that is, of sharing the same emotion as a consequence of another's emotional display. Although these responses are not empathic in quality since they do not derive from knowledge of the other's situation or condition, they are probably important precursors of empathy. Second, responses to another's arousal that are more clearly empathic in quality begin to appear midway through the second year of life. (p. 125.)

By the age of two to three months, Thompson and others point out, infants will involve themselves in face-to-face play with their mothers in a "nonverbal conversation" or "behavioral dialog" in which their responses influence each other. By two to five months infants are able to discriminate emotions from facial expressions and soon after they are able to use "social referencing," checking their mother's expressions before responding to situations positively or negatively. By one year of age, many children will respond with help-giving behavior, such as pats and concerned attention, to distressed children. Thompson believes that there is strong evidence for "the emergence of empathic responding midway through the second year and its role as a motivator of prosocial initiatives," (p. 133).

Randy Lennon and Nancy Eisenberg (1987) distinguish among three types of human responses to the situation of another: (1) personal distress, (2) emotional contagion, and (3) genuine concern or sympathy for another. They too find that empathic or sympathetic prosocial actions, such as "patting or touching the victim," begin in the second year of life.

In an article entitled "The Contribution of Empathy to Justice and Moral Judgment," Martin Hoffman (1987) takes the position that ". . . empathy contributes to caring and most principles of justice through empathic identification with victims and potential victims of society and its institutions," (p. 71). This is similar to my viewpoint, expressed in the *Psychology of Freedom* (1980), that empathic love for others is a cornerstone for most people's commitment to human rights and liberty.

More than two hundred years ago, as already noted, Adam Smith voiced a similar principle, that fellow-feeling or sympathy for others leads people to act generously on behalf of others. He also found that the reward of being loved motivates people to live justly:

What reward is most proper for promoting the practice of truth, justice, and humanity?—The confidence, the esteem, and the love of those we live with. **Humanity does not desire to be great, but to be loved.** *(p. 276.) [Emphasis added.]*

That concern for human rights is a function of love was confirmed by Oliner and Oliner (1988) in their study of the personalities of individuals who risked their lives to protect and save Jews during the Holocaust. They observe:

What distinguished rescuers was not their lack of concern with self, external approval, or achievement, but rather their capacity for extensive relationships—their stronger sense of attachment to others and their feelings of responsibility for the welfare of others, including those outside their immediate family or communal circles. . . . They remind us that such courage is not only the province of the independent and the intellectually superior thinkers but that it is available to all through the virtues of connectedness, commitment, and the quality of relationship developed in ordinary human interactions. (p. 249, 260.)

The human being is a social creature from birth onward and very early in life the infant develops the rudiments of what will become genuine empathy. The love dynamic is fundamental to human nature and to the development of human values, such as empathy, caring, and even abstract principles, such as justice and human rights. It is the primary source of what Oliner and Oliner identify as "moral heroism."

LOVE, CARING, AND NURTURING

Love often colors relationships with caring and nurturing. The feeling of empathic love and the activities of caring for and nurturing are probably at root one and the same, both originating in the parent-infant bond. Nurturing is the critical activity through which lessons of human relationship are initially learned. The mother socializes the child through feeding, bathing, changing diapers, burping, stroking, cooing, smiling, face-to-face play, and myriad other activities, conscious and unconscious.

Among our primate cousins, grooming is a critical expression of their social bonds, and it is also a primary method of conflict resolution among adult chimpanzees. (At the same time, of course, it helps keep the animals rid of parasites. The one function does not exclude the other.) In *Touching: The Human Significance of the Skin* (1978), Ashley Montagu suggested that touching, including caressing and cuddling, is a "basic need." He concluded:

. . . adequate tactile satisfaction during infancy and childhood is of fundamental importance for the subsequent healthy behavioral development of the individual. The experimental and other research findings on other animals, as well as those on humans, show tactile deprivation in infancy usually results in behavior inadequacies in later life. (p. 318.)

When love and direct, physical nurturing become separated, something is lost. This is exemplified by those men (and sometimes women) whose capacity to love is inhibited by their unwillingness or inability to nurture. They defend their love as real even though it is not expressed through tender actions; but however real it may seem to them, it impacts relatively little on their lives or on the lives of those around them. Often they are unable to touch or to embrace their children or to use the word "love." Typically, their families speak of them as "distant," "unemotional," or "unapproachable."

When fathers become more involved in nurturing their offspring, they generate more love with their wives as well. I have enjoyed observing the process on a weekly basis when a couple with their newborn infant continues in therapy with the baby. The men in these sessions, much more involved with daily nurturing than typical males, also share a more radiant love with their wives. Instead of competing for their wives' affections, they bask together in the glow of mutual love.

THE LESSONS OF FAILED NURTURING

Recent research discloses that the infants of depressed or with-drawn parents quickly begin to reject their own parents and to withdraw socially. Byron Egeland and Martha Farrell Erickson (1990) have been studying the effect on infants of parental failure to nurture and support them. Their conclusions are based on direct observation of parents and infants. They summarize:

We know also that infants who are not nurtured or comforted during times of distress will develop an avoidant pattern of at-tachment with their caregiver. At times of distress these infants avoid their caregiver because they have learned that their care-givers will not provide them with the needed comfort or support. We have found that avoidant babies continue to avoid close rela-tionships as they get older. (p. 32.)

Egeland and Erickson's empirical research bolsters the earlier observations of psychoanalysts, such as Bowlby (1973), who found that infants fail to thrive and become depressed when deprived of maternal love. Mahler, Furer, and Settlage (1959) reviewed the early literature on infants and small children subject to maternal or institutional abandonment, and described the devastating impact, including severe withdrawal and depression, psychosis, and death. When mothers fail to relate to their infants, the children can become autistic, displaying "a spectacular struggle against any de-mand of human—of social—contact," (p. 825).

Spitz (1946) studied the impact on children of being institution-alized and removed from their mothers for a period of two or three months at the age of six to eight months. The final result in many cases was a complete withdrawal, obvious dejection, and an ex-pressionless face. If the mothers were restored, recovery took place. If not, the infants deteriorated and a large percentage died.

John Bowlby (1973) has also presented evidence and reviewed the literature on anxiety generated in small children by removal from their parents, even into the best of circumstances. The re-sponses of the children were characterized by "*intense* protest, fol-lowed by despair and detachment," (p. 22). These responses, including "sadness, anger, and subsequent anxiety," (p. 22), were seen most dramatically in children two years and older, but less intensively in younger ones as well. Similar responses could be elicited by parents who were physically present but emotionally withdrawn or absent. How much children subsequently recovered depended largely upon how loving their environment later turned out to be.

The original studies on children suffering from infantile autism, a severe state of withdrawal, identified their parents as typically emotionally cold and unable to relate (Eisenberg and Kanner, 1958). Often these parents encouraged their children to do without human contact, attention, and loving support. It was then no surprise that these youngsters then went on to treat other people as if they did not have human qualities, often banging into them or staring through them as if they were inanimate objects. While modern biopsychiatry has tried to dismiss these early studies and to claim that autism is genetic or biological, they have no substantial evidence to support their claims (reviewed in Breggin, 1991). Thus clinical and empirical research confirms the existence of basic needs for love in the form of nurturing, comfort, and emotional support, and finds that the failure to fulfill these needs leads to psychosocial disorders.

Animal studies in the wild have confirmed the human research. Chimpanzees observed by Goodall in *Chimpanzees of Gombe* (1986) and mountain gorillas observed by Dian Fossey in *Gorillas in the Mist* (1983) have displayed profound mourning reactions, including what psychiatrists might label "clinical depression," in response to psychosocial losses and deprivation. Depending on their age and maturity, young orphans may or may not be able to bond again with another chimp or gorilla. If they are too young to bond after the loss of a parent, they may stop eating and caring for themselves, and die. Fossey describes feeding and stroking an orphaned baby gorilla back into health. Goodall also describes how chimps are capable of generosity and altruism toward each other, including sick or feeble relatives and friends. In *Toxic Psychiatry* (1991), I reviewed these primate studies and compared the responses of the animals to those of humans under similar circumstances, and found them largely indistinguishable.

It must be concluded that love is a basic need. In the infant, love may be the *most basic need*, because the infant cannot thrive without receiving it. It is more primary in some respects than food or water, because the unloved infant (human or primate) may refuse both and die. It is certainly the most basic need in terms of normal psychosocial development. Without being loved, and subsequently learning to love, an infant and child cannot grow up to function well as an adult.

LOVE AS A BASIC NEED IN CONFLICT RESOLUTION LITERATURE

In the literature of conflict analysis and resolution, we find an increasing awareness that people have basic needs for love, nurturing, affiliation, and meaningful relationships, and that these love needs must be satisfied to achieve more harmonious living on earth.

Among basic needs, John Burton (1990a) includes "bonding," "valued relationships," and "recognition." As an ideal, he promotes a "sharing society" with "close bonded relationships," (p. 50). Others of his basic needs or values, such as autonomy and control, would seem more related to the liberty dynamic (see chapter 3) than to love; but as we shall see, the development of autonomy, social role, identity and similar capacities requires some degree of prior fulfillment of the need for nurturing and love.

In "The Existence of Human Needs" (1988), James Chowning Davies speaks more directly of "the social-affectional or love needs." He places them second in a list of four basic-need categories that also includes, first, "the physical needs;" third, "the self-esteem or dignity or equality needs," and fourth, "the self-actualization needs."

Consistent with viewing the human being as a "social animal," Davies finds that love plays a crucial role in regard to the fulfillment of all other basic needs:

. . . the love needs form a continuously traveled bridge between a human being's most elemental physical needs and his/her more distinctly human needs as a unique individual. A person's demands for everything from food to recognition of his/her unique creativity are all transacted with other human beings. (p. 27)

Davies notes that chimpanzees and humans cannot develop normally without love and nurturing. He further believes that individuals require a loving upbringing in order to move on to self-actualization, and even as adults must return to socializing in order to recuperate or reenergize for the task of self-actualization.

In *Peacemaking Among Primates* (1989), Frans de Waal describes the tension between cooperation and aggression in chimpanzees, pointing out that both dominant and submissive animals actively promote reconciliation through vocalizations, facial expressions, posturing, grooming, and even hugging and kissing. Often acts of aggression end in reconciliations that tighten the bonds between animals.

Chimpanzee life is hardly a survival of the fittest struggle among the animals; rather it is a complex social enterprise involving a shifting balance between competition and cooperation between individuals and coalitions. While conflict frequently occurs, it rarely escalates to the point of social disintegration or lethality, in part due to a wide variety of conflict resolution techniques, including individual reconciliations and third party interventions on behalf of peace and cooperation. As de Waal cleverly puts it, "The law of the jungle does not apply to chimpanzees," (p. 49).

THE LOVE OF SCIENCE, TECHNOLOGY, AND KNOWLEDGE

The escalating development of science and technology is usually attributed to (or blamed on!) liberty rather than love. However, love for their work or the subject they are studying is extraordinarily important in motivating most scientists and technologists, as well as artists, historians, philosophers, social scientists, and others who contribute to human knowledge. Love for the pursuit of knowledge also helps to establish the international community of these individuals in their various specialties.

Albert Einstein's life and work illustrates the role of love in science. It is well-known that he viewed his theoretical work in part as an attempt to understand God's universe. The passionate, loving enthusiasm that he gave to these pursuits is captured by Ronald Clark in *Einstein: The Life and Times* (1984). Clark quotes a friend who witnessed Einstein's meeting with fellow physicist Hendrick Lorenz:

Lorenz sat smiling at Einstein completely lost in meditation, exactly the way a father looks at a particularly beloved son—full of secure confidence that the youngster will crack the nut he has given him, but eager to see how. It took quite a while, but suddenly Einstein's head shot up joyfully; he "had" it. Still a bit of give and take, interrupting one another, a partial disagreement, very quick clarification and a complete mutual understanding, and then both men with beaming eyes skimming over the shining riches of the new theory. (p. 240.)

Notice that the men are not only joyful about each other in the process of scientific analysis and discovery; they also cherish the product of their work.

In his book, *Therapeutic Studies* (1985), in a section entitled "Einstein; thinking and loving," psychiatrist Kenneth Artiss declares:

Now it is possible to compare the openness of Einstein's mind with that of the lover's. We are surprised by some similarities.

Artiss follows the discussion of Einstein's passion for truth with a few trenchant paragraphs headed "Freedom to Love." He declares that to love someone or something is to desire and to search for complete knowledge of the loved one's uniqueness. He quotes Goethe's maxim, "A man doesn't understand anything unless he loves it."

We shall return to the theme of love and knowledge as we further examine the role of love in conflict resolution. If love is indeed a path—and perhaps *the* path—toward understanding, its importance in conflict resolution becomes further magnified.

Einstein has not been alone in being motivated by a passionate love for knowledge. His predecessors—such as Copernicus, Brahe, Kepler, Galileo, and Newton—were motivated by a passion for science and understanding, and not purely by self-interest or competition. Some of them risked their careers and even their lives.

The community of scientists, as well as other truth-seekers, exists as a continuum in time that spans the ages. Einstein felt a strong affinity for his predecessors and was drawn to ancient institutions where they had studied and taught. The feeling we often have for those who have paved our intellectual way often transcends simple respect. It becomes loving and reverential. I am reminded of how one of my philosophy professors felt toward Plato and Aristotle. His feeling toward the old masters reached beyond the analytic, comprehended their flaws, and nonetheless took delight in them.

Often these communities of truth-seekers reach into the future as well, not only revering those who crèated the traditions of the past, but enjoying the prospect of contributing to the future. Einstein also expressed his love for future generations through his work in support of international peacemaking.

Through his biography of Einstein, Clark also documents how the community of scientists attempted, before and after World War II, to maintain itself across national borders despite the hatreds generated by war. To this day, international scientists frequently see themselves as members of a community that transcends individual and national interests.

THE HOPE OF LOVING COMMUNITIES

It is relatively easy to understand how love bonds and motivates people in families and in local community organizations, such as the many volunteer groups that serve the needs of Americans. A recent TV movie based on the rescue of baby Jessica McClure from a well shaft in Texas was described in its subtitle as a story of volunteerism and love. Unfortunately, love does not sufficiently motivate us in regard to the vast but more commonplace suffering found in our local communities, for example, among the poor and minority groups. But notice that, in the absence of love, we usually fail to come up with any benevolent, workable solutions.

Love also plays a role in many divergent worldwide movements aimed at solving our most difficult global problems, including the destruction of our environment and the increasing disparity between the rich and the poor of the world (see chapter 11). Here I want to emphasize that love can reach across national boundaries through a variety of organizations based on social justice, religion, shared cultural values, philanthropy, and common interests such as science and the arts. Often the individuals involved also see themselves as a part of a larger community extending through time, even into the future where they anticipate the good effects of their contributions.

Love is rooted in the whole human being—the biological, psychosocial, and spiritual—and binds human beings in positive, valuing relationships from the most superficial to the most intimate and intense. The capacity for love is inherent in the newborn infant, but it must be brought forth through nurturing. The infant requires love in order to thrive and then in order to join society as an adult. Love is *the* most basic psychosocial need; the individual cannot function autonomously or socially without a loving introduction into life.

The feeling associated with love is positive and, at its best, joyful. It inspires attitudes and activities of caring, nurturing, cherishing, and reverent treasuring. It encourages liberty and justice, sympathy and mercy. Empathic love transforms individual self-interests into mutual interests and becomes the final common pathway for those values leading to the resolution and prevention of deep-seated conflicts in the personal and political spheres alike.

▼ ▼

CHAPTER 3

Understanding Liberty

But we assure the socialists that we repudiate only forced organization, not natural organization. We repudiate the forms of association that are forced upon us, not free association. We repudiate forced fraternity, not true fraternity. We repudiate the artificial unity that does nothing more than deprive persons of individual responsibility. We do not repudiate the natural unity of mankind under Providence.

> **Frederic Bastiat, The Law (1850)**

Property rights are human rights, and are essential to the human rights which liberals attempt to maintain. The human right of free speech depends upon the human right of private property in newsprint.

> **Murray Rothbard, For a New Liberty (1973)**

I suggest that the greatest threat to the exchange system [the free market] is the claim that it can do everything. This leads to the equally absurd claim that it can do nothing. The real problem here is to appraise it in its setting and to get the right kind of setting for it.

> **Kenneth Boulding, Beyond Economics (1968)**

Whether complete identification of human nature with individuality would be desirable or undesirable if it existed is an idle academic question. For it does not exist. Some cultural conditions develop psychological constituents that lead toward differentiation; others stimulate those which lead in the direction of the solidarity of the beehive or anthill.

> **John Dewey, Freedom and Culture (1989)**

Love grows best in the soil of liberty.

> **Leonard Frank, unpublished letter (1991)**

From the dawn of humankind, communities have probably been aware of their freedom and the need to protect it; but personal or individual freedom is a more recent concept. It is not yet accepted in many cultures and nations of the world, especially for women, children, and minorities. In their personal lives, even in the United States, many people have little or no concept of how to exercise their own personal freedom.

THE IDEAL OF LIBERTY IN PERSONAL RELATIONSHIPS

In our personal lives we can determine to conduct ourselves with a maximum amount of respect for the rights of others. We can, with some success, make sure that our most intimate relationships are strictly voluntary in spirit and in fact (Breggin, 1980; see also chapter 6). I can, for example, decide on my own never to threaten or deceive my family or friends. I can also try not to exercise my advantages as a male when bargaining with my wife about matters such as domestic chores, money, or career. When we then sit down to discuss the division of labor within the family, there is some hope that the outcome will reflect, at least in part, a genuine bargain, a voluntary exchange.

The problem is of course more difficult for women, especially if they choose to raise children within a typical family. Their choices may be vastly limited compared to men's. Nonetheless, even in this arena there is a beginning awareness of the need for equal rights.

In personal and political relationships, and in conflict resolution, the aim is to maximize the voluntary nature of relationships, and within them, to maximize the mutual fulfillment of needs. To some extent, this is a three-step process from coercion through liberty to love.

To the extent that the principle of liberty can be built into relationships, it establishes the first step or initial context for the development and survival of love (see chapter 6).

WHAT IS LIBERTY?

Liberty can be understood and justified in many ways, including theories of natural or divine rights, human nature, property rights, or constitutional law. The subject has attracted volumes of attention over the centuries. I will not at this point examine the many debates concerning liberty, such as the validity of equating personal freedom with the right to own private property. My aim is to develop a narrow definition of liberty for use in contrasting it to coercion and to love.

Liberty will be defined in terms of "freedom from" rather than "freedom to." That is, it will be limited to the right to defend oneself from external oppression or control, rather than the right to have one's other needs fulfilled, such as those for food or medical care. These more complex issues will be taken up in the chapters that deal with business corporations, society, and international politics.

For many advocates of liberty, *self-ownership,* including the ownership of property and other presumed products of one's labor, is the basic axiom from which all other rights are derived. In *For A New Liberty* (1973), Murray Rothbard adopts as his "primary axiom" the "universal right of self-ownership, a right held by everyone by virtue of being a human being." Self-ownership further justifies the right to pursue one's own interests free of outside restraint:

Since each individual must think, learn, value, and choose his or her ends and means in order to survive and flourish, the right to self-ownership gives man the right to perform these vital functions without being hampered and restricted by coercive molestation. (p. 27.)

In the epilogue to the *Psychology of Freedom* (1980), I cited self-ownership as a fundamental ethical and psychological principle:

You own yourself; you possess yourself; you belong to yourself. You are your own natural resource, your own and sole source of life energy. You have complete rights to yourself. (p. 237.)

But self cannot so easily be separated from others, and I went on to describe love for others and for life as the highest expression of self-ownership.

Liberty can also be defined in terms of the "non-aggression axiom." According to Rothbard, "no man or group of men have the right to aggress against the person or property of anyone else," (p. 8). That is, the principle of freedom restricts the use of force to self-defense.

Self-ownership and the restriction of force to self-defense are basic principles of Dynamic II: liberty. Although they were initially developed as economic and political principles, I have applied these axioms to psychology and to personal living as well (Breggin, 1980). Personal autonomy, self-determination, and empowerment flow from self-ownership and nonaggression.

EMOTIONAL BULLYING

In the broader political and legal arena, force is defined as a *physical* intervention or the threat of it. In reality, there are many other forms of coercion, most of which are familiar from our personal lives. Sometimes authority is invoked, as "I am your father" or "I am your husband." One individual may attempt to control another by stimulating painful feelings. The victim is made to feel guilty, shameful, anxious, or numb about standing up for his or her own interests or principles. Sometimes threats of abandonment are used: "If that's the way you want it, I'll leave you."

In personal adult relationships, people have the right to reject emotional bullying and, if necessary, to leave the relationship. Emotional bullying cannot be made *illegal,* but individuals can personally refuse to subject themselves to interpersonal oppression. I will deal with this issue further in discussing coercion (in chapter 4) and family conflict (in chapter 6). Here I want to introduce the idea that all forms of bullying and threats are incompatible with voluntary *personal* relationships. They also corrupt political relationships, but they are difficult if not impossible to outlaw.

Because we are more directly in control of our intimate relationships, liberty is typically a more realizable ideal in the personal than in the political arena. It is not utopian to seek to make all of one's intimate adult relationships wholly voluntary and free of coercion; but it is utopian to expect such an outcome on a national or international scale in the foreseeable future.

Meanwhile, in the field of conflict resolution, it is generally agreed that only *voluntary participation* and *voluntary agreements* can advance parties from uncompromising conflict toward meaningful, lasting solutions (Burton, 1990a).

THE DIFFERENCES BETWEEN RESPECT AND LOVE

Respect or esteem is the emotion generated by Dynamic II activities. Respect or esteem says, in effect, "You have conducted yourself well. You are ethical. Be proud." Respect is very important in the lives of all individuals. Children need to be emotionally rewarded for their accomplishments and good attitudes. Adults want to earn similar approval for their accomplishments. In both the home and the workplace, human beings need to feel esteemed.

Respect or esteem is not the same as love. Love says, "You are valued for yourself." It is unconditional. Respect, by contrast, is a social reward or reinforcer. It is contingent on individual performance and accomplishment. Love reaches to the core or essence of the person; esteem concerns itself only with quality of performance.

Sometimes people can love without giving respect. A parent may not always approve of a son or daughter's conduct; but a parent should always strive to find love in his or her heart for a child. However, with people who are not dear to us, we may be able to respect them without loving them. This leads to an important principle in conflict resolution.

In the absence of love, respect can provide the starting point, at least, for a relationship and for the early stages of conflict resolution. If people do not show respect for each other in a negotiation or conflict-resolution setting, the relationships will further deteriorate. When beginning to work on conflict resolution as a third party or as a participant, it is important to insist upon mutual respect from the earliest stages.

The mistaken equation of esteem with love amounts to a denial of love. By confusing esteem with love we overlook the key human needs for bonding, valued relationships, or affection. Basic-needs theorist Paul Sites (1990), who has considerably influenced conflict resolution theory, has fallen into this error. Sites believes that animals and people become depressed because they lose the approval (esteem) they have been receiving:

In short, a feeling of depression occurs when a person's self-esteem is in some way threatened or damaged. Depression may occur, for example, when a family member or close friend dies. These are the people most likely to provide approval behavior and their death negates this.

Sites postulates no basic human need for contact or communication with people, or to "belong to a group." People and groups provide *opportunities* for need satisfaction, but they can also thwart it; therefore people are merely *potential* satisfiers rather than beings of inherent worth to each other. Thus humans are not fundamentally drawn to be with other human beings or to love them. From such a viewpoint, society must be seen as evolving from a hodge-podge of need satisfactions without a central, comprehensive need for social life.

Even caring seems absent as a human motive in Sites's framework. For example, in Sites's view we avoid shaming other people because of an implicit agreement that people will therefore not shame us. There is no appreciation that humans tend to empathize with each other's pain even without external rewards. Nor is there any acknowledgment that human beings spontaneously desire to nurture each other, to protect each other, and to relieve each other's emotional or physical pain. Yet the existence of such social needs or values is easily explained by his evolutionary perspective. The drive toward *mutual satisfaction* and *cooperation,* as Kropotkin suggested, can be understood as a necessary outcome of evolution (see chapter 2).

Consistent with what seems like a typical male hierarchical value system (see chapter 6), Sites places enormous emphasis on *control* as central to human behavior. Altruism is seen as one more method of controlling people, i.e., getting others to think and to do what we want. That people might want something *for other people* seems beyond his system. His passing mention of altruism and his dismissal of a need for human companionship or society is the closest he comes to discussing love.

Nothing is more important in resolving conflict than to get past this erroneous equation of respect with love. As already noted, respect establishes the possibility of a meaningful relationship, but only love and empathy move people to care about each other's problems and hence to seek mutually satisfying solutions.

INDIVIDUAL LIBERTY, AUTONOMY, AND LOVE

Autonomy or self-rule is the ability to think rationally for oneself, to exercise free will, and to make independent judgments. It may be viewed as "inner freedom" and is essential to effective functioning.

In "Psychotherapy as Applied Ethics" (1971), I made autonomy the central value and working principle of psychotherapy. It certainly is an important one. Without autonomy, people are unable to pursue any set of values and goals. Without autonomy, they grow afraid and distrustful toward other people who seem more powerful. In more recent years I have increasingly sought to place liberty and autonomy within the context of love and other social values and experiences. And autonomy no longer seems to me such an easy concept to define.

In a book originally published in 1959, Dorothy Lee has analyzed how autonomy depends upon a social structure and cultural philosophy that values or loves the individual. After describing the tightly-knit structure of the Navaho family and society with its many taboos and customs, Lee goes on to focus upon the autonomy granted to all individuals:

Within this structured universe and tightly knit society, the Navaho lives in personal autonomy. Adults and children alike are valued for their sheer being, just because they **are**. *(p. 10.)*

Love is so unconditional that there is no incentive to push for personal recognition through competition and achievement. If anything, the individual is suspect for doing so. The wealthy person may even be accused of having employed malicious witchcraft.

In her book, *In a Different Voice* (1982), Carol Gilligan continues the observations begun by Lee. She finds that men have placed the values of autonomy and independence at the top of a hierarchy of values, while the lives of women more typically emphasize caring, mutuality, and interdependence. Her position might be characterized as "Autonomy is not enough."

The position taken by Gilligan, and especially by Lee in *Freedom and Culture*, raises important, difficult-to-answer problems. While

autonomy in the English and American tradition has been connected to personal freedom, Lee connects autonomy to a feeling of
being unconditionally valued or loved. I believe that love is required for the initial development of autonomy, and to some degree for its maintenance in adulthood; but the autonomous person
as described and seemingly promoted by Lee is culturally restricted
in what he or she is allowed to think about. While individual
wishes are greatly respected in some of the societies that she cites,
the range of these wishes and their expression is narrowly determined by the cultures. The Navaho mother can permit her child to
make up his or her own mind in part because more threatening
options, such as rejecting the culture, are unthinkable. By autonomy, I mean a far greater degree of inner freedom, with considerably greater cultural support for a broad range of personal choices.

Sociologist Helmut Schoeck (1966), with a much stronger libertarian bent than Lee, takes a somewhat more cynical view of similar anthropological data. It may be closer to the truth. He points
out that envy plays an enormous controlling role in preindustrial
societies. Envy, often expressed through the evil eye and witchcraft, tends to suppress individual initiative and to enforce group
norms. For Schoeck, it is a double-edged sword. Envy enforces
group coercion and prevents the domination of the group by especially powerful or competitive individuals; but it also prevents
the individual from more freely developing special interests or endowments. A pragmatic theoretician, Schoeck believes that the
tension created by envy is inevitable because it is an indispensable
part of society's built-in checks and balances.

In an epilogue to the 1987 edition of Lee's *Freedom and Culture*,
Jeffrey Ehrenreich summarizes Lee's viewpoint and brings us face
to face with the dilemma of the individual and society:

*Lee believed that content, fulfilled, productive, autonomous indi-
viduals—people who could value the self—needed a social environment and structure which promoted freedom, dignity, and
individual diversity. She wanted to see such positive qualities
structured into people's lives and not just held as principles. She
wanted individuals to live in societies with social structures in
which there would be ". . . absolute respect for man, for all individuals irrespective of age and sex." (p. 180.)*

Ehrenreich then describes Lee's own struggle for autonomy, which brought her to reject mainstream academic life and, for many years, to refuse to write anything further. She did this by choice, but not without an identity crisis and personal suffering.

I believe that Lee's personal life, more than *Freedom and Culture* itself, expresses the sometimes inherent conflict between the individual and society. Autonomy and its corollary, personal freedom, cannot depend upon societal encouragement and reinforcement as fully as Lee had hoped. Autonomy requires facing the existential anxieties and the real life conflicts inherent in making one's own choices. Even the best of societies will paradoxically encourage autonomy while trying to discourage the individual from making unlimited choices.

Lee's work does make the all-important point that the autonomous person does not automatically spring into action with adulthood. As Lawrence Haworth has more recently elaborated in *Autonomy: An Essay in Philosophical Psychology and Ethics* (1986), autonomy must be nurtured, cultivated, and encouraged in the child. Autonomy is a natural striving within the infant who attempts, often to the consternation of its parents, to do things on his or her own without or even despite adult interference. Self-feeding by an immature infant, for example, can try any adult's patience. But, as Haworth observed, the flowering of autonomy requires the indulgence, encouragement, and support of adults. It has to be learned through its exercise in a social context. It is easily threatened and may not develop at all. Often it develops in relative degrees without necessarily becoming fully expressed.

As concentration camps and POW camps have demonstrated, even adult autonomy can be devastated by systematic undermining in controlled institutions. Erving Goffman (1961) and I (1991) have described a similar outcome in the lives of state mental hospital patients. Lenore Walker (1989) has documented how battered women can lose their autonomy and become psychologically helpless in the face of overwhelming abuse and control at the hands of men determined to rob them of their independence.

Nurturing and love in infancy and early childhood is required for the development of normal functioning in primates and humans (see chapter 2). Clinical experience shows that an unloved human being is likely to grow up lacking in basic capacities, such as autonomy (Miller, 1984; Breggin, 1991). Such an individual may become so insecure, fearful, and suspicious that he or she becomes labeled insane or incompetent.

Social and developmental psychologists have studied how children develop components of autonomy and self-determination, such as self-control, delay of gratification, mastery (the opposite of helplessness), and locus of control (the degree to which children believe that their own actions can influence the outcome of events in their lives). The research indicates that autonomy is fostered within families that warmly encourage children to be self-reliant and independent by means of nonauthoritarian, nonpunitive interventions, including praise and gentle, rational persuasion (for a review, see Seligman, 1991; Liebert, Wicks-Nelson, and Kail, 1986).

The dependence of autonomy upon normal maturation and, to some extent, on supportive conditions in adulthood is a central issue in conflict analysis and resolution. The question must always be asked, "Are all parties to the conflict in fact autonomous?" If not, then the weaker may be taken advantage of by the stronger. At the least, the nonautonomous individual will gain limited benefit from the process.

In individual psychotherapy, clients may not be able to benefit when lacking in autonomy and overcome with personal helplessness. A therapist may mistakenly encourage such clients to examine childhood trauma, only to find them becoming more overwhelmed in the face of the restimulated pain. Instead, the therapist should directly address the issue of autonomy and helplessness, helping nonautonomous persons strengthen their self-control and self-direction. In therapy, it can be futile and even damaging to emphasize other issues when clients feel relatively unable to control their inner life.

People lacking in autonomy often end up agreeing to destructive psychiatric treatments in the form of toxic drugs, electroshock, or psychosurgery (Breggin, 1991). Their psychological helplessness then becomes compounded by brain damage and dysfunction.

Whether we are talking about interpersonal or broader political conflicts, we cannot *assume* the existence of autonomous individuals without leaving relatively helpless people at the mercy of more powerful ones. A setting in which liberty is the only governing principle is advantageous to relatively competent individuals, but hazardous to relatively helpless ones. Without help from others, people lacking in autonomy cannot survive or protect themselves from exploitation. That help will only be provided where people are willing to love unconditionally and to offer gifts to others. These observations, as much as anything else, underscore the limits of liberty.

There may come a time when a person concludes that grandma or grandpa is no longer able to make decisions for herself or himself. Similarly, young children sometimes need adults to take over their lives for their own good or to prevent serious harm from befalling them. But with few exceptions, people will further their own lives and those of the people around them by standing fast for everyone's liberty. Within a context of personal liberty, individuals can far more easily develop themselves, help their loved ones, and settle their disputes and solve their conflicts through love (see chapter 6).

Mature individuals are in a position to most fully benefit from liberty. In their personal lives, they may wish to do everything they can to preserve and promote their own freedom and that of the other autonomous people in their lives. But this can never be a fully comfortable approach to life. It brings with it the anxiety of making one's own choices, often in conflict with prevailing social norms. The autonomous person may end up rebelling against society or particular social institutions when they become oppressive and when they fail to meet the basic needs of individuals.

POLITICAL LIBERTY AND LOVE

In the political arena, the problem of liberty and autonomy becomes more complex because many citizens are unable to take care of themselves or to compete adequately in the free market. Free market advocates believe that liberty is the engine of human progress—the source not only of modern technological and industrial advances, but the inspiration for human rights throughout the world (Weaver, 1947; Von Mises, 1966; Schoeck, 1966; Rothbard, 1982).

The utopian benefits of the free market have of course been challenged from many directions, including more recent fears that the "engine of progress" is in reality devouring the human community and nature alike (Galbraith, 1958, 1980; Berry, 1972, 1987; Fromm, 1976; Etzioni, 1988; Wachtel, 1989). Yet the former communist nations of Europe, as well as Asian communist nations, are beginning to experiment with the free market or capitalism as the only hope for economic survival and recovery (see chapter 9). *They* are informing *us* about the necessity of human freedom for human survival. Yet they face the most vexing problem of the free enterprise system: the degree to which it exploits less autonomous people.

The interactions between liberty and love within the larger community are complex and controversial, and will be dealt with in more depth in chapters 8–10, as well as later in this chapter. It is doubtful, for example, if liberty can be sustained without people feeling community ties with each other and without people feeling some degree of love for others beyond the immediate circle of their family and locality.

THE ORIGIN OF EQUAL RIGHTS

The principle of liberty holds that humans are equal under the law rather than equal in value. But can people have equal rights without *necessarily* having equal worth as well? If people do not have equal worth, then what is the source of equal rights? Why do we insist that strangers be respected and legally protected, even when it is not in our self-interest?

Perhaps some people do support liberty on selfish grounds, but certainly this is not true for most. Patrick Henry's rallying cry, "Give me liberty or give me death," hardly seems to reflect rational self-interest. Nor does the motto of the state of New Hampshire, "Live free or die." Whether we approve of them or not, these resounding battle cries reflect a higher ideal than personal self-interest or even survival. At the least, they reflect a *love* of liberty. To some extent, at least, they reflect a love of other people—for all human beings to be free, even at the potential cost of sacrificing one's own life.

Nor is it true that our self-interest is always best served by rejecting force and fraud. Often we can obtain a great advantage by bullying or cheating. Sometimes, as the lives of many dictators and other politicians have illustrated, force and fraud can yield enduring advantages with lifetime benefits for oneself and one's family and associates. Indeed, governments and their beneficiaries typically thrive on force and fraud. Self-interest by itself is an insufficient motive for respecting the rights of others.

Only when we care about or love people do we thoroughly and unequivocally grant them equal rights. Absent a real sense of the *inherent worth* of others, we are bound to fudge or hedge here and there about their rights. *With vast implications for conflict analysis and resolution, I believe that the lack of love among human beings is the chief cause for the rampant disrespect for rights nearly everywhere we turn. Love remains a flimsy fabric in world society, and therefore so do equal rights.*

FORCE IN LIBERTY AND LOVE

Liberty as a principle supports the use of force in self-defense, but love abhors the use of any force. Here is possibly the greatest incompatibility between love and liberty. To injure another person, even to kill someone, is considered ethical and sometimes admirable in defense of person, property, or the ideal of liberty itself. But to harm someone in a loving relationship—even in self-defense—is at best a horrible expediency. Usually it is viewed as repugnant and unacceptable.

Having stated the ideal, it must be repeated that a great deal of violence is committed in the name of love within the family and many social institutions, such as religion and psychiatry (see chapter 7). However, the experience of genuine love, which is rooted in empathy, is incompatible with violence against the loved one. This is not only an intuitive and an ethical conclusion, but an observation based on experiences with loving people. In chapter 11, the equation between love and nonviolence will be examined through the work of Gandhi, Schweitzer, and Martin Luther King, Jr. As a person develops most fully in his or her capacity to love, the use of force, even in self-defense, becomes increasingly abhorred; and nonviolent approaches to conflict resolution become increasingly valued.

SELF-INTEREST AND ALTRUISM

Advocates of liberty, such as Rothbard (1973) and Von Mises (1966), usually describe self-interest as the most natural, proper, and overriding human motive. Sometimes they view self-interest as the only *possible* human motive. Altruism then becomes a kind of hypocritical rationalization or a mere derivative of self-interest.

Most people are not motivated by self-interest all the time, not even in their economic or work relationships, let alone in their personal ones. Altruism, concern for others, the desire to maintain good will, a sense of fairness, patriotism, religious devotion, and many other constraints and ideals motivate the activities of people. Personal motives such as greed, envy, and the desire for power also affect people, sometimes causing them to act against any commonsense notion of self-interest.

Consider the actions of an art dealer who discovers that a valuable painting is being sold unwittingly for a mere ten dollars in a second-hand store. The dealer might, if he had no prior relationship with the store owner, quickly buy the underpriced art. But if he had a long-standing business relationship with the store owner that he desired to maintain, he might share some of his profit with him. This might be called "practical altruism," something still closely associated with the pursuit of self-interest. But if the dealer felt sympathy for the store owner, or if he were a close friend to him, he might announce the painting's true worth and then join his friend in celebrating his good fortune.

To argue that altruism is essentially selfish because it brings self-satisfaction is to miss the point. As the art dealer's story illustrates, acting selfishly and acting altruistically are different phenomena with frequently opposing outcomes.

The idealization of the pursuit of self-interest is, to a great extent, a male viewpoint. Women, in their nurturing or homemaking roles, cannot live by it. It is one thing for Von Mises the man to declare that most people prefer to fill their own bellies; it would be another for Mrs. Von Mises to say it. She was in all likelihood filling a number of people's bellies ahead of her own, including Mr. Von Mises's. In *Justice, Gender and the Family* (1987), Susan Moller Okin observes that theories of economic self-interest ignore or take for granted the existence of women who, at great personal cost, typically devote themselves to taking care of other people.

COMPETITION AND IMBALANCES IN POWER

In his well-known metaphor of the invisible hand, Adam Smith argued in 1759 in *The Theory of Moral Sentiments* and in 1776 in *The Wealth of Nations* that when people pursue their own self-interests (without the use of force), they unintentionally end up serving each other's needs and the needs of the society. In order to sell my product to you, I must make it conform to your expectations. Similarly, I will reject your offer, unless it meets my expectations. Thus selfish exchanges inadvertently or unintentionally cater to the needs of others and create a kind of practical altruism. This leads to a vast web of exchange, which no individual or state could artificially construct, wherein people end up satisfying each other's needs while pursuing their own.

Adam Smith's theory works smoothly as long as the ideal of voluntary exchange between equal partners is reasonably approximated; but in *most exchanges* and *most relationships*, built-in imbalances of need, competence, and power predetermine the outcome.

In the economic arena, for example, if a desperate father decides to pay his last peso, ruble, or dollar for the food or medicine necessary for the life of his wife or child, he is hardly in a bargaining position with the wealthy owner of the food market or pharmacy. Even if he has sufficient resources to strike a meaningful "voluntary" exchange with the local store owner, he is in no such bargaining position in relationship to still greater forces that determine the cost of the food and medicine, such as monopolistic industries, international banks, or global markets. If the desperate father is also relatively unsophisticated or incompetent, then he is further disadvantaged in the exchange.

In *Toxic Psychiatry* (1991) I have described how the drug companies spend millions to buy the good will of psychiatry and the endorsement of individual psychiatrists, thereby creating a psychopharmaceutical complex that dominates the drug marketplace. Individual drug experts, psychiatric organizations, the Food and Drug Administration (FDA), the National Institute of Mental Health (NIMH), and the media have contributed to the effort to promote psychiatric drugs, to the consumer's detriment.

I've come to the conclusion that the ideal of liberty—voluntary exchanges between relatively equal partners—is unattainable as a practical matter on a large scale or societal level. In a pure free market, most people would probably find themselves decidedly unfree.

Power imbalances also exist in family and male-female conflicts. As Marilyn French in *Beyond Power* (1985) has pointed out, these imbalances are built into gender relationships through the institutions, customs, and economic relations of all "civilized" societies. In the United States, for example, if a wife and mother takes a job outside the home, and then tries to bargain with her husband to get him to assume his share of the domestic chores, the outcome is predetermined. In nearly all cases, her husband is likely to refuse to help at all with the domestic chores. If the woman in turn refuses to take over *all* of the domestic duties, the children will suffer from lack of care. Motivated by love for her home and children, by a sense of obligation toward the family, and by societal imperatives placed upon her, the working mother is typically saddled with an outside job *and* an inside, domestic one at the same time.

Most relationships and exchanges do not fit the pure model of voluntary exchange in our personal lives or the free market in our economic activities. To make believe that they do is to rationalize injustice—to force the father to give up his last dollar to save his child's life or to force the mother to hold two jobs in order to maintain a home for her children is to expose the vulnerable to enslavement by those with greater power. In sum, one or another party to an exchange too often has an advantage of such proportions that the mere rejection of force by no means guarantees a "voluntary" exchange.

COMPETITION IN LIBERTY AND LOVE

Ideally, liberty or voluntary exchange leads not only to competition but to cooperation. Adam Smith pointed out how, in the making of a pin, innumerable people in the pursuit of their own profit will cooperate in the process of transforming the metal ore into a useful instrument. Despite Adam Smith, Von Mises and others who believe that competition leads to a kind of practical altruism, competition also tends to breed conflict. Cooperation may develop *within* specific business organizations or affiliations, but ferocious competition typically develops among rivals (Kohn, 1986). Unhappily, as I mentioned in regard to the psycho-pharmaceutical complex (Breggin, 1991), even the desired competition between rivals in the marketplace may be compromised when they collude to the disadvantage of the consumer.

Sports teach us a great deal about cooperation and competition. To a remarkable degree, professional sporting events are based on the uncompromising Dynamic II model that is supposed to characterize the free market. The rules are the same for all the players involved, infractions are carefully monitored and punished by objective referees or umpires, everyone participates by their own choosing and gets paid for it, and violence is usually limited to self-defense. In most sports, such as baseball and basketball, the individual competitor is not even allowed to use force in self-defense. The enforcement of self-defense remains in the hands of the umpires and referees.

What is the result of this perfect model of competitive human activity? While cooperation is greatly enhanced within each team by the common goal of winning, conflict escalates between rival teams and among their respective fans. We do not have to remind ourselves of European soccer matches to see that violence can be generated in seemingly harmless sporting competitions. High-school students in America frequently come to blows at sporting events both on and off the field.

The ideal of liberty places strict limits on the competition by excluding the use of force and fraud. But keeping the competition within these bounds, in the absence of valued relationships or loving affiliations, is hard to do. And even when the competition is contained within the ethics of liberty, it can become extremely fierce and conflicted.

The concept of liberty is an adequate prescription for how to write legal contracts. It is also workable in some bargaining situations in which no one obviously has the upper hand. It is ideal for drawing up the regulations for sporting events between relatively well-matched competitors. It is a necessary condition if people are to begin examining their conflicts with each other.

When people are embroiled in deep-seated conflicts, the principles of liberty can help define the initial framework or start-up conditions. They will not by themselves prove effective when there is marked suspicion, distrust, desperation, or hatred. They will not work where power imbalances overwhelm the seemingly voluntary exchange. Nor will they work in situations, such as "undeveloped" nations, where the principles of liberty and ethical business practices are not understood or valued. Even in a so-called developed nation, the United States, former president Ronald Reagan's inspiring rhetoric and deregulation on behalf of the "free market" helped to spawn one of the worst orgies of financial greed and fraud in the history of the country. Nonetheless, the principles of liberty are critical in establishing some of the ground rules necessary for conflict resolution.

BASIC NEEDS IN LIBERTY AND LOVE

The basic needs categorized as Dynamic II: liberty include self-esteem, autonomy, mastery, and self-determination. They are essential to effective functioning as an agent and are closely related to the principle that human beings can earn their value through accomplishments. However, we have already noted that the full expression and satisfaction of these needs are dependent upon a foundation of nurturing and love in childhood. Other Dynamic II needs overlap with love. They include security, identity, role, and meaning. It is somewhat arbitrary to place them within one or the other category. Security at an early age is dependent on love, while it later depends on liberty as well. Identity, role and meaning in life are at times generated by living according to the principle of liberty and at others by living according to the principle of love.

Most of the basic needs categorized as Dynamic I are clearly discernable from those in Dynamic II. These love needs include nurturing, empathy, bonding, oneness with people and with nature, and community. They are closely related to the principle that human beings and other expressions of life have inherent worth. They are basic to the formation and maintenance of society.

The line between liberty needs and love needs is not hard and fast, but there are very significant differences. This analysis suggests that the deepest or most complete conflict resolution involves the satisfaction of love needs.

ARE LIBERTY NEEDS INNATE?

Animals and humans alike seem to desire freedom for its own sake or for some purpose as general as maximizing opportunity for exploration, stimulation, experimentation, and choice-making. Our family pet turtle, for example, is constantly pushing the limits of her ten-gallon water tank. If she were but stronger, she would have broken through the glass barrier long ago. While she moves less vigorously after a full meal, she still shows a curiosity and interest in her environment, exploring the niches of her tank, pushing her nose into the glass walls as if to get to the places beyond, or looking about the room from her rock.

Even the patriarch of behaviorism, Ivan Pavlov (1957), postulated a "freedom reflex," in part because his dogs so vigorously resisted the confinement of his laboratory experiments. In his paper, "Lectures on the Work of the Cerebral Hemisphere," first delivered in 1924, Pavlov made clear that he meant an even more global urge for freedom:

It is obvious that the freedom reflex is one of the most important reflexes, or, to use the more general term, reactions of any living being. But this reflex is seldom referred to, as if it were not finally recognized. . . . As we know, in some animals the freedom reflex is so strong that when placed in captivity they reject food, pine away and die. (p. 184.)

Thus when modern zoos attempt to replicate natural surroundings, some animals still do not survive in captivity. One of our nearest relatives, the mountain gorilla, is among these, and therefore subject to possible extinction in the near future.

The potential for love is an innate capacity (see chapter 2). While love, as humans understand it, seems beyond her, even our turtle shows an interest in our voices and appearance, and at times seems to enjoy being handled. This reaction to humans might be a conditioned response to food, but members of her species are typically seen in the wild congregating together while sunning themselves on logs. Most likely the heaping up of bodies represents at least in part a social drive rather than competition for scarce log space. Among turtles, then, there probably is a basic need for liberty (freedom) and for love (social contact).

While it may be anthropomorphizing somewhat in regard to the turtle, it is probably correct to see these basic needs expressed in higher animals, especially primates. All the basic needs are expressed and satisfied through their social relationships. Thus both liberty and love are *psychosocial dynamics*—basic needs expressed through specific social arrangements—in animal and human society. In talking about the various characteristics of liberty or love, one is really describing their dynamics.

Is liberty a single need or several, such as freedom, autonomy, and self-esteem? Is a unitary liberty need the source of the drives to explore, to investigate, to roam about, and to seek stimulation? The same question can be asked in regard to love. Is love unitary or a combination of nurturing, caring, touching, and a variety of other needs? There is no simple answer to these questions, which are in part semantic and in part practical in nature. Whether naming a few or many basic needs, most or all of them can be classified within the liberty or love dynamics. Distinguishing when possible between liberty and love can be a great aid in understanding how our needs become expressed in society and with what consequences.

Liberty and love, as dynamics, sometimes seem to be opposed to each other, the one striving toward independence and the other toward interdependence, or the one striving toward separateness and the other toward togetherness. On the other hand, liberty and love often enhance each other. Love provides a basis for granting liberty to others and liberty provides the optimal conditions for love.

COMBINING LIBERTY AND LOVE

Before adults can love each other, they usually need to respect each other's rights, including each other's autonomy and self-determination. Before people will become vulnerable enough to love each other, they usually need guarantees that none of the involved parties will use arbitrary force. They also need to feel safe from being defrauded by lies, cheating, or misrepresentations.

Both liberty and love are basic human needs as well as social dynamics. Sometimes these dynamics seem in opposition, or at least at opposite poles, and sometimes they are complementary. In personal and group relationships there is typically an interaction between the two, with one or the other often taking central stage. Liberty is the optimal setting for the development and expression of love between adults. On the other hand, love in childhood is necessary for the development of autonomous capacities, and in all likelihood, love for other humans is the basis upon which we recognize their equal rights and liberties. Ultimately, love is the more basic human need and the necessary dynamic for the resolution of deep-seated human conflict in the personal and the political arena.

CHAPTER 4

▼▼▼▼▼▼▼▼▼▼▼▼▼▼▼▼▼▼▼▼▼▼▼▼▼▼▼▼▼▼▼▼▼

Understanding Coercion

If certain human needs are not satisfied there will be conflict. The conflict will be of such a character that no suppressive means will contain it. . . . It is mistaken not only in theory, but also pragmatically when coercive and authoritative processes of control are used in an attempt to preserve existing interest and institutions. . . . There is empirical evidence that no bargaining, negotiation, mediation, or any other such process is acceptable to authorities when they believe they have the coercive power at least to contain a situation. . . . This is the case at all social levels, in industry, in community relations, and internationally.
      John Burton, **Conflict: Resolution and Provention (1990)**

Love lets the other be, but with affection and concern. Violence attempts to constrain the other's freedom, to force him to act in the way we desire, but with lack of concern, with indifference to the other's own existence or destiny. We are effectively destroying ourselves by violence masquerading as love.
      R.D. Laing, **The Politics of Experience (1967)**

Civilization is a process in the service of Eros, whose purpose is to combine single human individuals, and after that families, then race, peoples and nations, into one great unity, the unity of mankind. . . . But man's natural aggressive instinct, the hostility of each against all and all against each, opposes this programme of civilization. This aggressive instinct is the derivative and the main representative of the death instinct which we have found alongside of Eros and which shares world-dominion with it. And now, I think, the meaning of the evolution of civilization is no longer obscure to us. It must present the struggle between Eros and Death, between the instinct of life and the instinct of destruction, as it works itself out in the human species.
      Sigmund Freud, **Civilization and Its Discontents (1930)**

Coercion involves outright force or the threat of force. It also includes more subtle methods of intimidation, bullying, or manipulation. Lying, cheating, and misleading people are also coercive.

The aim of coercion is to gain power over another, to put one's own will in place of another's. In short, coercion attempts to *make* people do what they do not wish or choose to do. To refrain from coercing others, and to resist being victimized by it, we must be able to identify coercion and find better alternatives. This is true in both our personal and our political lives.

COERCION AND CONFLICT RESOLUTION

Coercion is a form of conflict resolution or, more accurately, conflict *suppression*. There is widespread agreement within the field of conflict resolution that genuine problem solving is incompatible with the utilization of coercive power (Burton, 1990a).

The use of force, except in self-defense, is the most limited and hazardous approach to relationships and to conflict resolution. It leaves little room for either party—especially the victim—to fulfill any liberty or love needs. In part because coercion encourages people to manipulate each other, to lie, and to hide their vulnerabilities and needs, coercion obstructs the resolution of deep-rooted conflict.

Oppressive actions are frequently cloaked in the language of love: "I did it because I love you" or "If I didn't love you, I wouldn't care so much." Sometimes love of God, country, or other "higher values" are invoked to justify horrible atrocities against others. In reality, both the perpetrator and the victim become impaired in their ability to love others outside the coercive dynamic. Thus coercion is the great impediment to conflict resolution.

DEFINING COERCION

According to the *American Heritage Dictionary of the English Language* (1979), to coerce means "1. To force to act or to think in a given manner; to compel by pressure or threat. 2. To dominate, restrain, or control forcibly." Most dictionaries mention compulsion and restraint, both of which attempt to thwart the individual from acting on his or her own wishes or intentions.

Based on the definition of liberty in chapter 3, *physical* coercion will be defined as the use of force for any purpose other than self-defense, as well as the use of excessive force in self-defense. *Emotional* coercion will be defined more broadly to include all forms of threats and emotional manipulation. This sweeping definition can be justified on the grounds that all forms of coercion, physical and emotional, have somewhat similar negative effects, including the subversion of autonomy and self-determination, and the compromise of self-esteem.

Physical force is not necessarily the most potent means of compelling, restraining, and demoralizing people. Battered women, for example, report that the verbal humiliation they endure is often more debilitating than the beatings (Gelles and Straus, 1988). In clinical practice, the more subtle forms of coercion often have at least as devastating an impact on children as physical brutality. Sometimes the more subtle forms, because they are difficult to identify and to resist, have an even more corrosive effect on personal development. The definition of coercion will therefore include *any* form of emotional oppression, including manipulation and emotional intimidation.

It is not easy to define the more subtle forms of coercion, such as manipulation. Manipulation can include lying or deception, using hidden agendas, providing incomplete information, or playing on someone's personal weaknesses or vulnerabilities. By stirring up fear and helplessness associated with past injuries, the oppressor can pressure the individual to alter his or her chosen course.

While the broad definition of coercion raises many unanswered questions, it can be turned to practical use with very specific applications. In particular, it reminds us that *all threatening and manipulative actions or communications, for any purpose whatsoever, have somewhat similar negative outcomes.*

THE NEGATIVE EFFECTS OF COERCION

Coercion by the most well-meaning person, for the most well-intentioned purposes, still has untoward consequences. When the outcome does seem largely beneficial, coercive methods are likely to have some negative effects, including the subversion of free will and personal freedom. As Gandhi and others have observed (see chapter 11), even force in self-defense is not free of harmful side effects, although it will not be defined as coercion.

The principle that coercion always has some negative consequences is probably not subject to proof or disproof. Rather it is an assumption or viewpoint of use in organizing experience. In testing such a hypothesis, one must rely mostly upon personal experience, including one's own inner reactions to being coerced, as well as one's perceptions of the responses of others. Beyond that, there is each person's general knowledge of human affairs. One of the aims of this book is to demonstrate the usefulness of viewing all coercion—including that which seems culturally or generally accepted, routine, and innocuous—with caution and concern. This includes the emotional bullying that routinely takes place in the family and social lives of many people, the frequently oppressive control of children in the home and schools, the similar oppression of women throughout most of the society, involuntary treatment in psychiatry, and many or most government interventions.

These two fundamental assumptions—that all forms of coercion create negative effects and that these effects are somewhat similar regardless of the form of coercion—have practical importance in how conflict resolution is approached. They encourage a close scrutiny of any and all attempts to use coercion, and they discourage its use as much as possible in human affairs. This has vast implications for many spheres of human activity in which coercion is frequently the sanctioned or most commonly accepted approach to resolving conflict, including family relationships, childrearing, most governmental activities, involuntary psychiatry, authoritarian religion, and war. This chapter will focus on interpersonal coercion, while others will focus on broader societal issues, including coercion by the state.

COERCION IN PERSONAL LIFE

It is the individual's right in his or her personal life to define coercion from a strictly personal and subjective viewpoint (Breggin, 1980). A person has the right to say "I *feel* coerced" and then to take nonviolent protective actions, such as rejecting or avoiding another adult or a situation that merely *feels* or *seems* coercive. The right to make a subjective definition of coercion, and to remove oneself from the oppressor, is central to personal freedom. Yet many people become confused and believe that they must or should submit themselves to family, friends, and other people whose attitudes and actions feel oppressive.

The principle must be modified in regard to dependent children, as well as disabled adults, especially those with whom we have contracted to help. We cannot tie a fellow mountain climber to our rope and then decide to cut it. We cannot have a child and then abandon it. We cannot agree to care for physically helpless people and then walk out on them. But in dealing with most adults in personal relationships, it is critical to retain the right to remove ourselves from situations that feel oppressive or coercive, even if love or other considerations lead us not to exercise the right at any given moment.

The subjective definition of coercion does not guarantee that an individual's perceptions will be rational. People often react with irrational fear to current situations on the basis of past negative experiences (see chapter 5). Nonetheless, any attempt to limit the right to define coercion on a subjective basis will vastly encroach upon personal freedom. A person must have the right to say, "I'm not comfortable with Harold, and I'm going to avoid him."

However, if the use of actual force is being considered, coercion must be limited to self-defense. We cannot hit people because we don't like them, their ideas, or their looks.

FORCE IN SELF-DEFENSE

Force in self-defense can become excessive and hence coercive, and therefore constraints on self-defense have been embodied in Western law. If we have disarmed an assailant, we do not then have the right to shoot him in retaliation for the harm he has done. If a relatively small child or weak adult strikes us, we do not have the right to unnecessarily injure the perpetrator in the process of defending ourselves. These issues become important in family life where adults too often find flimsy excuses for battering children and where men frequently respond to a slap in the face from a woman with a jaw-breaking counterpunch.

Within our personal lives, we can and should apply the same principle of the least possible amount of force in self-defense to emotional interchanges.

A MINIMAL STANDARD

The prohibition against the use of force except in self-defense should be seen as a minimal standard for developing loving relationships and for resolving deep-seated conflict. Often we must go beyond this standard, enduring a certain amount of aggression out of love, out of the desire to avoid doing any harm even in self-defense (see chapter 2), and out of a conviction that patience and kindness may at times encourage much better long-term results than swift or knee-jerk self-defense.

When genuine efforts are being made to end long-standing conflicts, it may be necessary for all parties to the conflict to refrain from using force even in self-defense. When conflicts have a long history, everyone involved tends to see himself or herself as a victim of aggression who is merely reacting in self-defense. This is true of married couples (see chapter 6) and nations at war alike. Restraint, even in self-defense, becomes critical to the early stages of conflict resolution. Each side is likely to continue seeing provocation as part of the now endless chain of violence, and each side will have to make every effort not to retaliate.

Love, which abhors force and rejects injuring the other person, is the most potent antidote to the use of force in self-defense. But individuals and nations who sit down at the conflict-resolution table are not initially likely to feel or to admit much affection for each other. In the beginning, restraint on the use of force can best be encouraged through a rational cost analysis. Both parties need to understand that the cost of tit-for-tat, or more massive retaliation, is too great once they have committed themselves to conflict resolution. The momentary "gratification" of striking back must be replaced with a long-range perspective on the infinitely greater rewards that will come from ending the conflict. It is the task of the therapist or conflict resolver to communicate this vision of the future.

THE PRICE OF COERCION: THE IMPACT ON THE PERPETRATOR

From the start it is important to realize that coercion has many negative effects on the perpetrator as well as the victim.

Consistent with the proposition that coercion of most kinds has certain more or less inevitable and uniform consequences, the categories of *perpetrators* and *victims* will be addressed broadly, at times referring to physical assault and at others to more subtle intimidation and manipulation. The term perpetrator will be broadly used to include anyone who coerces another. The models include more extreme forms of coercion, including violent dictators, Nazis involved in extermination programs, "madmen" who commit heinous and seemingly unprovoked violence, rapists, and wife and child abusers. Other models are drawn from family life as seen in clinical practice, including the more or less commonplace verbal and emotional abuse seen in many families. Through my psychiatric reform and forensic activities, I also have extensive experience with psychiatrists and other physicians who injure and oppress their patients.

The idea that perpetrators themselves suffer from what they do to others is foreign to many people; but in understanding why coercion should be eschewed even by the powerful, it is important to grasp the price that coercion extracts from all parties involved. Besides, most perpetrators were victims to start with. Their destructive activities are spawned in part by their own experience at the hands of oppressors. This does not mean that all abused people become abusers. Most do not. It does mean that most severe abusers were themselves victims, usually as small children.

It is also true that perpetrators often seem to benefit emotionally from their actions. Murderers and rapists, for example, often report feeling empowered and even euphoric for a time after their assaults on others. On the other hand, many brutal crimes seem perpetrated in a kind of fugue state with little overt feeling attached. Regardless of whether or not there is something akin to pleasure involved in perpetrating, there are typical negative consequences for the perpetrator as well.

PERPETRATOR DENIAL AND RATIONALIZATION

Perpetrators do not necessarily recognize, accept, or even recall their harmful actions or their consequences. Frequently, for example, they fail to acknowledge that even the most brutal violence causes suffering among its victims. Men who rape women and husbands who beat their wives almost always deny the severity of the brutality involved, including the amount of force employed, as well as the amount of physical and emotional pain that it caused. On the political scale, we recently saw the American attack on Iraq as a rather bloodless war because the United States lost so few soldiers. To wholeheartedly cheer such an outcome required denial or disregard for the hundreds of thousands of civilian and military victims on the "other side," as well as among friendly populations, such as the Kurds (see chapter 10).

Women, children, ethnic and racial minorities, slaves, mental patients, the enemy in wartime, and the poor are often the objects of systematic persecution and abuse. Perpetrators of violence against these groups frequently declare that their victims are somehow relatively immune or unresponsive to the suffering inflicted upon them. Often perpetrators and their apologists will argue that coercion and abuse is good for these victims and even that they want it. Frequently, of course, it is said that they deserve it.

Denial and rationalization of the impact of coercion is routinized in establishment theory. Women labeled witches were once systematically tortured and burned at the stake and nowadays people labeled mental patients are subjected to electroshock, lobotomies, and toxic drugs—always for their own good. Learned books have been written to say it is for their own good.

As I describe in *Toxic Psychiatry* (1991), psychiatrists commonly argue that extremely toxic drugs, such as the neuroleptics (e.g., Haldol, Thorazine, Mellaril, Prolixin), don't cause physical or emotional suffering to "mentally ill" people because their brains are different. To embellish the argument, it is said that these unfortunates suffer from biochemical imbalances that the drugs correct, thereby in fact reducing their suffering. I have heard survivors of psychiatry protest in outrage when "drug experts" make these claims. Yet the rationalizations continue, despite patient protests and mountains of research to the contrary.

Similarly, psychiatrists explain that involuntary patients often say in retrospect that they are glad they were incarcerated, drugged, or shocked against their will. These psychiatrists remain oblivious to the fact that the patients have to tell them this in order to get released or to stave off further assaults against their minds and bodies (see p. 82). Nor do they take into account that the desire to be controlled against one's will can be a sign of a self-defeating, self-hating approach to life. In my own psychiatric practice, for example, when a patient seems to want me to take over his or her life, I encourage the patient to adopt a more autonomous, self-determined outlook.

Dictators are especially fond of explaining how their efforts are directed by God for the common good. Why abject terror is required to keep their supposedly blessed citizens in submission is never fully explained, except perhaps with references to outside agitators and enemy nations.

Denial and rationalization also takes place on a more personal level. The rapist explains that women like to be forced to submit to sex. The perpetrator of incest argues that it is good for his children. There is no end to these rationalizations, both institutionalized and personal.

Truth, then, is one of the costs of coercion to the perpetrator. The perpetrator loses contact with reality. The oppressed, for example, may shock him by unexpectedly rebelling or fighting back. If the perpetrator has any genuine interest in helping or relating to the individuals he is oppressing, there will be little chance of his knowing what to offer.

SELF-DECEPTION

It is common for perpetrators to deny to themselves the very existence of their crimes. In traditional psychoanalysis, the deed is said to have become "unconscious" or split off from awareness. But when men "forget" that they have hit their wives or when mothers cannot recall that they have humiliated their children, it seems more useful and enlightening to think of these perpetrators as *lying* to themselves much as they would lie to others.

In couples and family therapy, perpetrators frequently describe their actions without "remembering" that a blow was struck or a violent epithet hurled at the victim. If the event was recent, and if the victim is present, it is usually possible to get the individual to admit to recalling what actually happened. Then rationalization replaces denial: "Oh, it wasn't so bad, was it?" or "You provoked me." When weeks, months, or years have passed, the perpetrator frequently continues to deny any recollection of the events, even when reminded of them in detail by the victim or bystanders.

Furthermore, if the victim is not available to present his or her side, the perpetrator can easily fool himself and the therapist alike. This is perhaps the gravest disadvantage of individual psychotherapy—the ease with which perpetrators neglect and cover up their harmful actions.

Has the perpetrator's "forgotten" deed become truly unconscious—locked outside his or her awareness? What does "unconscious" mean in such a context? Again, I find the concept of lying to oneself and others more useful. It can become impossible to determine who the lie is aimed at, oneself or others, and often it makes little actual difference. Nor should a deed that has become "unconscious" be treated as ethically less reprehensible. Often it simply means that the person has started lying to himself or herself as well as to others.

In summary, perpetrators often develop elaborate forms of denial, including self-deception, in dealing with their destructiveness. This can be considered one of the costs of being a perpetrator. It often prevents the perpetrator from understanding the conflict surrounding his or her activities, making the perpetrator unable to respond to the situation in a rational or effective manner.

IMPACT ON PERSONAL RELATIONSHIPS

Among the most serious effects on the perpetrator are those generated in the relationship between the perpetrator and the victim. Violence tends to break the social bonds that attach people to one another. Detachment from the victim is often accomplished by dehumanization—placing the victim in a category of lesser being, one especially deserving of manipulation, punishment, injury, or even extermination. All people outside the dominant social group are at risk for being dehumanized, including racial, religious, and cultural minorities; women; children; enemies in wartime; and various "social deviants," such as mental patients and criminals. Frequently perpetrators assign them specific negative labels, including various racial, national, or cultural epithets. Whether an enemy in wartime or a wife in domestic conflict is being abused, the tendency to dehumanize is basically the same.

Why do perpetrators dehumanize their victims? They do so in part to control or obliterate their own tendency to empathize and to love. Few people, including very oppressive ones, are wholly devoid of empathy. Perpetrators often find it hard to accept that they are treating people unjustly or inflicting pain upon them, especially if the victims are seen as "just like us" or "just like our family and friends." So perpetrators make believe their victims are different. In my own field of psychiatry, diagnosis has served this purpose for centuries. The individual labeled schizophrenic is turned into a non-person. An endless variety of brain-damaging treatments become justified, sometimes including a lifetime of incarceration under the most horrendous circumstances.

Again in order to detach themselves from what they are doing to their victims, perpetrators often convince themselves that their victims want or need to be coerced, despite evidence to the contrary. At a recent professional debate in which I participated, a psychiatrist defended involuntary treatment by citing studies that found that some patients will state in retrospect that they are glad to have been forced into treatment. I pointed out that the patients in the study were interviewed by the same doctors who had incarcerated them against their will and that the patients continued to be exposed to repeated involuntary treatment at their hands. However, the psychiatrist refused to acknowledge that the continued threat of involuntary treatment might have influenced these patients to say what the doctor wanted to hear.

We would hope that psychiatrists would have special sensitivity to the impact of coercion on their victims, yet they regularly deny that incarcerating people, or drugging and shocking them against their will, has negative effects on them. When I worked in state mental hospitals as a college student, I was told by psychiatrists that "schizophrenics" were less sensitive to changes in temperature. Thus, it was rationalized, they did not suffer from the seasonal extremes of freezing cold and suffocating heat on the poorly heated, poorly ventilated wards.

The labeling can even become microscopic. Well-known psychiatrists once argued that shock treatment works by killing sick brain cells while somehow exempting the healthy ones (Breggin, 1979, 1991).

Blaming victims is another method used by perpetrators to salve their consciences, as well as to mislead others (Ryan, 1976). Women and children are routinely blamed for the physical, sexual, and verbal abuse heaped upon them. Somehow they have elicited or evoked the violent responses against themselves. The violent madman image has been used for centuries to justify the incarceration, torture, and even death of millions of helpless mental hospital inmates (Breggin, 1991). As a psychiatrist working in mental hospitals, most of the violence I witnessed was in reality initiated by the staff. In response to involuntary incarceration and treatment, inmates do sometimes become violent, thus leading the doctors to justify further coercion.

Despite these self-protective attempts to justify coercion, many perpetrators continue to feel badly about their actions, and therefore they try to dull their feelings of empathy. They must "disconnect" from their own feelings, particularly their feelings for others. The caring place within their hearts is cauterized. This psychospiritual lobotomy is probably the most frequent psychological cost of chronic perpetration.

Perpetrators thus dehumanize their victims and themselves. This alienation from self and others is marked by a suppression of their own social feelings and their ability to love. One of the most violent offenders I have interviewed expressed more remorse than usual about what he had done, but his most marked feeling was despair for himself that he could not feel close to people.

It is of course difficult to determine whether the alienation felt by so many perpetrators is the cause of their violence or the result of it. Clinical experience indicates that violence is frequently motivated by alienation, and that violent acts then reinforce the alienation. However, it seems that even emotionally responsive people, after committing violence, suffer from alienation. This can be seen in soldiers who find themselves committing unexpected acts of violence. One reason the Nazis developed relatively aseptic murder techniques in closed gas chambers was to avoid the emotional toll that more openly brutal mass killing had taken on the soldiers carrying them out.

Although we might wish it were otherwise, *overt* or *expressed* guilt is not a common response to injuring others. Guilt, at least expressed guilt, is ironically more common in victims then in perpetrators. Former Nazis, for example, almost never displayed guilt or shame when interviewed. The same is true of men who rape and batter women. But the *victims* of Nazi brutality and the victims of male brutality frequently feel guilt and shame. Why victims feel guilt and shame will be discussed in chapter 5.

Overwhelming shame and guilt does sometimes well up within perpetrators. Many mass murderers end up turning the gun on themselves. Many Nazis committed suicide, at least after being accused or captured. However, it is unclear how much these suicides were in reaction to recognizing the monstrousness of their crimes. Some of the suicides may have resulted from shame and fear over having to face the consequences of their actions, including the humiliation of public disapproval. They would rather die than go on trial or face a death penalty. Other Nazis who killed themselves may have been trying to thwart the authorities from using them to indict others or to discredit the Nazi party.

Psychotherapists frequently conclude that the alienation found commonly in perpetrators is actually a veneer that covers unbearable guilt and shame. While this is perhaps true, the perpetrator's guilt and shame is not usually felt toward his or her victims, but toward those who have victimized the perpetrator in earlier years. For example, a man who was sexually abused as a child may feel guilt and shame about it and yet inflict the same cruelties on another generation of children without remorse. To repeat, the victim, not the perpetrator, tends to feel guilt and shame.

Most perpetrators never express any negative feelings about harming others. As Lonnie Athens dramatically documented in *The Creation of Dangerous Violent Criminals* (1989), people who commit horrendous physical assaults against innocent victims almost always have themselves been extraordinarily abused and humiliated while growing up. They feel shame about what was done to them in the past, not about what they have done more recently to others. Instead, they consider their own acts of violence to be justified in defense of their own "pride." The hapless victims of their murderous rage "deserved it" due to some real or imagined slight or insult.

Consistent with their alienation and lack of remorse, perpetrators rarely seek psychotherapeutic help. When they come to therapy, it is usually under duress from the courts or under the threat of being rejected by their spouses. In therapy, they tend to be nonreflective and "out of touch" in regard to themselves. They have little awareness of their own feelings or motives. Sometimes they can be helped by reexperiencing the humiliations they have undergone, typically in childhood; but it is much harder to help them gain sympathy for those whom they have gone on to oppress. Instead they often blame their victims for provoking them and restimulating their previous feelings of humiliation.

While some perpetrators can get in touch with their prior experiences of personal humiliation, more typically they are too emotionally cut off from their own feelings. As a result, they are also cut off intellectually from these past experiences and tend not to understand or grasp their own personal histories of being oppressed by others. Male perpetrators of sexual violence, for example, were frequently abused as children either physically or sexually by older boys and men; but often they do not recall it. If the abuse was physical, they may remember some of it, but interpret it as normal and justifiable. They "deserved" to be hit or being hit was "the way it was" in their family. If the abuse was sexual, it becomes almost impossible to get them to talk about it.

Jerome Miller, director of the Center for Institutions and Alternatives, recounted to me the stories of two men who confessed to him that they had been raped by the men they had later murdered. However, they would not let Miller tell anyone they had been raped, even though the mitigating circumstance might have saved them from the electric chair. These men were so ashamed of having been raped, they literally chose to die rather than to let a judge or state governor know about it.

As an aside, relevant to the psychospiritual approach required of healers and conflict resolvers, I asked Miller how he could maintain such profound sympathy for the extremely violent criminals with whom he often works in his rehabilitation program and in his attempts to save murderers from execution. He replied, "It comes from understanding them." He further explained that once you understand what someone has been through, it is hard to hate them for what they themselves go on to do. He didn't mean to excuse perpetrators; he meant to say that they almost always begin as victims of other perpetrators. Miller's profoundly caring viewpoint is precisely what perpetrators themselves become unable to feel or to express.

Recognizing that he himself was abused would require the perpetrator to face his own abusive ways. Conversely, to recognize his own abusive ways would require grasping what others did to him, especially in childhood. The perpetrator becomes locked into a cycle where he cannot face how he has been abused or how he has abused others.

In *Escape from Freedom,* Erich Fromm described the "authoritarian personality" produced by suppressive, rigid, and often physically abusive family life in Germany. Instead of realizing what had been done to them, and rejecting similar violence against others, the victims too often went on to become perpetrators. Later, they filled the rolls of the Nazi party.

It is commonly thought that perpetrators excuse their actions on the basis of how they grew up. To the contrary, as I've noted, they tend to deny childhood abuse. Miller, who has worked with hundreds of murderers, rapists, wife abusers, and other perpetrators states that he has never seen a case in which a perpetrator used his own childhood to excuse his conduct. I am also unaware of any such cases in my clinical experience. Oppressive authorities from childhood are often excused while the person blames himself, or more frequently, blames the people he has victimized.

EFFECTS ON PERPETRATORS OF BREAKING SOCIAL BONDS

Perpetrators often grow afraid that others will retaliate, and partly as a result of this, perpetrators tend to escalate their violence. They do so as if to deny or to defy their fear, and they do so to intimidate and control the victims from whom they fear retaliation. Perhaps their own violence convinces them that it is indeed a dog-eat-dog world as they had been taught as children. Sometimes it appears as if there is a kind of demonic potential in people, perhaps the residue of our own past hurts and our evolutionary endowment, that once allowed to express itself violently tends to grow more bold. Perhaps it is a matter of breaking the social bonds. Once the "human connection" to others has been cut by violence, all restraints are removed. Whatever the cause, violence sometimes feeds on itself, and perpetrators often tend to grow more violent with repeated acts of coercion. At the same time, they will grow more out of touch with themselves and with others.

Grandiosity is a another consequence of perpetration. Once the bond of respect and love between humans is broken, once the line is crossed in restraint toward other people—perpetrators tend to grow more grandiose. Having taken a god-like stance toward others, they begin to live the part more fully, becoming more controlling, more dominating, more self-centered. It is as if the bonds between people, and the constraints inherent in them, are necessary for our maintenance of perspective on ourselves. If we separate ourselves from others by acting violently against them, we risk becoming focused on ourselves as the center of the universe. We imagine powers that we do not have and we lose track of our vulnerability. This can lead perpetrators to do seemingly self-destructive acts, such as repeating their crimes until they get caught or until they drive their victims into violent counteractions.

This cycle of increasingly compulsive and eventually self-defeating violence can be seen in men who batter their wives until their victims rebel and even kill their tormentors (Walker, 1989). It is found in rapists and other violent persons who repeat an obvious pattern of crime until they are caught. It can be seen when political leaders initiate wars they cannot possibly win. As a medical expert in malpractice suits, I have testified in cases involving psychiatrists and other physicians who have injured their patients with drugs, electroshock, and even lobotomies, and then repeat the "treatments" again and again despite obviously worsening damage. In one case, psychiatrists nearly killed a woman with a dangerous combination of drugs and then immediately resumed it even before she was fully recovered. In another, neurosurgeons lobotomized a patient on three separate occasions. In these cases, the physicians typically refer to themselves as using "heroic treatments."

In order to control their victims, perpetrators must learn to hide from them their real intentions and agendas. A battering husband, for example, will often disguise his intent, and make promises of complete reform. So will a dictator bent on controlling or exterminating another group. By hiding themselves from their victims, perpetrators further break the social bonds between themselves and their victims. In that process, the perpetrator also begins to fool himself. Humans are such social creatures that they often prefer to lie to themselves rather than to admit that they are lying regularly to others. The perpetrator thus becomes further alienated from himself in the process of denying his own ill-intentions and malevolent actions.

As Alfred Adler (Adler, 1969; Ansbacher and Ansbacher, 1956) observed decades ago, all people want to believe they are doing the right or good thing, and that impulse, again a social one, further leads perpetrators to fool themselves about what they are doing.

Perpetrators end up tangled in a web of lies that they themselves often come to believe. Out of feelings of insecurity and inferiority, people strive for power and superiority. The power-seeking individual also loses contact with himself and with reality. He or she develops subjective "fictions"—rigid, false beliefs aimed at bolstering a flagging sense of worth.

According to Adler, the individual who strives for superiority eventually becomes "self-bounded":

The self-bounded individual always forgets that his self would be safeguarded better and automatically the more he prepares himself for the welfare of mankind, and that in this respect no limits are set for him. (Ansbacher and Ansbacher, 1956, p. 112.)

Thus individuals devoted to coercing others actually abandon their true interests, their connectedness with the human community.

Karen Horney (1950) described the fundamental "neurotic" problem as the individual's attempt to fulfill his or her idealized or glorified self-image. When this happens, according to Horney, "The energies driving toward self-realization are shifted to the aim of actualizing the idealized self," (p. 24). Instead of fulfilling the basic needs for love, creativity, and genuine human relationships, the individual pursues "the search for glory" and his or her "will to power" takes on "magical proportions." Power and control over others become the ultimate aim, with increasing alienation from self and from others.

Ultimately, perpetrators cannot genuinely love. Nor are they in turn truly loved. They cannot empathize with the individuals they seek to injure and control; and those whom they victimize must withdraw from them in self-defense. Writing in the year 1552 or 1553, Etienne de la Boetie declared:

The fact is that the tyrant is never truly loved, nor does he love. Friendship is a sacred word, a holy thing; it is never developed except between persons of character, and never takes root except through mutual respect. . . (p. 83.)

THE PERPETRATOR SYNDROME

We can now summarize the perpetrator syndrome: the constellation of attributes found in most people who persistently coerce others. Perpetrators tend to:

1. *Deny or minimize the damage they are doing to others,* for example, by failing to recognize their own coercive actions, by under-estimating the sensitivity of those they are abusing, and by imagining that the victims like what is being done to them.

2. *Rationalize the harm they are doing,* for example, by alleging that the perpetrations are ultimately in the best interest of victims, better than other alternatives, a necessary last resort, or otherwise inevitable and unavoidable.

3. *Blame the victim.* This is a derivative of denial and rationalization, but is worth mentioning in its own right. Typically, perpetrators accuse the victim of being the malicious or dangerous one, or the provocateur. By blaming others, they reject responsibility for their own actions.

4. *Suppress their own feelings of empathy,* thereby blunting their emotional responsiveness to their victims. Often they blunt their empathic responsiveness toward themselves and all other people as well, and become unable to love. They become withdrawn from themselves and others.

5. *Deny or rationalize their own prior victimization at the hands of others,* including the abuse they were subjected to as children and adults. They do not tend to excuse their perpetrations on the grounds that they themselves have been previously victimized.

6. *Persistently react with anger and blame toward others based on much earlier feelings of shame and humiliation.* Sometimes the anger is very covert and indirect in its expression. Often the feelings of shame are denied. While guilt and anxiety can also drive people to abuse others, shame seems by far the most common emotional basis for perpetration, especially in its most severe forms. Rapists and murders, for

example, are almost always driven by childhood shame. Shame will be discussed in greater depth in chapter 5.

7. *Dehumanize their victims.* The victim is defined as inferior due to his or her status or condition as a man, woman, child, criminal, mental patient, foreigner, racial minority, etc. Perpetrators try to overcome their own feelings of inferiority and to elevate themselves to a superior status by dominating others.

8. *Feel empowered through their perpetrations.* They do not feel guilt or shame about the harm that they do to others. When they do feel guilt or shame, it is in response to their own earlier victimization by others. Their perpetrations are motivated by their earlier victimization.

9. *Seek to resolve conflicts through authority, power, and domination,* sometimes directly through physical violence, sometimes indirectly through socially sanctioned authority. When they feel threatened with possible exposure or censure, they often tend to escalate their perpetrations, and may not be stopped unless confronted with overwhelming power.

10. *Become grandiose and self-centered.* They imagine that they have the power and the right to obtain their ends through force, and feel a certain degree of invulnerability, at least when they are in the act of perpetration. This can lead to the self-destructive escalation of their perpetrations to the point that they are confronted or exposed.

11. *Become alienated from their genuine basic needs,* especially those related to love.

The perpetrator syndrome is found in almost every sphere of life. It includes men and women who abuse their spouses and children, rapists and murders, bullies on the playground or in the workplace, conmen and others who prey upon the vulnerabilities of other people, most biological psychiatrists, police who resort to brutality, political tyrants, and anyone who seeks to dominate and manipulate others.

The syndrome is not always present in all its aspects, but very often it is. It can be difficult to determine which traits are derived from earlier victimization and which are the result of the actual perpetrations. The shame and humiliation tend to originate from the earlier victimization (see chapter 5) and the alienation probably results from both victimization and perpetration.

THE COST OF COERCION: THE IMPACT ON THE VICTIM

One might wish that perpetration would cause the perpetrator to feel guilt, shame, and anxiety, but more typically their victims do. While it seems easily understandable that victims might experience anxiety, and perhaps even shame, it seems at first glance more puzzling that they also experience guilt. The key, I believe, is the psychological helplessness that is engendered in the victim, making him or her vulnerable to guilt, shame, or anxiety. For example, after a young boy is beaten up in a fight, he may feel guilt for getting into a fight, shame over not performing better, or anxiety over what may happen to him in the future—all depending on his circumstances and his learned style of responding.

It is extremely important to understand the development of negative emotions as a result of victimization. It is impossible to analyze conflict without such an understanding (see chapter 5).

VICTIM DISHONESTY

While perpetrators lie to others and sometimes to themselves in order to cover up their abuses, victims learn to lie and to dissemble in order to avoid or minimize further oppression. When a victim habitually lies about his thoughts, feelings, and actions, it can become a serious impediment to conflict resolution.

Often parents ask me what to do about their child's lying to them. Their attitude generally suggests that something more should be done directly to the child. Instead, I explain that children lie out of fear and distrust. Typically, they feel unfairly coerced. Therefore, the parents need to change in order to create an environment that is relatively free of fear and distrust.

In dismay, the parents may ask me, "But what would you do if your child lied to you?" And I tell them that I would try not to punish my already intimidated child. Instead, I'd try to understand why my son or daughter was in such fear of me.

Children lie because they don't believe that telling the truth will gain them a fair hearing or a fair punishment, let alone a sympathetic, caring ear. Often lying has become a useful and even necessary defense against arbitrary authority and coercion. It can be more effective than lapsing into psychological helplessness (see chapter 5). The abused adult or child may have no other protection against arbitrary authority, capricious punishment, and hateful or insensitive authorities. As helplessness deepens in response to chronic abuse, the individual may even give up lying, throwing himself or herself on the mercy of the oppressor.

Children and other oppressed people also lie in order to manipulate the situation as much as they can. Doubting that the authority in power is genuinely interested in supporting their most basic needs for self-determination, self-esteem, or love—they seek ways around the authority through flattery, fakery, or the like. Meanwhile, they avoid at all costs becoming still more vulnerable and dependent by admitting or displaying their basic needs. "I don't need nothin' from you" is the typical response of the victim, as long as some shred of dignity remains.

No one wants to be coerced. As we have seen, humans and non-human alike value their liberty. In human beings, this need becomes quite elaborate. It includes the desire to think for oneself, to make choices, to exercise reason, to seek justice. As already described, the need for liberty dovetails with the need to love and to be loved. When the individual feels subject to abuse or arbitrary control, he or she tends to hide these needs in order to seem less vulnerable.

The tendency of victims to hide their basic needs is one of the great costs of oppression. A battered child or an abused woman, for example, may be the last to express his or her needs for self-respect and love. In self-defense and in defense against the pain of oppression, these needs have been buried. Often the victim no longer believes that he or she deserves to have a better life. Even when the oppressor lets up, or is gone, the compulsion to hide one's needs and feelings of unworthiness or worthlessness may persist. Thus the people most in need of great doses of self-respect and love are often the least likely to show their needs or to reach out for their fulfillment.

When the victim hides his or her needs, this can also create a cost to the oppressor. Thus abusive parents drive their children into hiding and cheat themselves of the capacity to connect to them in a loving way.

IS COERCION A BASIC NEED?

Conflict analysis and resolution theory often equates basic needs with "good" or pro-survival needs. Tendencies toward violence, greed, or envy are thus not seen as "basic needs" but as perversions or distortions, usually in reaction to frustration and helplessness.

It seems possible that built-in violent tendencies served evolutionary purposes, and became basic needs; but they now have no place in larger, more complex societies in which huge numbers of people must get along in close proximity. For example, fear and violence toward strangers could have had survival value when humans lived in smaller, more widely dispersed groups. The group that best protected itself and its territory may have most readily reproduced. It has been speculated that human beings killed off all their near-human hominid competitors. In particular, homo sapiens and Neanderthal man crossed historical paths, but only homo sapiens kept going. If we did murder our nearest of kin 100,000 years ago, it is consistent with our modern behavior as well.

Murdering strangers or upright creatures who look a little different from us did not threaten our own survival when fists, rocks, or spears were our only weapons. But violent impulses toward others is obviously self-defeating in the age of atomic weapons.

I am not wholly wedded to the biological basis of human violence. But unfortunately, it seems highly probable that human nature has not evolved in perfect harmony with the needs of a modern global community. There is every indication that it has not. This reality must be taken as a challenge rather than a cause for despair.

It is also possible that the demands of culture itself, or the inherent problems in raising human beings, inevitably create aggressive or even violent tendencies in some individuals. I see no way to come to final conclusions on these matters.

There are, of course, many dangers in the sociobiological view, as represented by E. O. Wilson (1978), that human beings are genetically aggressive. I am cautious as I suggest that the evidence favors a built-in tendency toward coercion and even violence. The socio-biological view can lead to glossing over the environmental stresses that clinical (Miller, 1984) and sociological studies (Gelles and Straus, 1988) often find at the root of extremely violent behavior. Most perpetrators were themselves victims, often in their child-hood. Genetic theories of violence can lead to an overemphasis on police control at the expense of ameliorating underlying causes in society. Often they are used to justify racism and xenophobia. Genetic explanations also encourage denial of the patriarchal influ-ences that cause male-dominated society to place a positive value on power, control, and aggression (French, 1985; Eisler, 1987). Within modern psychiatry, genetic and biochemical theories of violence are used to justify the diagnosing and drugging of so-called hyperactive children (Breggin, 1991). As a result, the underlying environmental causes of upset in these children, including child abuse, usually go unattended. Even obvious toxic causes, such as lead poisoning, may not be investigated. Overall, scientific arguments for genetic and constitutional causes of violence are weak (Fausto-Sterling, 1985).

Most important, *individual variations in violent behavior have no known relationship to genetic or constitutional factors* (Fasto-Sterling, 1985). There is no evidence that chromosomal aberrations, race, or other factors increase violence. The problem is not that some hu-mans are genetically more violent than others; it is that all humans have these tendencies.

Destructive behavior is sufficiently widespread and culturally universal that it seems an aspect of human nature. The desire to use excessive or unwarranted force is something most or all people seem to struggle with, and too often it is expressed in arbitrary and damaging ways. Gandhi, for example, referred to the constant struggle within himself to tame these reactions (Bondurant, 1988). Jane Goodall (1986) was disillusioned to discover that chimpanzees can become murderously violent, and she has publicly warned that human beings must also recognize and surmount this same ten-dency within themselves.

The evidence suggests that while human beings are a violent species, the manner and degree to which that violence gets ex-pressed is determined in large part by environmental experience within the family and the culture, as well as by individual self-determination (see chapter 5). A great deal of male violence, for example, is directly attributable to culture values, including patriarchy with its emphasis on domination and control (French, 1985; Eisler, 1987; Yllo and Bograd, 1988). Group support for male violence, as in wartime, mobs, and gangs, also seems to bring out the worst in men.

From my research and from my personal and clinical experience, I have come to the following conclusions: (1) All people struggle with violence within themselves, although sometimes they seem unaware of the meaning or implications of their hostile thoughts, feelings, and actions; (2) The intensity and direction of the feelings are greatly influenced by victimization in childhood and adulthood; (3) Patriarchal values of power and control encourage men to indulge in physical violence, as well as emotional abuse, often directed most viciously toward women and children; (4) Humiliation in the family and culture pushes many women to feel persistent bitterness and anger that typically becomes expressed verbally rather than physically; (5) While nearly all severe perpetrators of violence have been victims of physical abuse and/or humiliation earlier in their lives, most victimized children do not grow up to become perpetrators; (6) The human spirit can, and frequently does, overcome early environmental and later cultural pressures in order to live a more principled life.

In conclusion, coercion always has a cost for the victim. Most obviously, it creates psychological helplessness, including guilt, shame, and anxiety in the victim (see chapter 5). It encourages victims to lie and to dissemble. It also exacts a price from the perpetrator in terms of the perpetrator syndrome with unrealistic self-appraisals and an alienation from oneself and others.

Coercion, in all its many manifestations, has little or no place in conflict resolution. At best it is a stopgap measure that temporarily suppresses conflict, ultimately increasing its ferocity. Even when coercion seems a necessity, it interferes with liberty and with love, and ultimately with the resolution of conflict.

From the psychological to the interpersonal and the global, the resort to coercion remains one of the greatest obstacles to conflict resolution. Those who seek to help others resolve conflict must stand forthrightly for the values of liberty and love. Instead of pretending or attempting to take a value-free stance, they should openly seek to educate people on the hazards and costs of coercion and on the merits and benefits of liberty and love.

Part II
▼ ▼

Applying the Three Dynamics to Conflict Resolution

CHAPTER 5

▼ ▼

Resolving Psychological Conflict: Overcoming Childhood Helplessness and Vulnerability

It is easy to substitute our will for that of the child by means of suggestion or coercion; but when we have done this we have robbed him of his greatest right, the right to construct his own personality.
Maria Montessori, in E. M. Standing, Maria Montessori (1957)

Every defect of character is due to some wrong treatment sustained by the child during his early years.
Maria Montessori, The Absorbent Mind (1969)

[C]hildhood is the key to understanding a person's entire later life. By becoming sensitive to childhood suffering, I gained emotional insight into the predicament of the totally dependent child, who must repress his trauma if there is no sympathetic and supportive person he can talk to. . . . The child in his or her helplessness awakens a feeling of power in insecure adults and, in addition, in many cases becomes their preferred sexual object.
Alice Miller, Thou Shalt Not Be Aware (1984)

When people are enduring stress and conflict, there comes a crucial moment when they either take control of their thoughts or lapse into helplessness. At these critical times, the central question of the individual's mental life becomes, "Will I become helpless or instead take charge of myself?"

The decision can take place out of habit and without thinking, but frequently there is an instant when the individual begins to feel overwhelmed and then consciously decides, "I give up." Often a corresponding moment can be identified when the person instead determines to "keep my head" or to "stay calm" while deciding how best to proceed. Optimally, the individual may even remain loving when confronted with hostility and rejection.

Once helplessness takes over under stress, all is lost. The person becomes a victim of overwhelming emotional reactions, other people, and circumstance. Even if circumstances turn out favorably, the victim of psychological helplessness will continue to suffer from painful feelings, and will eventually fail.

In my clinical practice, I find that psychological helplessness must be overcome before any progress can be made. When people feel helpless, learning about painful childhood experiences does more harm than good. Recalling the trauma justifies continued feelings of helplessness. If they experience good luck, such as being handed a better job or inheriting money, they will greet it with fear and dismay, and ultimately ruin the opportunity.

Nothing matters more in life than our attitude toward it. If we approach life with feelings of helplessness and doom, we'll find our prophecies coming true. If we approach life with an attitude of self-determination and hope, we will make the best of whatever situation comes along, and often we will triumph.

I use the term "overwhelm" to designate the experience of lapsing into helplessness. Overwhelm can take many forms, from the emotions of guilt, shame, anxiety, numbing, and chronic anger to the larger experiences of anxiety, depression, and even madness (Breggin, 1991).

CHILDHOOD FEELINGS OF HELPLESSNESS AND VULNERABILITY

Children begin to feel helplessness when their lives are taken out of their control or when they are abused, neglected, and abandoned. When small children are left by their parents, even for relatively brief periods, they at first protest with anger and resentment. Then they go through despair and ultimately detachment (Bowlby, 1973). They can grow up believing that detachment equals liberty, when in reality it is a form of helpless withdrawal. If we include this kind of unintentional abandonment as a form of coercion or oppression, then most helplessness can be seen as resulting from coercion and oppression.

Adults who have been conditioned to be helpless in childhood will more readily lapse into it under pressure. But all adults must struggle against helplessness when stresses or conflicts become severe enough.

The negative psychological effects of being victimized by coercion will receive the most attention in this chapter. This is relatively easy to do because coercion tends to reduce options or to limit choices. Coercion tends to breed helplessness and thus to stifle human potential. Therefore, the impact of coercion is somewhat routinized and repetitive from person to person. By contrast, liberty and love inspire individual uniqueness.

Because the individual's mental processes develop in response to interpersonal relations, an analysis of them must deal extensively with childhood. However, childhood experiences reflect values implemented by the family and other social institutions, such as religion and the state. Therefore, it is important to be aware of the family as a social institution and childhood as, to some extent, an indoctrination into society's values.

CHILDHOOD EXPERIENCES AND CONFLICT RESOLUTION IN ADULTHOOD

Coercion, liberty, and love each have their psychological or mental parallels or representations. People take attitudes toward themselves much as they do toward other people. They coerce and hate themselves, have esteem and grant liberty to themselves, and love or treasure themselves.

How people relate to themselves vastly affects how they treat others as well. It is difficult, if not impossible, to hate oneself and to love others. It is equally difficult to love others and to hate oneself.

Whenever people enter conflict situations, childhood experiences of helplessness become restimulated. To understand conflict resolution among adults, we must see how their childhood experiences rear up under stress.

CHILDREN AND COERCION

Childhood often smacks of coercion. It is an involuntary relationship. No one, as far as we know, chooses to be born or hand picks his or her parents. Despite the best-intentioned parents, children will at times feel like prisoners, if not of their parents, then of childhood itself.

The power imbalance between parents and children—in size, authority, experience, economic resources, etc.—is so great in the early years that children are bound at times to feel intimidated and overwhelmed. Since parenting inevitably requires a certain amount of enforced control, even in an ideal family, all children will be acutely aware that they are at times being coerced. It is virtually impossible to get through childhood without a legacy of feeling helpless.

Even within the most harmonious families, children will *typically* feel that they cannot entirely trust their parents. Under the best of circumstances, people will often disagree on issues important to their lives. Conflict is commonplace between husbands and wives, for example, on issues of money, sex, communication, domestic chores, and childrearing. It is also frequent between bosses and employees. But the likelihood of substantial disagreement is increased when one party to the conflict is a child and the other is an adult. Their viewpoints, for innumerable reasons, including maturity and generational differences, are likely to differ. Yet the parents have the resources with which to win any conflict. The result is that almost any child will monitor what he or she tells to a parent. Conflict is not "resolved" but submerged, sometimes to break out at a later date. Often it merely adds to the unspoken gulf between parent and child.

In many if not most families, the situation is much worse. Many children grow up under extremely unfavorable circumstances. Children are frequently hit by their parents, and often sexually abused, neglected, or abandoned (see chapter 4). They also suffer dreadfully from watching their parents abusing each other (Jaffe, Wolfe and Wilson, 1990; Yllo and Bograd, 1988). Most children feel, to one degree or another, threatened and unloved. Often they witness severe conflict and even violence directed at other members of their family by one or both parents. While children are no longer legally considered to be property, often they are treated by adults as if they were.

The emotional, physical, and sexual abuse of children, and its aftermath, has now been documented from many directions. Sources include early psychoanalytic studies of children (e.g.,

Bowlby, 1973; see also chapter 2); decades of clinical literature (e.g., Miller, 1984; reviewed in chapter 4); and a recently burgeoning research literature (Wyatt and Powell, 1988; Wolfe, 1987; Green, 1989; Athens, 1989; Jaffe, Wolfe, and Wilson, 1990; Gelles and Straus, 1988; see also chapter 4). What once was commonsense observation and clinical hypothesis—that childhood abandonment and abuse scars the individual, sometimes for life—is now a demonstrable fact.

Not only families, but schools and religious institutions often neglect and abuse children. The schools in particular have recently come under increasing criticism (Carnegie Council on Adolescent Development, 1989). Children often feel like unwilling inmates of their homes, schools, and churches.

Nowadays children are also exposed to an enormous amount of violence outside the home. In many inner cities, the violent death of young people has become commonplace. Gunshots can frequently be heard down the block. Everywhere children are watching violence on TV news and especially in TV features and movies. Beyond violence, there is a variety of other expressions of coercion routinely accepted in the "real life" dramas presented on TV and in the movies.

The amount of coercion experienced or witnessed by children has many negative consequences. In their intimate lives, they often internalize the problem, turning aggression on themselves, or they attack others who have not offended them. As they grow up in society, they come to accept coercion as an inevitable part of life. Oppressive governments, for example, often pale in their violence against adult citizens compared to what children experience within their families. The child then brings to adulthood the viewpoint that conflicts large and small can and should be handled by coercion. Rarely does the child grow into adulthood believing that voluntary agreements can be trusted and that love can ameliorate extreme or hard-to-resolve conflict.

THE BASIC STRESS PARADIGM: HURT, FEAR, AND HELPLESSNESS

When people undergo prolonged or severe emotional pain, they develop what I call the Basic Stress Paradigm. Three words summarize the essence of this negative experience: *hurt, fear,* and *helplessness.* This analysis parallels Bowlby's description of the child's response to abandonment: protest (against the hurt), despair (extreme fear), and detachment (helpless withdrawal).

The Basic Stress Paradigm can be summarized:

1. *Hurt:* Any negative experience and the painful emotions associated with it.

2. *Fear:* The *inevitable* response to severe or prolonged feelings of hurt.

3. *Helplessness:* In children, the *inevitable* outcome of severe or prolonged fear.

By hurt, I mean any feelings of discomfort, from physical pain through all the variations of emotional distress. The word *pain* will at times be used instead of hurt; but hurt has the value of suggesting both the painful cause of the discomfort and the subjective response of feeling injured. The response to intense hurt is fear; and the response to severe or chronic fear is helplessness, including feelings of overwhelm, incompetence, inability to think straight or to cope, and withdrawal. Fundamentally, the individual "gives up trying" and accepts the role of victim.

The Basic Stress Paradigm can be linked to basic-needs theory. Individuals feel hurt or injured when their basic needs are thwarted. These include *all* the basic needs, such as the needs to be loved, to be self-determining, to have security, and so on.

THE NEED TO AVOID PHYSICAL PAIN AND DEATH

Survival needs are often mentioned in conflict resolution analyses, but typically they are given little attention. The specific need to avoid physical pain is not usually addressed at all. Nonetheless, the need is among the most urgent. It provides the basis for the commonplace use of corporal punishment to control children, as well as for the male abuse of women. It is also the basis for torture in the political arena.

The need to avoid pain is closely associated with another basic need that is rarely examined in the field of conflict resolution—the need to avoid death. It too is sometimes subsumed under survival needs, but the specific threat of death plays an important role in human psychological, interpersonal, and political life.

Unlike some other basic human needs, the need to avoid pain and to avoid death are obviously shared with most if not all forms of animal life. The two needs are so primary that they find expression in all three dynamics. For example, they motivate the Dynamic II right to self-defense. They also motivate Dynamic I values. The fear of death has long been recognized as a major contributor to the search for spiritual values, such as the importance of lasting and loving relationships and the belief in God and an afterlife. But in Dynamic III: coercion, the needs to avoid pain and death play the most obvious role. In every aspect of life, coercion gains its strength by threatening individuals with pain and death. Even in their domestic lives, women and children, and more rarely men, learn to conform their behavior before these two grave threats.

THE BASIC STRESS PARADIGM AND LEARNED HELPLESSNESS

Helplessness is the debilitating end product of a Basic Stress Paradigm. In the *Psychology of Freedom*, I spoke of psychological or emotional helplessness. Martin Seligman's term, learned helplessness, is more familiar and probably better. In his latest book, *Learned Optimism* (1991), Seligman describes learned helplessness as "the giving-up reaction, the quitting response that follows from the belief that whatever you do doesn't matter," (p. 15). The following analysis, while using his term, is based on my own observations.

Learned helplessness is the opposite of autonomy and self-determination. Helplessness is usually learned after severe, chronic coercion. That is, the Basic Stress Paradigm is frequently the result of coercion.

The key to defining learned or psychological helplessness is the limitation it imposes on the individual's use of his or her full faculties. Learned helplessness is self-defeating in any situation other than that of propitiating hostile authorities. Sometimes an individual can learn to feign helplessness when faced with hostile authorities. The person remains self-determined and autonomous, but fakes a helpless role. That is not what is meant by learned helplessness, which is a role that the individual actually accepts for himself or herself.

Learned helplessness is a mental state or emotional reaction, rather than a realistic response. An individual may in reality be more or less *physically* helpless if partially paralyzed, tied up with ropes, or imprisoned in a small room. But the most physically helpless person, if conscious, need not be overcome with psychological helplessness. He or she can still do everything possible to remain self-determining—to control his or her own mind or spiritual state. This individual realizes his or her realistic limitations, but refuses to adopt an attitude of helplessness.

People who suffer from developmental retardation often act helplessly, mostly because they have been so frequently humiliated and victimized. But even these impaired persons will not display learned helplessness if they have been encouraged to use their existing capacities to the fullest. Psychological helplessness is an attitude about ourselves rather than a reality.

In my experience, learned helplessness is frequently a more active process than simply quitting. The individual, having been rewarded for helplessness, displays it in the hope of pleasing authorities, gaining their sympathy, or avoiding their antipathy. Young women, for example, are taught by the culture that helplessness in regard to physical danger is appealing to men. Young men, perhaps to justify future demands upon their wives and to emulate their fathers, become helpless about household chores, such as cooking or doing the laundry. Too often parents find helplessness in their children endearing. Or parents find it easier to deal with their children when they lack self-determination or spunk. People who want to substitute their own will for the will of others will encourage learned helplessness in their victims.

ORIGINS OF LEARNED HELPLESSNESS

Small children easily respond with helplessness when faced with what seems to them to be overwhelmingly difficult challenges. Most parents and teachers know the importance of helping children not to give up in frustration or panic when faced with learning something new. When children are not given this support by their parents or other authorities—or worse, if their parents or authorities actively undermine them—children easily adopt an attitude of helplessness toward specific challenges or toward life in general.

Helplessness can be learned as an adult and also as a child. The strongest people can lapse into helplessness immediately after a severe physical or emotional trauma. An otherwise self-empowered individual abruptly becomes frightened, irrational, confused, overwhelmed, unable to make decisions, and simply unable to cope. I have worked with male rape victims who have been diagnosed "schizophrenic" as a result of one assault. The growing literature on post-traumatic stress disorder shows that a single trauma, such as rape, or more prolonged stress, such as chronic wife abuse or warfare, can leave a legacy of lingering helplessness, sometimes to a seriously debilitating degree. In general, the reaction is most severe where another human being, rather than nature or chance, is a perpetrator. Being intentionally victimized by another person disrupts our Dynamic I connectedness to other people.

Authoritarian religions, cults, schools, and other institutions also encourage helplessness in order to enforce their control. In a total institution (Goffman, 1961), such as a prison or a mental hospital, or in the home of a severe wife and child abuser (Walker, 1989), victims learn to be helpless in order to avoid further abuse and even death. In Nazi concentration camps, almost everyone learned to be helpless, including captured military officers and political leaders.

It is difficult to "act" helpless without ultimately becoming helpless. Individuals who develop a particular role in order to placate their oppressors will tend to adopt the role as their viewpoint.

The role or identity of helplessness will often be strongly defended by individuals. They will argue that their helplessness is inevitable. For example, they will insist that they cannot learn to think straight under pressure, and will resist attempts to help them learn to do so. This resistance indicates that they feel that being helpless has some (usually unidentified) advantage, such as staying out of trouble or gaining sympathy. Or they may feel that their condition or the situation is so utterly hopeless that it is not worth risking further defeats and failures. Simply ignoring their problems and conflicts may seem the best alternative when all hope is gone.

GUILT, SHAME, ·ANXIETY, AND NUMBING

Guilt, shame, and anxiety, as well as emotional numbing and compulsive anger, can be understood as derivatives of learned helplessness (Breggin, 1980). They can usually be traced back to Basic Stress Paradigms in childhood, or to overwhelming adult experiences, such as rape, torture, and solitary confinement.

The human mind is complex and tends to seek explanations or reasons for the hurt, fear, and helplessness that it experiences. The Basic Stress Paradigm tends to become integrated into a broader understanding of life. Guilt, shame, and anxiety are, to some extent, attempts by the victim to label, explain, or channel his or her hurt, fear, and helplessness.

The literature on guilt, shame, and anxiety is too enormous to review here (e.g., Kaufman, 1989, and Morrison, 1989, on shame; Freud, 1936, Sullivan, 1953, May, Angel, and Ellenberger, 1958, and McCullough and Mann, 1985, on anxiety). Instead I will summarize my own understanding of these three emotional reactions (also see Breggin 1980, 1991).

Whenever we trace the roots of these emotions into childhood, we shall find a Basic Stress Paradigm. Occasionally the hurt will be a circumscribed event or series of closely related events, such as a death in the family or identifiable episodes of abuse; but more frequently there would be a pattern of estrangement, abandonment, neglect, or oppressive interactions, sometimes lasting an entire childhood, involving one or more family members and other significant children or adults.

NUMBING AND ALIENATION FROM SELF

When emotions become unendurable, they will sometimes be blocked, wholly or in part, from consciousness. The individual can become emotionally numbed. Often, but not always, guilt, shame, and anxiety will be found not far beneath the surface. Even deeper down, of course, is the original hurt, fear, and helplessness. As already discussed in chapter 4, perpetrators of severe abuse tend to experience a numbing or an alienation from their own feelings.

THE ESSENTIAL CHARACTERISTICS OF GUILT, SHAME, AND ANXIETY

There are a number of different ways to distinguish among guilt, shame, and anxiety. The following is a sketchy psychological shorthand intended for practical use, rather than as thoroughgoing analysis.

1. *Blame:* The direction of blame helps identify the emotion being felt.

   In guilt, blame tends to be directed inward. The individual sees himself or herself as the source of the problem. The essence of guilt is "I am bad, evil, harmful. I do this to myself. I deserve what I get." Instead of feeling accused by others, the individual feels deserving of blame.

   In shame, blame is almost always directed outward. Other people are humiliating, controlling, or rejecting the victim. The essence of shame is "People make me feel like I am worthless, a defective, a nobody, an outsider." Where no specific outside source is named, the individual feels inferior in comparison to other people or by societal standards. Shame almost always encourages a person to hide or withdraw from others, unless the individual overcompensates with a defiant public display.

   In anxiety, blame is assigned nowhere. The individual experiences something closer to the original basic stress triad—hurt, fear, and helplessness—but without identifying any source. Anxiety is experienced as a kind of emotional know-nothingness. The essence of anxiety is "I don't know what is happening to me; I'm unable to cope; I can't make decisions; I'm overwhelmed and helpless."

   In summary, guilt directs blame inward, shame directs blame outward, and anxiety directs it nowhere.

2. *Anger:* Anger follows blame.

   In guilt, anger is directed inward, and suicide is its most extreme result.

In shame, it is directed outward, and causing harm to others is its most extreme expression. Because one feels humiliated and impotent in relation to others, one tries to triumph over others. Most people who commit murder do so in the midst of a shame or humiliation reaction: "You can't do this to me. I'll show you." As described in chapter 4, shame tends to fuel the perpetrator syndrome.

Anxiety leaves the individual unable to direct anger toward anyone or anything. The person feels hopelessly confused and frustrated by the onset of emotion which seems to come not from a source but from "out of the blue."

3. *Potency:* The sense of power or powerlessness differs in each emotion.

People who feel guilty often believe that they do have an impact on others, albeit a negative one. Typically they have been taught by their parents, "You have made me miserable," or by their religion, "You are evil."

People who feel shame tend to see themselves as impotent, as if they cannot affect others; and in outrage over this, they will do extreme things to others. They have been taught by their families, "You don't count, you are ridiculous, you don't fit in."

People who become overcome with anxiety tend to feel something close to impotent, but it has a different coloration. It feels more like incompetence or helplessness. They have been taught, "You can't do it; you can't handle it; you might as well give up."

THE FUNCTIONS OF ANGER

Anger, as already noted, can be generated as reaction to guilt or shame, and ultimately, as a reaction to any injury. In chapter 4, I discussed the probability that there is a built-in tendency toward violence in human beings; but whatever the ultimate roots of anger and violence in human life, it is clear that pain and hurt, and especially humiliation, usually acts as the trigger for violence against others.

Most psychotherapists will confirm that persistent or seemingly unprovoked rage is usually traceable to chronic victimization in childhood. The defensive reaction becomes fixed in place, especially if the individual identifies with his or her anger, feeling that "It's all I've got." To stop being angry seems tantamount to "giving in" and to becoming vulnerable to further injury. Often pride leads the angry person to declare, "I'm not hurt at all, I'm outraged." Being angry rather than being hurt becomes a matter of pride.

Because it usually occurs as a defensive response to emotional pain, anger should be viewed as a superficial emotion. The "deeper" emotion is the original hurt. When the person then decides to stop expressing anger, he or she becomes more able to feel and to deal with the underlying painful emotions and frustrated basic needs for liberty and love.

In resolving conflict, people need to accept that their anger is driven by feelings of injury. When two embattled individuals acknowledge to each other that they feel hurt, they can feel both more potent and more vulnerable at the same time, and both feelings facilitate the resolution of conflict.

People feel more potent when they learn that they do have the power to inflict pain on each other. Often this comes as a shock to both parties because each has been feeling unable to impact on the other. "You mean, I'm really getting through?" is a typical response. Nothing fuels violence more than feelings of frustration and impotence; and so when people feel more able to affect the other person, they usually feel less driven to attack.

When people learn they are hurting each other, they also become vulnerable to each other. This allows a husband and wife, a parent and child, or even political antagonists, to work on the underlying pain, hurt, and frustrated needs. It can come as a relief to have it out in the open: "Yeah, all this fighting hurts me." It allows people to begin to address their overall pain in the relationship.

Venting anger is of little help in relieving it. If anything, the chronic expression of anger tends to become a compulsive pattern. Having demeaned and injured other people, we want to rationalize what we have done. We fan the fire of our own anger as a means of justifying our past offenses. This leads to a cycle of violence. To achieve self-insight and to resolve conflict, it is usually necessary to inhibit anger and to feel the underlying pain.

Does anger serve any useful function? It can be important in self-defense to discourage an aggressor who won't respond to reason or to appeals for more peaceful conflict resolution. It can signal to ourselves and others that we are hurt and need to be treated more gently. People who are *unable* to feel their anger will need to get in touch with it. But in general, anger generates far more conflict than it ever resolves.

The person who gives up anger as a method of conflict resolution loses very little, and opens the way to more ethical and loving approaches.

PATTERNS OR LIFESTYLES OF REACTIVITY

Typically a person's life will be colored by a tendency toward one or other of these responses, or a particular combination of them. Thus, the same stress may provoke entirely different reactions in individual people, depending upon the person's pattern. If, for example, a pet gets loose from the house and is run over, each will respond differently. Guilt-ridden persons will find themselves at fault, blame themselves harshly, and declare that they do not deserve to have a pet. Shame-ridden people will feel that others will blame them, that they will be seen as "dumb" or "stupid" for allowing it to happen. Anxiety-ridden persons may feel that life is fragile, that there is danger everywhere, that they are not competent to take care of themselves or a pet. The numbed person will, of course, not experience his or her feelings, but rather an increase in remoteness from them.

IDENTITY AND EMOTIONAL REACTIVITY

People often identify themselves with their patterns of emotional reactivity. They believe that feeling humiliated, guilty, anxious, angry, or numb is "a part of them" or basic to their personality.

A great deal has been said about shame as the most basic threat to identity. Kaufman states:

Shame is the affect of inferiority. No other affect is more central to the development of identity. None is closer to the experienced self, nor more disturbing. Shame is felt as an inner torment. (p. 17.)

In a similar vein, Morrison connects shame to narcissism—the core feeling of self-worth. The shamed person feels fundamentally defective.

However, identity is a stake in any of the emotional reactions. I have already noted that people often make anger central to their identity. People also become identified with their feelings of guilt, shame, anxiety, and even numbness, especially when these emotions are overwhelming. The guilty person's identity is that of "bad person" or "source of trouble"; the anxious person's is that of "incompetent, unable to cope"; and the ashamed person's is that of "worthless" or "defective." Meanwhile, the numbed person is likely to feel "out of touch" with his or her identity.

Surprisingly, people sometimes struggle to hold onto these negative identities, perhaps because they seem so integral to their personalities and their life experiences; perhaps because they are afraid that there is nothing else for them to feel. I find it useful to suggest to people that love can become a more solid and far more satisfying identity.

GUILT AND REMORSE

Can guilt be deserved? Doesn't it ever result from wrong-doing? In my experience (Breggin, 1980), guilt is rarely if ever a direct response to actual bad deeds. As I described in some detail in the previous chapter, perpetrators typically do not react with guilt to their crimes. Guilt is an emotional reaction, derived from helplessness, and usually based on childhood experiences of hurt and fear. Indeed, the origins of guilt are usually no longer within the individual's consciousness.

When adults do feel guilty in relation to something bad they have done, it is usually due to restimulation of childhood guilt. There is an emotional association between the bad deed and a guilt-provoking childhood experience. In short, guilt is an irrational reaction rooted in childhood helplessness rather than in adult remorse. In my practice, I have seen murderers who show no guilt and innocent people who are overwhelmed with it.

But does guilt serve a useful purpose in inhibiting destructive behavior? Sometimes, perhaps. But more often it tends to make people irrational and resentful, and thus it motivates destructive actions.

Remorse is another matter. It lacks the self-hate and self-loathing characteristic of guilt. It does not mire the person down in helplessness. The person who is genuinely remorseful feels autonomous and self-determining, and eager to take new and better actions. Often the remorseful person experiences an increase in self-esteem through recognizing the wrong deeds and correcting them. Remorse is usually very easy to distinguish from guilt, which instead overwhelms and demoralizes people, makes them feel badly about themselves, and frequently leads to helpless inaction or further destructiveness.

Even genuine remorse is probably not a significant motivator for benevolent human conduct. Instead, the motivator comes from a much more positive source. Oliner and Oliner's study of *The Altruistic Personality: Rescuers of Jews in Nazi Germany* (1988) provides evidence that the most seemingly sacrificial behavior, risking one's life for Jews during the holocaust, was *not* the result of guilt or even lofty ideals. It was motivated by empathic bonding—love.

According to Oliner and Oliner, children who became rescuers as adults were treated tenderly and leniently while they were growing up. Their eventual "moral heroism" was the result of extensive social ties and empathy, rather than guilt or even a sense of duty or obligation. Oliner and Oliner described the development of empathic social connectedness in the future rescuers:

It begins in close family relationships in which parents model caring behavior and communicate caring values. Parental discipline tends toward leniency; children frequently experience it as imperceptible. It includes a heavy dose of reasoning. . . . Punishment is rare. (p. 249.)

To repeat, guilt and other painful or burdensome feelings are not a reliable source of benevolent behavior. Empathic love *is* that reliable source.

DYNAMIC III: COERCION AS THE ROOT OF THE BASIC STRESS TRIAD

Basic Stress Paradigms and their derivative negative emotions usually result from experiencing the effects of the coercion dynamic.

Often these reactions result from obvious oppression in the form of emotional, physical, or sexual abuse. Often they are caused by emotional neglect which, in the case of the dependent child, is itself a form of abuse. This neglect need not be intentional—it can be the product of an emotionally damaged and withdrawn parent—but the impact on the young child can be overwhelming. If we categorize neglect as coercion, then Dynamic III includes nearly all of the worst things that happen to children.

Sometimes, however, the Basic Stress Paradigm is caused by misfortunes, such as illness, death, natural catastrophes, or war, that are beyond the control of anyone in the child's life. However, as already noted, clinical experience and recent studies of posttraumatic stress disorder confirm that the most debilitating emotional responses result from direct actions by people. For example, the British found during the London blitz of World War II that being in terrifying bombardments was not nearly so stressful for a child as being sent away from one's parents to the safety of a countryside nursery (Bowlby, 1973). Furthermore, even when a child is seemingly injured by a severe trauma, such as the death of a family member, the most stressful part of the experience is frequently associated with neglect or abuse by other adults. For example, the child may have been ignored while the family member was dying in the hospital or the child may have been made to feel guilty about the death.

SELF-DEFEATING REACTIONS

Guilt, shame, anxiety, numbing, and chronic anger are ultimately self-defeating reactions. In childhood, they may have served some limited purpose. If the sexually abused six year old blamed herself rather than her father, this may have kept her from being further injured by him. Or it may have maintained her much needed faith in her parent's ultimate good intentions. If the "mamma's boy" acts helpless, it may endear him to his mother and postpone her rejecting him because of his "manliness." If the shy girl learns to shrink away in the presence of parents or authoritarian teachers, it may keep her out of trouble and earn her approval as a "nice child." Similarly, if emotions are overwhelming, temporary numbing may enable the person to continue a semblance of normal activity. Chronic anger may be useful to a child in fending off oppression or in bolstering his or her pride.

But in the long run—and especially as the child grows into an adult—guilt, shame, anxiety, numbing, and persistent anger become self-defeating. The individual's emotional signal system will arbitrarily push the person one way or another—toward feeling guilty, ashamed, anxious, numb, or angry—without regard for the individual's basic needs, interests, or rational values. Actions required for successful living, or even for survival, may be stifled by overwhelmingly painful feelings. A woman, for example, may feel too guilty to leave an abusive husband. A man, out of shame over his "cowardice," may die in battle or in a bar fight, rather than retreat or get out of trouble. Overcome by anxiety, an individual may fail to deal with a life-threatening emergency involving himself or herself, or a loved one. People may become numb or angry in situations in which other emotional responses, such as love, are needed.

The emotions that grow from the Basic Stress Paradigm suppress the fulfillment of our basic needs. They interfere with rationality and with love; they are the source of low self-esteem and even self-hate; they prevent the individual from pursuing his or her self-interest, as well as the interests of loved ones. Indeed, any one of the negative emotions is likely to rear up at times when the individual has the opportunity to improve his or her life, for example, by choosing a new career, going to school, making a relationship, or even pursuing a healthy lifestyle. The negative reactions tell the individual, "No, you cannot do or get what you want." They do so by overwhelming the individual with guilt, shame, anxiety, numbness, or anger when faced with opportunities. Many people have little or no idea about what they want out of life or how they would like to live their lives, because the mere thought of these issues brings up their typical helpless responses.

OVERCOMING BASIC STRESS PARADIGMS AND LEARNED HELPLESSNESS

Overcoming Basic Stress Paradigms and their effects is an aspect of psychotherapy and conflict resolution in general, and hundreds of volumes have been written about it. Indeed, the Basic Stress

Paradigm is itself a simplified way of looking at psychological causation, a somewhat crude model that I hope will be helpful in conflict resolution. The overall problem of the origin and amelioration of irrational, self-defeating conduct is of course too large for this book. For practical purposes I want to focus on some of the basic steps in handling the Basic Stress Paradigm, learned helplessness, and the associated emotional reactions of guilt, shame, anxiety, and numbing, as well as compulsive anger.

IDENTIFYING THE NEGATIVE EMOTION AND REJECTING ITS IMPACT

As a start, the individual suffering from self-defeating emotions should learn to identify each of them by name. The descriptions I have provided of guilt, shame, anxiety, numbing, and anger can be helpful. People can feel considerably liberated simply by knowing that they suffer from a specific kind of irrational emotion. Consciously recognizing, "I'm being driven by shame," can help to subdue and control the emotion. The individual can now reject the emotion as a foreign intruder, an alien response from earlier hurtful experiences.

People are surprised and encouraged by the idea that they can both identify and refuse to respond to an emotion. I often compare these emotions to wild beasts and explain, "If you refuse to listen to them or to do their bidding, they lose their power over you. But if you respond to them and act according to their dictates, they grow stronger and more demanding." After such an explanation, a motto like "I won't feed my anger," can be very helpful.

Of course, simply deciding not to act in response to an emotion is easier said than done; but it is an important beginning, one that people often do not think about.

SUBSTITUTING BETTER PRINCIPLES OF LIVING

Once self-defeating emotions are identified, it is possible to consciously practice replacing them with more rational and loving principles. Understanding Dynamic I: love and Dynamic II: liberty can provide people with better ways of looking at their internal and external conflicts. The individual can learn to replace their coercive internal messages with attitudes consistent with liberty and love, including self-respect and self-love, as well as respect and love for others.

Helping people understand how to satisfy their basic needs is another important step. They can learn that emotional reactivity is not the answer, and that implementing liberty and love in one's life and in the lives of others is the best approach.

REEXPERIENCING BASIC STRESS PARADIGMS

If the participants in a conflict are willing, more intensive therapeutic approaches can be taken to relieve the underlying Basic Stress Paradigms. This is an accepted and essential part of couples or family therapy (see chapter 6), but it can sometimes be done as well in workshops dealing with racial, cultural, and other societal and even international conflicts (see chapters 9 and 10).

Early in his career, Freud experimented with relieving childhood stresses by encouraging the patient to reexperience or "abreact" them. Nowadays a variety of cathartic methods are used. The individual recalls and reenacts the original hurts, sometimes by using role-playing, mild suggestion, guided fantasies, or other methods to encourage childhood recollections. The adult may end up reexperiencing not only the childhood feelings, such as guilt or shame, but the original more painful Basic Stress Paradigms of hurt, fear, and learned helplessness. This same uncovering process is possible when the original trauma is of more recent origin, such as a severe accident or the death of a loved one. It is useful for focusing on isolated trauma or on lifelong patterns of hurt in the form of rejection, abandonment, and other stresses.

If a person can discover and relive the original childhood trauma or stress, the exaggerated adult reactions can often be reduced. Awareness of the raw feelings of childhood hurt can defuse their impact. The adult can learn that there is no longer any reason to feel so much hurt, fear, and helplessness. The source of the compulsive emotional reaction—the earlier Basic Stress Paradigm—becomes placed correctly in an earlier time, and no longer seems so appropriate. When the source is identified, the individual can declare, "This isn't reality today; it's something out of my past," this makes it easier to reject the negative emotion.

To defuse the original hurts, they must be reexperienced *from the viewpoint of an autonomous adult*. The cathartic experience must not become overwhelming. This last point is critical. Individuals should not be encouraged to reexperience earlier feelings of hurt, fear and helplessness unless they can do so as self-determining adults. It is the therapist's task to support the individual's sense of mastery and to approach the original trauma or stress only when the individual feels ready to handle it in a confident and competent fashion. Reexperiencing old hurts in a helpless fashion can reinforce them.

Sometimes it is helpful to explain that different people respond very differently to the same stress, depending on their own particular style of reactivity. That is, the reactions are not inevitable. A person doesn't have to react with guilt to a particular experience. Someone else might respond with anxiety or shame. And still another person might manage the stress in a rational and loving manner. It is the person's style, not the stress, that determines the undivided response. And a style can be changed.

It is, however, important not to ridicule the person in making comparisons to others. The point, instead, is that all people have these reactions, but they are particular to each person, and that no one is required by the stressors to respond in one way or another.

EXTERNALIZING THE INTERNAL CONFLICT

Guilt, shame, anxiety, numbing, and compulsive anger can be viewed as internal conflicts. They are analogous to conflicts between separate persons. Often they are experienced by the individual as if "two personalities" are contending, the one with the positive desires to fulfill basic needs, the other with negative responses to any such suggestion. When Freud developed his ideas of the Id, Ego, and Superego, he was adhering to that tendency to separate our inner conflicts into seemingly separate parts of ourselves, a metaphor for internalized persons.

Role-playing and psychodrama methods can be helpful in externalizing internal conflicts by having the individual or other persons play the internal parts. In this manner the individual gets a chance to reexperience and defuse the underlying hurts, and also to see them in greater clarity as events external to himself. Indeed, that is much of their origin—in social events external to the individual.

Again, the principles do not differ substantially from those involved in resolving and preventing conflicts between separate individuals and groups. The ultimate answer is a cleansing love for self and others that declares one's mind a guilt-, shame-, and anxiety-free zone, an arena in which painful emotional reactions from childhood are replaced by more independent and loving attitudes. Instead of self-hate, the individual learns to accept his or her individual rights and inherent worth as a human being.

EMOTIONAL REACTIVITY IN INTERPERSONAL CONFLICT

External conflict tends to stir up our earlier conflicts and hurts. We end up not only in conflict with another person in present time but with people from our past, and hence with ourselves. People who wish to manipulate and control others often capitalize on the victim's negative emotions. If clever about it, they may zero in on the victim's chronic style of guilt, shame, anxiety, numbing, or anger. A car salesman, for example, might play on any number of themes: (guilt) "You're not going to buy after all the time you have taken and the trouble you've caused?"; (shame) "You mean you can't even afford that much?"; or (anxiety) "Do you think this car or any other like it will be around forever?"

When Freud spoke of transference, he was identifying the tendency of adults to reexperience emotional reactions from childhood when in stressful adult situations. In the classical psychoanalytic situation, few of the client's basic needs were met. The "blank screen" analyst did little, for example, to show respect or love for the client. Faced with this real-life rejection, the client often "projected" onto the analyst feelings from earlier relationships in childhood. Clients would love or hate their analysts much as they loved or hated their parents. In fact, the so-called transference was complicated by the fact that the therapist was being abusive by withholding basic need satisfaction in an intimate relationship. Under such frustrating conditions, the individual is indeed likely to be overwhelmed with reactions originally generated during childhood experiences of hurt, fear, and helplessness. These early childhood reactions are likely to be stirred up in any new situation, including therapy; but they are not as likely to become overwhelming if the therapist is warm and caring rather than hostile, remote, or "objective" (see chapter 6).

Interactions between people, compounded by their own inner conflicts, can become complex. In couples or family therapy, however, they often become readily apparent (see chapter 6). Both members of a couple, for example, may feel so much shame about themselves that they will not "give in" for fear of risking further humiliation. The man who dominates his wife may fear looking like a "wimp" if he gives up his macho attitudes. His wife, in turn, may be afraid to stop tongue-lashing him, for fear she will lose her only defense against humiliation. While each may be aggravating the other's negative emotions, each is also reacting to experiences buried in the past.

A man feels so guilty about hurting his girlfriend that he repeatedly tells her that he has done "everything possible" to be good to her. She in turn reads this to mean that he is telling her that "no one will ever be able to relate to you," which inspires in her feelings of both anxiety and shame. Meanwhile, since he hardly ever feels anything but guilt, he cannot understand her anxiety and shame reactions; and similarly, she cannot figure out his intentions, because she has little inner experience with guilt. Thus these emotional reactions, if not identified and controlled, can disrupt an otherwise loving relationship.

EMOTIONAL REACTIVITY IN POLITICAL CONFLICT

Earlier Basic Stress Paradigms are frequently reactivated when people confront political coercion and conflict. Guilt and shame over the Holocaust, for example, has been identified as a force that keeps Israelis from reaching a compromise with the Palestinians. Similarly, shame over being overpowered and defeated by the Israelis can keep many Palestinians from resolving their conflicts with the Israelis (see chapter 10). Often these emotional reactions have still deeper roots in the family life of the respective cultures and their tendencies to foment guilt, shame, or anxiety. All this vastly complicates the problem of conflict resolution on any level, but it cannot be overlooked.

The examples in the discussion of interpersonal conflict could easily be translated into examples of political leaders in a conflict resolution setting. When two leaders who have opposed each other for years finally sit down to try to resolve their conflicts, they may react as irrationally to each other as any other feuding couple.

A leader's childhood reactions of guilt or shame can make it nearly impossible for him to hear correctly what someone else is saying. Or they may prevent him from making an otherwise reasonable compromise. Perhaps he is so prideful (a shame reaction) that he is more interested in his public appearance than in solving the actual problems. Perhaps he cannot make any concessions for fear of feeling shamed. Perhaps he feels so guilty that he is afraid to do anything that will cause his own constituents to be angry at him.

AN OVERVIEW OF PSYCHOLOGICAL CONFLICT AND CONFLICT RESOLUTION

The interaction between personal emotional reactivity and conflict resolution is addressed throughout this book. Here I want to summarize some of the salient points.

First, Basic Stress Paradigms, including learned helplessness and the associated negative emotions, usually result from experiences along Dynamic III: coercion. They can also motivate people to perpetrate against others. They play a major role in the generation of conflict and in disrupting conflict resolution.

Second, in any conflict situation, people will bring in their personal style of reactivity, whether it is guilt, shame, anxiety, numbness, chronic anger, or, most frequently, various combinations of them. When the reactions seem to impinge on the individual's identity, they may utterly disrupt progress in conflict resolution. Most people will defend their identity at almost any cost, including death. This can lead to an absolute unwillingness to show "weakness" by compromising or changing one's position.

Third, conflict of any kind tends to restimulate and exaggerate earlier Basic Stress Paradigms, vastly complicating conflict resolution. This is true whether the people at the conference table are husband and wife or opposing political leaders. Being in a leadership role does not make one immune to the effects of childhood trauma and stress.

Fourth, the prospect of attempting to resolve a conflict can so restimulate Basic Stress Paradigms that an individual will reject entering into the conflict resolution process. Or having entered in, the individual may disrupt it. The therapist or conflict resolver may have to work with all parties to help them control their reactivity before they come together.

Fifth, it can help the participants in the conflict if deeper therapeutic techniques can be introduced. However, this should only be done voluntarily and without shaming anyone. Often it may be necessary to apply them before or separately from the conflict resolution process (see chapter 6). Unfortunately, a deeper therapeutic approach is not something that a national political leader is likely to consent to. Therapeutic techniques aimed at handling emotional reactivity are being applied in conflict seminars for potential leaders and for others somewhat below the level of president or dictator (see chapter 10).

Sixth, not only individuals but institutions (e.g., churches, schools, military organizations) and entire cultures implement their own styles of emotional reactivity. America had prided itself in never having lost a war, and this undoubtedly reinforced President Nixon's and President Johnson's reluctance to withdraw from Vietnam under the humiliating shadow of defeat. Their need for "peace with honor" may have long delayed the resolution of the conflict. Similarly, as we shall discuss further, the shame of losing in Vietnam may have in part motivated America's massive attack on Iraq in the Gulf War. President Bush was clearly able to manipulate these feelings to further his policy.

Obviously, the personal reactions of leaders are not nearly sufficient to explain political events like war; but they are contributing factors. They can become especially important during the conflict resolution process.

Lastly, the presence of emotional reactivity should never be used to undermine or deny the reality of other issues in a conflict. A battered woman, for example, will frequently react with seeming "paranoia" and debilitating anxiety when in the presence of her abusive husband. After prolonged brutalization, she may even react this way in his absence. A child may indeed seem "hyperactive" as a result of abuse. American psychiatrists diagnosed Saddam Hussein as a madman, but this was rhetoric to rationalize our own ferocious attack on the Iraqi people (see chapter 10). It will be suggested that Arabs and Israelis are burdened by their own characteristic emotional reactivity; but there are *real reasons* for this, rooted in their political and personal history.

Although an individual style of emotional reactivity contributes to the conflict, it may not be the cause of it. It may even result from it. Furthermore, other more contemporary issues are often of overriding importance. Psychological analysis should never be used to discredit an individual or group's viewpoint or claims during a conflict.

Psychology should enable people to liberate themselves from all coercive influences, both internal and external, so that they can more fully live by the principles of liberty and love.

▼ ▼

CHAPTER 6

Resolving Interpersonal Conflict within the Family

[M]ature **love is union under the condition of preserving one's integrity,** *one's individuality.* **Love is an active power in man;** *a power which breaks through the walls which separate man from his fellow men, which unites him with others; love makes him overcome the sense of isolation and separateness, yet permits him to be himself, to retain his integrity. In love the paradox occurs that two beings become one and yet remain two.*
Erich Fromm, The Art of Loving *(1956)*

For one human being to love another: that is perhaps the most difficult of all our tasks, the ultimate, the last test and proof, the work for which all other work is but preparation.
Rainer Maria Rilke, Letters to a Young Poet *(May 14, 1904)*

There are situations, moments in life, in which unawares, the human being confesses great portions of his ultimate personality, of his true nature. One of these situations is love. In their choice of lovers both the male and the female reveal their essential nature. The type of human being which we prefer reveals the contours of our heart.
José Ortega y Gasset, On Love *(1957)*

Members of a couple are in an extraordinary position to grow in their ability to love, and to help each other to live ethical and happy lives. The focus in this chapter is on professional couples therapy or conflict resolution; but any person can apply these same principles to resolving his or her own problems or disputes with family, friends, and coworkers. Conflict resolution is an essential part of personal growth and the development of more fulfilling relationships.

COERCION IN COUPLES CONFLICT RESOLUTION

Much of what has already been said about coercion may be summed up in one principle: coercive reactions always produce negative reactions, whether immediate or delayed, and have little or no place in conflict resolution (see chapter 4). This applies to couples as well as countries. In *Getting Together* (1988), Roger Fisher and Scott Brown make the same point in their summary of "An Unconditionally Constructive Strategy." Under the rubric of "non-coercive modes of influence," they write "Even if they are trying to coerce us, neither yield to that coercion nor try to coerce them," (p. 38). They devote a chapter to practical alternatives to coercion, including "attack the problem" (and not the person), "treat negotiation as joint problem-solving," "remain open to persuasion," "explore interests," "invent multiple options," and "try to persuade them of what's fair," (p. 139). They also encourage finding a beneficial way to leave a conflict rather than to resort to coercion.

From the start, coercion must be "left at the door"—outside the office or conflict resolution setting. For a fully successful resolution, both partners must eventually forsake all such tactics in their everyday lives. In personal relationships, this means giving up not only threats of force and abandonment, but subtle manipulations through deception, or through stimulating guilt, shame, anxiety, and numbness.

Often people learn each other's "emotional buttons" and then press them. Jane knows that Jim can't stand it when she cries (guilt) or when she suggests he is an inadequate wage earner (shame). Jim knows that Jane can't stand it when he hints that he might start drinking again or leave (anxiety).

By the time most couples seek help, they typically are deeply enmeshed in Dynamic III: coercion. Often they are bullying each other with threats of leaving, having an affair, or getting family and friends to choose sides. Often the children are being manipulated into the conflict. Sometimes men are openly using or threatening force. Almost always, both parties are trying to inflict a spectrum of guilt, shame, and anxiety on each other. Abusive language and attitudes are commonplace.

The therapist can and usually should quickly intervene to point out the nature of coercion and its various manifestations. The therapist's initial role, it can be explained, is to help the partners stop abusing each other. Generally, agreement can be relatively easily reached on the benefit and even *necessity* of stopping hostile communications. It can take much longer for the couple to believe that the aggression can in fact be stopped. It may take still longer for them to trust each other's intentions and convictions.

While each person will have to struggle through the process of personally rejecting force, threats, and emotional manipulation— some progress can often be made in this regard after one or two sessions. One week later, Jim may be able to boast that he has not once threatened to leave or to start drinking again, and hopefully Jane will acknowledge that it is true. One or two such steps in the right direction can begin to instill mutual confidence. Giving up coercion is often much easier than learning new, positive ways of relating. It is usually a prerequisite as well.

If one of the partners resists personally giving up oppressive tactics—such as abusive, accusatory language—then conflict resolution is greatly slowed down. This individual is probably so stuck in childhood Basic Stress Paradigms—so driven by hurt, fear, and helplessness—that giving up hostility now seems too dangerous. In his or her mind, being "tough" (meaning angry and hurtful) is the only way to "get anywhere."

The person who is compulsively destructive usually feels deeply humiliated, nearly worthless, and unable to forgo revenge and retaliation. Sometimes he or she has experienced too much abuse from the partner to easily set it aside. Often these reactions require individual work outside the couple's therapy. The hurt individual feels too vulnerable and humiliated in front of the partner, and therefore cannot explore patterns of emotional reactivity that predate the relationship.

The feeling and expression of anger, in Adler's words, can become a lifestyle (Ansbacher and Ansbacher, 1956). The person identifies with anger as an essential aspect of his or her personality and fears becoming too vulnerable to attack without its regular exercise. In childhood, this chronic rage may have given the injured youngster a sense of pride and security against attack; in adulthood, it injures other people and drives them away, and makes every encounter a source of fear and anxiety. The adult must learn that the defensive and aggressive strategies developed to cope with an abusive childhood are no longer appropriate or effective. The very trait the individual most prizes, his or her capacity to fight back, may have become the cause of unending failure in social relationships.

Compulsive withdrawal or numbing presents an equally if not at times more difficult problem. The person who is numbed often presents a veneer of rationality that can be difficult to penetrate. Because this person is literally unaware of his or her own basic love needs, progress is again slowed down. In withdrawing behind a façade of rationality and objectivity, the individual feels superior and secure, but loses out on connectedness to others. Again, the individual's most-prized trait, the defensive capacity to remove himself or herself from seeming danger, becomes the cause of chronic failure. The lifestyle learned in childhood must be abandoned for effective adult living.

When abuse has reached severe proportions within a relationship, especially if it has escalated to violence, then a cessation of the abuse should be an absolute requirement. An immediate end to abuse is most urgent when a man is battering his wife, but it can also be important when a man or woman is verbally abusing his or her spouse. Especially in regard to physical violence or threats, the therapist should immediately intervene and explain that battery is not only unethical and antithetical to the principles of conflict resolution, it is illegal and criminal.

The victim should be informed that any assault on her is a criminal act and that if she feels threatened, she should take appropriate defensive actions such as moving out, calling the police, or obtaining a restraining order. The batterer should also be instructed that physical assault is criminal and that any hint of a physical threat is wholly unacceptable. Recent research on family violence confirms that a firm policy against male violence, including involvement of the criminal justice system, is a powerful deterrent to battering (Gelles and Straus, 1988). While assuming this "tough" stance on abuse, the therapist should show concern for *both* parties to the conflict.

Withdrawal or numbing, especially when masquerading as rationality, is also very destructive. It is important from the start to try to define numbing as a "problem" rather than as a strength. This can be difficult for men to accept, but little progress can be made as long as a man identifies strength with being emotionally unresponsive. Similarly, if a woman equates strength with being able to get viciously angry, she must overcome this obstacle as well. Since anger is a natural response to feeling chronically humiliated it may be hard for her to experiment with more gentle approaches to expressing her hurt and resentment.

The therapist should acknowledge to the abuser the difficulty of abruptly and completely abandoning his or her habitual tactics. Especially with the man, it is important to explain that he will become much more effective in satisfying his basic needs through a more respectful, loving attitude. It should be explained that the ability to create a loving relationship is the most powerful way to create a happy life for oneself.

Of course, if a person is unwilling to acknowledge any under-lying Dynamic I needs, there is little or no hope for a loving conflict resolution. But at least in the private practice of voluntary psychi-atry, few participants are totally out of touch with these shared human desires and values. At any rate, teaching a couple to control and reject coercion is inseparable from teaching them about vol-untary exchange and eventually about love.

LIBERTY IN COUPLES CONFLICT RESOLUTION

Liberty permits the use of force in self-defense. While retaliation and legally defined self-defense continues to play a role in societal relationships, in personal relationships even force in self-defense has too many adverse consequences. Both parties usually feel so injured that they view all of their coercive actions as defensive or retaliatory. In insisting upon the right and even a need to verbally degrade a partner, an individual may repeat a litany of offenses by the partner extending years and even decades into the past. Typ-ically both the husband and wife believe the other to be ultimately responsible for the hostile and destructive quality of the relation-ship. At some point, they must become willing to surrender their resentments in the interest of making a new beginning based on the principles of love and even forgiveness. Short of this, conflict resolution will remain limited.

An attempt should be made to discourage the use of force, even in self-defense—except of course where physical safety or important property are at stake. This helps people give up being aggressive even when they feel it is justified on the grounds of self-defense.

It helps to point out that both parties are inextricably enmeshed in emotional preemptive strikes and in retaliation, and that the couple take a brief holiday from it during the sessions. It is also helpful to remind them that if they love each other, they also feel pain when they inflict pain. Often there is quick mutual agreement about this, and each may be pleasantly surprised to discover that the other feels badly about causing hurt. Despite the various gratifications involved in "fighting back" (e.g., retaliation, getting even, pride in standing up for oneself), each partner usually does find it distressing to hurt the other.

My general experience in couples work indicates that most people can and will control their more violent tendencies when they realize that forgoing coercion will better enable them to fulfill their basic Dynamic I and II needs. As a therapist or conflict resolver, I am willing to appeal to a whole array of principles, from self-interest to morality and empathy, depending on what helps the individual forgo emotional or physical bullying.

The principles of liberty focus on the contractual part of relationships—voluntary exchange with each other. Often this dynamic is in disarray when couples are in serious conflict. Agreements about sharing responsibility, for example, are usually confused by feelings of guilt and resentment. Often the individuals in conflict have no idea about distinguishing between exchanges and gifting. Indeed, they may feel they are doing favors for each other simply by carrying out routine responsibilities.

Almost any loving relationship also has an aspect of voluntary exchange. Friends do favors for each other not only out of love, but often out of an awareness that kindnesses will be returned. Friends also spend time together because they need partners for special activities, such as playing tennis or cards. In romantic relationships and especially in marriage, exchanges are important, but too often they are arranged without any real discussion of each person's desires. In the traditional family, the husband earns the money to support the family and the wife takes care of the household and probably the children as well. As already noted, this model tends to persist even when both partners are working outside the home. In most of these families, the exchange is unfairly tipped toward the husband. Many feminist theorists, with good reason, doubt if truly voluntary exchanges can take place between men and women in patriarchal society (French, 1985).

There are many subtle exchange issues between couples. Few

people have exactly the same sexual desires or experience the same sexual rhythms. Few people prefer exactly the same restaurants, movies, TV shows, or vacations. Again, bargaining and compromise may take place. But even in these instances, a genuine mutual concern with each other's preferences may lead individuals to work toward solutions in which each feels satisfied. It may become difficult to differentiate which they end up enjoying more: their own need satisfaction or that of their loved one. In the process, the couple will grow in their trust and their love for each other.

Often basic needs find differing expressions. One person wants to be held and another wants to be listened to. One likes continual companionship, another more alone time. One person needs financial security, another likes to take risks. Meeting these needs within the marriage may require negotiation, at least in the beginning, before love leads to mutual satisfaction.

Respect and self-esteem are generated in the voluntary exchange process. People feel good about themselves and about each other when they can successfully negotiate their way through a conflict toward mutual basic need satisfaction. Love is generated when people reach beyond negotiation and seek to help each other.

Recognizing the distinctions between esteem and love, between exchange and gifting, can help people begin to make sense out of their conflicts. A woman realizes that her husband's offers of affection always have "strings attached." They are really attempts at exchange. Both develop a better idea about love as unconditional. Both realize they have never given or received it, but determine to try to learn.

A man realizes that he loves his wife but doesn't respect her. A woman realizes she respects her husband but doesn't love him. Both partners realize that they once loved each other very much, but that the love has become lost in the bitter fighting. A woman realizes she is tired of being told "I love you" when she isn't being given a modicum of respect.

Mediation in itself is not the ultimate role of the therapist or conflict resolver. The aim is to teach principles of conflict resolution that the individuals can use for themselves. Often this can be done through example by helping them resolve problems during the session; but the ultimate goal is to give people the tools for resolving disputes without outside help. Relating through love is the single most important principle.

LOVE IN COUPLES CONFLICT RESOLUTION

Practical guides to conflict resolution often suggest the importance of love without explicitly or fully dealing with it. In *Getting Together*, Fisher and Scott discuss unconditional acceptance as a basic concept. They refer to the Bible as teaching "Love thine enemy," (p. 153), but do not fully explore the implications. Similarly, in *No-Fault Negotiating* (1987), Len Leritz declares "The degree of our success in negotiating is usually determined by the quality of relationship we have with the other person," (p. 7) and "Negotiating is a process of creating mutual understanding," (p. 10). Again, the implications are not fully explored. The concept of negotiation may itself be the stumbling block. Thoroughgoing conflict resolution reaches beyond bargaining or reconciling competing interests. It reaches toward a loving affiliation that recognizes the equal importance of each other's basic needs. In love, people treat each other's needs as if they were their own.

It will usually become apparent rather early on that there are limits to bargaining, compromising, and otherwise achieving voluntary exchanges in the absence of love. Helping people experience love requires patience. This is not surprising. Since love tends to resolve conflicts, loving couples do not as often end up in a therapy or conflict-resolution setting. On the other hand, love can also motivate people to save or to improve their relationship. Furthermore, the three dynamics do not exist in a rigid hierarchy of progression: love and hate, tenderness and violence, often coexist.

People may love each other very much, while nonetheless behaving very badly toward each other. Due to the ravages of their own Basic Stress Paradigms, or due to misunderstandings or serious practical problems, people who already love each other may nonetheless find their relationship failing.

Sometimes the couple may be aware of loving each other despite their conflicts; more often they can recall a time years earlier when they were "in love," a feeling that now seems tragically remote. If they never loved each other and are starting from scratch, the eventual flowering of romance is less promising, but not altogether out of the question. If the therapist can help them recapture feelings of love from earlier years, conflict resolution can be expedited.

THE FEAR OF LOVE

Love can be frightening, and when people "fall in love," they usually fall into fear as well (see chapter 2). Because romantic love can become the most intense expression of our adult social needs, it can amplify all of our social fears as well. Love not only heals the vast reservoirs of hurt within us, it can also hurl us into them (Breggin, 1980).

Love, especially romantic love, usually reactivates early childhood experiences of rejection, betrayal, and loss. It confronts us with how our parents and other relatives related to each other. It also recharges any previous adult hurts associated with love. Often an individual made one attempt at romantic love, perhaps in his or her teens or early twenties, and then, feeling badly hurt, "gave up on love." Now that protective barrier is threatened and fear sets in again.

Because of its intensity, romantic love brings out the worst—as well as the best—in us. On falling in love, it is commonplace for previously independent men and women to turn into helpless dependents. After they have committed themselves to a new love relationship, partners are likely to be shocked by the abrupt display of irrational conduct by their loved ones, as well as by themselves.

It is no wonder that people find it so hard to begin and to maintain passionate love relationships. It can be helpful for a therapist or conflict resolver to acknowledge the inevitability of fears and irrationality, and to teach people to break through them in order to get in touch with their loving feelings again.

ENCOURAGING LOVE

How does one "teach" or encourage love?

There are many different approaches to this, including explaining and discussing the nature of love, identifying it as an important aspect of life, and asking people about their personal experiences. A variety of popular books can also be useful. Didactic presentations should be limited to a brief few minutes and specifically addressed to the clients' thoughts, feelings, and experiences. Hopefully these brief presentations stimulate greater hope for the possibility of love in their lives.

When face to face with each other in a session, people can be encouraged to make eye contact or even physical contact, such as holding hands, and to risk feeling their more tender feelings toward each other. If people are feeling shy or defensive, they can experiment with feeling these emotions without expressing them. Guided activities such as these are only useful, however, if both partners feel ready to experiment with feeling or displaying more love and if both freely wish to enter into these potentially embarrassing interpersonal experiments. No pressure should be applied to get anyone to participate.

People often feel more hopeful about feeling love when they recall and consider less threatening experiences of love, such as their affection for a childhood friend, a pet, a work of art, a plant, or a place. They realize that they have the capacity for unconditional love and that they have experienced it in other circumstances. Very frequently the individual will then respond, "Oh, but it's so much safer to love my cat or my plants . . ." That revelation provides the opportunity for exploring the fears surrounding love for other human beings.

In helping people understand love, the aura, beingness, or personal attitudes of the therapist is probably the single most important factor. Does the therapist love, cherish, or treasure his or her clients? Does the therapist radiate pleasure or even joy on seeing them? Does the therapist really care about their well-being? Does the therapist take pleasure in learning more about each one of them? Does the therapist take delight in seeing them happy, both as individuals and with each other? Does the therapist love his or her work as a therapist or conflict resolver? Does the therapist display a zesty enjoyment of others and of life in general?

Ever since Carl Rogers (1961) first began to study the beneficial effect of the therapist's positive regard for the client, studies have continued to confirm his findings. In his review, James McConnell (1989) summarized:

Psychological change almost always occurs in a supportive, warm, rewarding environment. People usually "open up" and talk about things—and try new approaches to life—when they trust, admire, or want to please the therapist. (p. 509.)

In *Toxic Psychiatry* (1991), I described studies confirming that a warm, supportive, empathic approach is the most effective therapeutic approach regardless of how disturbed or incapacitated the patient may be.

Consciously or not, the client will evaluate the therapist as a person, and will be inspired or disillusioned by what he or she perceives. In chapter 10, in regard to Jimmy Carter's work as a peacemaker, it will be observed that the conflict resolver can play the same inspiring role in larger political conflicts.

Love, as it is defined in this book, is a joyful awareness characterized by treasuring, caring, mutuality, a desire for closeness, and empathy. If the therapist expresses these attitudes toward his or her clients, other people, and life in general, then the therapist is creating a healing environment.

I am not suggesting that the therapist or conflict resolver should fake a loving viewpoint. The therapist should actually develop these attitudes, for his or her own personal sake and for benefit of everyone involved in his or her life, including clients. Furthermore, if the therapist has a special difficulty feeling love for a particular client, it is up to the therapist, as a paid professional, to search out why his or her natural caring response to people is being withheld. The therapist should seek to open his or her own heart to the client or diplomatically suggest that the client seek another therapist. Every effort must be made not to communicate any rejection of the client.

No one is likely to meet an ideal standard of loving all or most of the time. What *is* required is a basically loving attitude and a profound conviction that love is the best way of life and the ultimate method of conflict resolution.

THE THERAPEUTIC OR CONFLICT-RESOLUTION SETTING

A well-constructed and maintained therapy setting greatly facilitates the possibility of people loving each other. Earlier in my career (Breggin, 1975), I described psychotherapy as a mini-utopia in which the client has the opportunity to experience a more protected and loving relationship than might otherwise be possible.

In general, people put in close proximity for periods of time will tend to feel affinity for each other. If the encounters include emotional sharing, love gains still more encouragement. In short, people who get to know each other tend to get to love each other. This principle has proven itself true in a variety of professional settings from psychotherapy to politically oriented conflict resolution workshops involving avowed enemies. It is obviously at work as well in other social and occupational settings.

Of course, people sometimes learn to dislike each other when they are thrown together. The therapist's or conflict-resolver's task is to minimize that possibility, while maximizing the more positive outcome.

The therapist's capacity to love in the therapy setting is enhanced by the rules that protect the integrity and separateness of the setting. The therapist limits social contact to the sessions themselves, avoiding the complexities and pitfalls of trying to extend it outside the office. The client deserves a quality of relating that is often beyond the ability of both the therapist and client outside the safety of the sessions.

Even if therapist and clients alike seem potentially capable of intimacy outside of the office, they are not likely to manage it while dealing with the most intense and painful issues in the clients' lives. Few, if any, experienced therapists would try to be a therapist or conflict resolver with friends on any regular on-going basis. A therapist might use his or her skills on occasion to help a friend, but a routinized therapy relationship is a whole other matter.

Within the therapy setting, sexual intimacy is unacceptable. Because of the inherent power imbalance between the therapist and client, romance too easily becomes exploitation. Therapy is disrupted and becomes potentially abusive when passion intervenes.

The therapist also places time and energy limits on the relationship so that it will not become overtaxing. Finally, the therapist is committed to being completely ethical in the treatment of all clients, and in demanding the same in return.

The therapist does not allow himself or herself to be abused physically or emotionally. This is an important point: therapy or conflict resolution is not the place where the client gets to "unload" on the therapist. Verbal attack, or any other form of coercion, is not good for the perpetrator and certainly not good for the victim, even if the victim is an experienced professional.

Unfortunately, the same warning must be given to therapists.

"Treatment" must never become an excuse for verbally or physically abusing the client. All people, regardless of their emotional problems, deserve the same respect for their dignity. In regard to biological psychiatry, physical treatments such as medication, electroshock, and lobotomy can easily become thinly veiled expressions of violence on the doctor's part (see chapter 7).

These built-in protections make the therapy a kind of mini-utopia of interpersonal relations in which the therapist is protected from stress, enabling him or her to be as rational and loving as possible. Meanwhile, the same protections encourage the clients to more easily and freely communicate with each other and with the therapist. However, the therapist is paid with money and with the satisfactions inherent in the work, but not specifically with love. Some clients may reciprocate with love, but the therapist must be prepared to help people who remain unwilling or unable to do so.

The therapist must be sure that he or she is not using "love" to manipulate the client. Furthermore, the therapist must be careful not to overwhelm the client. Most people are limited in how much love they can accept at any given time. The therapist's task is to remain sensitive to client responses so that the expressed caring or affection is not experienced as threatening or faked by the client.

Maintaining sufficient restraint is not very difficult, as long as the therapist does not try to satisfy his or her own basic love needs through the therapy. If the therapist remains oriented to the clients's feelings, he or she will not reach out in a frightening manner. Nor is it artificial or "fake" for the therapist to consciously control personal expressions of love. People restrain expressions of positive and negative feelings throughout daily living in response to multiple factors, including social convention, etiquette, the needs of others, and their own inclinations.

While therapists with specific religious convictions might differ from me, the aim of couples therapy or conflict analysis and resolution is *not* to assure the survival of the relationship or marriage. The aim is to help resolve deep-seated conflicts. The relationship or marriage may or may not prosper, depending on the wishes and abilities of the partners.

The conflict-resolution process also offers other benefits to the individuals, including self-realization through a better understanding of themselves and others, and a greater awareness of the principles of liberty and love in everyday life.

BASIC STRESS PARADIGMS

It is worth repeating that any current conflict will restimulate the negative results of past conflicts and their related Basic Stress Paradigms. Hurt, fear, and helplessness—expressed as guilt, shame, anxiety, numbing, and anger—rear up from the past to affect our current conflicts. The individual's childhood reactions become part of the current problem. A man who was often abandoned as a child, perhaps by being left alone at night when very small, may overreact to any hint of abandonment in adulthood. A woman who was screamed at or who heard a lot of screaming as a child may become frightened and irrational the moment a voice is raised.

People in conflict also undergo new Basic Stress Paradigms. After frequent episodes of abuse, betrayal, or abandonment, the hurt turns to fear and eventually to helplessness. I have seen men driven to suicidal despair by relentless guilt-provoking verbal assaults from their wives, and, more frequently, I have seen women driven into helpless outrage by the humiliating attitudes and actions of their husbands.

Some psychoanalysts would say that the *real* roots of each person's problem predate marriage and adulthood; but in my experience, a destructive relationship can, in and of itself, wholly demoralize an otherwise sound human being. Often a person needs, more than anything, to find the courage and confidence to leave an oppressive relationship.

SOCIAL INSTITUTIONS AND INDIVIDUAL PSYCHOLOGY

Individuals are of course enormously influenced by social institutions and the values they implement, including how these institutions cause, worsen, or prolong conflicts. The family, through its child rearing function, usually leaves the most indelible marks on the individual. Educational, religious, fraternal, military, and other institutions also play a role. TV, Hollywood, and the news media are major contributors to individual value systems.

Nearly all of society's institutions have one set of values in common—male patriarchy. The influence of patriarchy must be taken into account on every level of conflict resolution, from spousal to international disputes (French, 1985; Lerner, 1986; see chapter 11).

Patriarchy promotes and implements the values of "power over" and domination. It views human relationships in terms of hierarchies: who is superior and who is inferior.

In personal relationships, in both obvious and subtle ways, men tend to subordinate, ridicule, and control women. While either a man or a woman may be the chief abuser in any particular relationship, most men in most marriages are imbued with a sense of superiority over their wives and seek to impose controls upon them. Often men express their superiority by claiming to be more rational and sane (see Breggin, 1991). By withdrawing and inhibiting their feelings, they create a façade of autonomy and competence. By the time most couples seek help, the woman feels deeply humiliated by her husband's attitudes, which have reinforced her earlier humiliating experiences as a woman and girl.

In couples therapy, it is difficult to imagine an in-depth understanding or resolution of serious conflicts without dealing with issues of patriarchy and male domination. Most couples in therapy are enacting or resisting typical male-female stereotypes (described in detail in Breggin, 1991). Very often, the husband assumes a viewpoint similar to that of a biologically oriented psychiatrist. He is aloof, "objective," seemingly rational, and believes that his wife is emotionally unstable and mentally ill. He feels she makes demands on him emotionally that make no sense. He yearns to be "let alone." In turn, the wife feels humiliated, deeply emotionally deprived, and overtly angry. She feels controlled and rejected by him, and longs for deeper communication.

Typically the husband injures her by withdrawing emotionally and by looking down upon her; she injures him by verbally attacking and ridiculing him. He gives her no help with the domestic chores, even if she is working full time; and she undermines his sense of worth and potency, often by rejecting him sexually.

Both the husband and wife feel victimized by the other and justify their aggressive tactics as retaliation for injuries perpetrated by the other. But beneath these gender stereotypes both are feeling thwarted in their basic needs for respect, love, companionship, and security.

In international politics, the male dominator viewpoint prevails in nearly every conflict through the exercise of economic power and the threat of war. Patriarchal politics exerts an influence on all of society, from the TV and the media to the little boys playing guns or bullying each other in the school yard. Violence is treated as a rational solution to conflict. As in the attack on Iraq, war is reported by the media as if it were a computer game. The destruction or suppression of other people is rationalized on the grounds that they are "different" and "inferior" (see chapter 10).

CHANGING VALUES IN THERAPY AND CONFLICT RESOLUTION

In several of my earliest publications, I stressed that the principles of the free-enterprise system are essential to the conduct of psychotherapy. Not only does the client pay the therapist or clinic, the client is encouraged to develop Dynamic II ethics of autonomy and independence. I urged therapists to recognize that therapy is a form of applied ethics and politics, and suggested that they make free enterprise values central to their practice.

Experience has continued to confirm the essentially ethical and political nature of psychotherapeutic processes, but also the need for a more subtle awareness and a more complex analysis of the values involved. First, I have come to place increasing emphasis on the negative influence of patriarchal values, especially the use of power to suppress conflict. Power and coercion as values impinge on people in their everyday lives, including outright sexism and more subtle forms of authoritarianism. Second, I now see more pitfalls in rigidly free-enterprise values. Third, and closely related, I more openly embrace the role of love in therapy and in life. And finally, it now seems inescapable that there are inherent and sometimes unresolvable contradictions in trying to live by the principles of both liberty and love, even though we must strive to reconcile these two ideals.

ILLUSTRATING THE CONFLICT BETWEEN LIBERTY AND LOVE

I recently had a session with one of my patients, Jeb, that underscored the potential conflict between liberty and love in professional relationships, such as therapy and conflict resolution. The issue was fees.

When Jeb first came to see me six months earlier, he was hard pressed to pay my usual fee, and so I reduced it by about ten percent. Now he unexpectedly sold the rights to a project he had been working on for years, and overnight he had become wealthy.

It rather quickly occurred to me that he could now easily afford to pay my original fee and that it would be fair to ask him to do so. However, as far as I could recall, I had originally neglected to raise the possibility of readjusting his fee at a later date, and so I wanted to ask his permission to do so. I also didn't want to seem greedy or insensitive, and therefore hesitated to follow up on his good fortune by immediately asking for more money. So I waited a couple of months before bringing it up.

Jeb is a very quiet but extremely intelligent young man who has trouble knowing and expressing his feelings; but when I said that I would like to increase my fee to its original level, he flushed with color, became silent, grinned uncomfortably, and generally looked uneasy. After a few minutes, he explained that my request seemed entirely reasonable and ethical. He agreed that he could and would pay the increase, but . . . but that he felt somehow . . .—the words were hard for him to find—"confused, upset, disappointed, hurt."

Our conversation went on to traverse territory I've frequently covered around the issue of fees, but with more mutual openness than usual. There were moments when I too flushed, became silent, grinned uncomfortably, and generally looked uneasy. The following summary of our conversation highlights some fundamental issues of liberty and love, of capitalism and caring.

Although Jeb kept reassuring me that my request was reasonable and that he planned to comply, he wished in his heart that our relationship was more like a friendship, that I cared about him more as a person than as a paying client, and that therefore it wouldn't have occurred to me to think about money. My asking him for the few dollars more, he said, reminded him of his childhood feelings that no one cared about him—that he as a person simply wasn't important. Indeed, expressing these feelings brought up some important new insights into his childhood.

Perhaps some therapists would have played up Jeb's own references to his childlike feelings. They might have felt and even said that Jeb was being childlike by "wanting something for nothing," and so on. But it did not strike me that way at all.

Among other things, I was noticing my own "childlike" feelings, and sharing them with Jeb as well. While he had wished that I cared enough not to even think about money, I had wished that he cared enough to realize, as a newly wealthy man, that it was only fair to pay the original fee.

While I was expressing this part of myself to Jeb, I was also reassuring him that in no way were my feelings rational. That is, I did not in reality want him or expect him, as my client, to be focusing his attention on my needs. But I did think it might be helpful for him to know that he was not alone—that his therapist was also struggling over the contradictions between free-market principles and love in a therapeutic relationship.

I had also hesitated to bring up raising my fee because I didn't want to hurt Jeb's feelings. I did genuinely care about him. Indeed, as I told him, I would have reduced my fee further had it been necessary to allow him to come to therapy while working on his long-term project. I didn't want him to have to give up either his therapy or his much-loved work. And to compound my ambivalence, I felt that *not* bringing up the fee would deny an important issue. After all, the fee had been reduced because he was financially in need of it, and that was no longer the case. I wanted to address his feelings about it, and if helpful to him, to share mine as well.

Perhaps some mental health professionals would conceptualize my session with Jeb in psychoanalytic terms. They would say that Jeb was suffering from "transference" (his childhood emotional reactivity directed at me) and that I was suffering from "counter-transference" (my childhood emotional reactivity directed in turn at his transference). I did not view it in that manner, and the session turned out to be very productive. Jeb expressed his tender feelings more openly than ever before in therapy. I also shared my own feelings with him. He was able to affirm that all of his reactions, including the conflicted ones, were acceptable and understandable; and that we two men could share ourselves at an awkward moment and come out the better for it.

I now believe that all people, deep down, want to be loved for themselves. The nuances will differ from person to person; but all persons want to be loved and cared about. These desires make it almost inevitable that conflicts will come up in therapy about paying fees.

It also seems apparent that on a larger societal scale, capitalism and caring are bound to conflict. There is nothing in the profit motive that necessitates caring about anything but money. Other values must contain and ameliorate the drive to maximize profits (see chapter 8).

Put in more abstract terms, there are inherent contradictions between liberty and love. While liberty can be the staging ground for love, it can also get in the way of it. It *is* difficult at times to have both a capitalistic and a caring relationship, and this is true in both the personal and the societal arena.

PROFESSIONALISM AS A SOLUTION

In professional relationships, in part to ameliorate these contradictions, restraints are usually placed on the profit motive. Although I know at least one psychiatrist who has acted differently, the vast majority of mental health professionals do not believe that they are supposed to charge each individual person as much as he or she can be pushed to pay. Yet that is a basic free-market principle: to charge what the traffic will bear; to maximize profits.

In Jeb's case, for example, I did not try to raise his fee beyond my usual one, even though he could have easily afforded it. In my experience, few professionals, including lawyers, try to charge each client as much as possible. The usual terse explanation is "I'm a professional" or perhaps "I'm in a service profession."

But there's a deeper, if unsaid, reason why professionals don't usually try to squeeze every penny they can from their clients. There is an element of *caring* in being a professional. There is an imperative to orient to the client's needs as well as toward one's own. Gilligan (1982) has pointed out that women often make mutual satisfaction one of their highest values; professionals often do the same, without necessarily acknowledging it.

It is not merely a matter of "good business practices" or "wanting to keep my customers." In professionalism, there's a *higher standard* than mere profit. That standard includes regard for the client's interests. When regard becomes unconditional—separated from the profit motive—it moves from Dynamic II: liberty toward Dynamic I: love. Unhappily, there has been an increasing tendency among some professionals to become "mere businessmen," but most people lament this as a breach in ethical standards.

When people know each other, affection or personal regard more easily modifies the unbridled pursuit of self-interest. The conflicts become more difficult to resolve on a societal level where members of the community have little or no personal contact, no obviously shared tasks, and few cultural ties (see chapter 9).

INVOLUNTARY CONFLICT RESOLUTION WITH COUPLES

Involuntary conflict resolution is probably a misnomer. When one or another participant has been compelled to participate—for example, by court order, civil commitment, or threats of harm from another person—conflict resolution becomes badly distorted. As discussed in chapter 4, threats and force make honest, open communication almost impossible, and instead encourage lying and deception. Basic needs cannot safely be disclosed in situations of such great vulnerability and so their satisfaction is prevented. When coerced into anything, most people focus their attention on doing whatever is necessary to escape from the coercion or to limit its impact. The agenda of "staying out of trouble with the authorities" is not conducive to conflict resolution.

Even in seemingly voluntary situations, power imbalances obstruct the resolution of conflict. If one side has vastly greater resources or authority, a situation tends to become coercive. Dynamic III, with its untoward consequences, slips into place.

Every effort should be made to make any conflict-resolution effort as voluntary as possible. When this cannot be done, the therapist or conflict resolver should weigh the possibility of ending the process or refusing to participate. Other avenues may then prove more useful. For example, if a man has been battering his wife it may be necessary to institute criminal proceedings before attempting therapy or conflict resolution. Once the criminal matter is resolved, the perpetrator can more freely decide whether or not to enter into a therapeutic or conflict-resolution program.

IMPLICATIONS FOR PSYCHOTHERAPY

Psychotherapy is best understood as a form of conflict resolution. The therapist helps clients resolve internal conflicts, as well as conflicts with family members and society. As the vignette about Jeb and myself illustrates, the therapist's conflicts with his or her clients are also grist for the therapeutic mill. Some conflict is unavoidable over one or more routine issues, such as fees, scheduling, therapeutic approaches, and the length and content of sessions.

In these conflicts with clients, the therapist's ethics and caring are most sorely tested, and yet this aspect of therapy has great potential benefit for the client. If the client discovers that the therapist relates, at times of conflict, in a respectful and loving manner, then the client will probably develop an increased sense of personal worth, and improved skills in dealing with people.

As I discuss in *Toxic Psychiatry* (1991), adherence to the highest principles of conflict resolution becomes even more important with severely disturbed individuals. These severely hurt people are often more easily overwhelmed by coercive, uncaring tactics or attitudes. Unfortunately, these emotionally injured people are most likely to find themselves victimized by destructive psychiatric interventions, such as involuntary "treatment," massive drug doses, and electroshock.

OVERVIEW

Any thoroughgoing interpersonal conflict resolution process must address all three dynamics: coercion, liberty, and love. The parties to the conflict must learn to forsake the use of force, except in self-defense, and to negotiate agreements according to the principles of liberty. But that is not the end of it, and at some point in the relationship, the parties to the conflict ideally will begin to care about each other in new and more loving ways.

They will see themselves in each other, and mutually address each other's needs and values. Where they perceive differences, they will be pleased and delighted by them. They will look out for each other as they do for themselves. They will at times find themselves so deeply concerned about the fulfillment of each other's needs that distinctions between self and other, selfishness and altruism, will be rendered meaningless. They will take care of each other's needs on a level that neither one could possibly do alone.

The above description of a loving relationship is not farfetched.

It is, in fact, a commonly held ideal of family life, marriage, and friendship. While it is rarely fulfilled in all aspects, it is often approximated.

As described in chapter 2, empathy and the desire to help begin within the first year or two of life, and they can be cultivated throughout life. Parents, spouses, lovers, and friends frequently put the needs of loved ones above their own. Ethical professionals, as well as people in general, often find themselves "not taking advantage." Sometimes at great personal cost, they promote the interests of others in their family, social, and occupational lives.

In all spheres of life, people often take better care of each other than they could take care of themselves on their own. Often people freely sacrifice for each other without even considering it a sacrifice. While the therapeutic and conflict-resolution fields have not paid sufficient attention to the love dynamic, it remains the foundation of individual well-being, the critical ingredient of social life, and the ultimate source of both individual happiness and harmony among people.

▼ ▼

CHAPTER 7

The Role of Psychiatry in Conflict Resolution

Some paradox of our nature leads us, when once we have made our fellow men the objects of our enlightened interests, to go on to make them the object of our pity, then of our wisdom, ultimately of our coercion.

Lionel Trilling, The Liberal Imagination (1979)

Psychiatry is a method of social control. It gives the power to confer exemptions and excuses; it gives the power to lock people up and throw away the key.

Jonas Robitscher, The Powers of Psychiatry (1980)

By its very nature, psychotherapy must pretend to supply an objective, kindly, and human atmosphere to those who wish to express their deepest feelings of pain and sorrow. The tragedy is that this legitimate need is exploited, even if with the best of intentions, by "experts" who claim to offer what has never been theirs to give.

Jeffrey Masson, Against Therapy (1988)

The most severe personal conflicts have been relegated to the mental health profession. If a person becomes despairing, suicidal, or seemingly mad, almost everyone agrees that psychiatry has the best answers. Many societal conflicts, like crime and homelessness, also lie within the province of psychiatry. Yet modern principles of conflict resolution, including the concepts of liberty and love, have had almost no impact on the mental health profession.

As a psychiatrist, I have been dismayed to watch modern psychiatry reduce psychological problems and conflicts between people to biochemical defects within one specific individual. While there is little or no scientific basis for the new biological psychiatry (Breggin, 1991; Cohen, 1990; Coleman, 1984), the ideology has gained widespread support. Ironically, psychiatry's growing reliance on genetic and biological theories comes at precisely the moment that clinical and empirical research is confirming the childhood origins of adult problems and emotional pain (reviewed in chapters 4 and 5).

A child who rebels in a dysfunctional home or fights the burdensome routine of school is labeled hyperactive and given Ritalin. An elderly woman who becomes depressed over being ostracized and abandoned is labeled major depression and given shock treatment. A man who cannot find work or housing is labeled schizophrenic and forced into a state mental hospital.

Too often, little or no effort is made by psychiatry to identify and satisfy the individual's basic needs. While the patient is seen as incompetent, no attempt is made to support his or her autonomy and independence. No attention is given to the conflicts between the individual and other people, such as his or her family, school, or community. Instead, psychiatry takes a short cut: It diagnoses the person as mentally ill, explains away the problem as genetic and biochemical in origin, and subdues the patient with drugs, electroshock, and hospitalization (Breggin, 1991).

To say that psychiatry rejects Dynamic II values, such as liberty and self-determination, is no exaggeration. Psychiatrists intervene as outside authorities to diagnose people and to prescribe for them, often against their will. As I describe in "Iatrogenic Helplessness in Authoritarian Psychiatry," (1983), physical treatments, such as drugs and electroshock, tend to make the patient more helpless and dependent—more suggestible and amenable to psychiatric control.

To say that psychiatry is a loveless approach is also no exaggeration. Psychiatric training encourages the doctor to relate in an aloof, controlling and authoritarian manner, rather than with a warm and caring approach (Breggin, 1991). Contemporary psychiatric principles and practices are at odds with those of conflict analysis and resolution that seek to empower the individual and to encourage collaborative decision-making.

PSYCHIATRY AND INTERPERSONAL CONFLICT RESOLUTION

When psychiatrists treat a patient, they usually single out one member of an interpersonal conflict for their attention. Others involved in the conflict escape diagnosis and treatment but may in reality be more the source of the problem. The conflict is then suppressed by locking up, drugging, or shocking one of the members into a more submissive state.

When psychiatrists intervene in family conflict, they will single out one or another member of the family as "mentally ill." A child, for example, is restless or rebellious at home and is labeled hyperactive. A wife is despairing about her marriage, stops doing the housework, won't get out of bed. She is diagnosed depressed. A husband is filled with rage, much of it stemming from childhood Basic Stress Paradigms, and tries to stifle his pain by drinking. He is labeled alcoholic.

Many individuals who become diagnosed by psychiatrists are in reality suffering from oppression. This is especially apparent in children because they are more obviously subjected to events outside their control. The psychiatrically labeled child is, in most cases, a victim of obvious family conflict, often including emotional, physical, or sexual abuse (Breggin, 1980, 1991; Miller, 1984; Green, 1989). Sometimes the child is directly reacting to marital discord. At other times, the child simply has too much energy and creativity to be contained within stultifying homes or classrooms.

Whether the problem lies in the child's family or the school, the child is further injured by being diagnosed and treated. The family or the school should be helped to respond better to the child's basic needs for love, security, and stimulating education.

Childhood stresses eventually become internalized as Basic Stress Paradigms and psychological conflict, and many adults suffer from the result of experiences they can no longer recall. The adult who hallucinates voices talking to him through the walls of his house may be reexperiencing the dread of overhearing his parents speaking in a threatening manner through his bedroom wall when he was a small child. The grown woman who thinks her insides are rotting may be driven by the horror of incestuous abuse as a child (for further discussions, see Breggin, 1991).

Basic Stress Paradigms or internalized conflicts from childhood often impinge on adult conflicts in a marriage (see chapter 6) and other areas of adult life. A woman becomes immobilized by fear whenever her husband looks at all aggressive; a man collapses in guilt whenever his wife complains about anything.

However, not all adult emotional problems result from childhood experiences. More often than generally realized, women are driven to despair by physical, sexual, and emotional abuse in their ongoing marriages (Walker, 1989). Sometimes, men are pushed into severe depression when they cannot cope with continuous verbal abuse from their wives.

In summary, when psychiatrists "treat mental illness," they are manipulating and controlling people who instead need someone to address their basic needs and conflicts. The psychiatric interventions tend to suppress conflict, often at great cost to the person labeled "patient." The conflict model is far more appropriate and effective than its psychiatric counterpart.

PSYCHIATRY AND THE HOMELESS

Psychiatrists also enter the arena of conflict resolution on a social and political scale. The profession originated during the industrial revolution as a method of bypassing legal restraints on the incarceration of homeless street people (Foucault, 1965). Civil commitment proceedings were instituted throughout the Western world permitting the indefinite incarceration of homeless, unemployed, and sometimes mad people. State mental hospitals, within which the profession originated, were lockups for the poor. Some became self-sustaining feudal systems in which the once homeless inmates now became completely self-supporting with their own dairies, farms, mechanics, tailors, and so on.

By the 1930s these giant lockups, which shoved the problem of poverty under the institutional rug, had become too large and unmanageable. Lobotomy and various shock "therapies" were developed for subduing the inmates (Breggin, 1979, 1983a). In the 1950s, drugs were developed that induce chemical lobotomies (Breggin, 1991). These drugs—called neuroleptics, antipsychotics, or major tranquilizers—remain in widespread use in institutions of all kinds, and in clinics and private practice as well.

Despite the new drugs, the hospitals remained overflowing. Then in 1963 the federal government's disability payment programs began to cover psychiatric diagnoses, and, for the first time, patients declared psychiatrically disabled could receive a meager sum to help them live at home, in nursing homes, board-and-care homes, and sometimes on the streets. Thus began so-called deinstitutionalization, which was mostly a transfer of patients to private facilities, with the cost shifted from the state to the federal government. This series of events is better described by the term transinstitutionalization than by deinstitutionalization (Brown, 1988; Mosher and Burti, 1989).

The economic policies of the Reagan and Bush administrations resulted in a vast increase in the numbers of homeless. The real wages of the poor dropped, low-cost housing subsidies decreased, housing costs went up. The result was a massive escalation in people who could not afford housing.

Now psychiatry is attempting to reinstitute its old policies in what might be called reinstitutionalization. Here psychiatry moves into an area of societal conflict—what to do about the poor and homeless—and offers an easy political solution: lock them up against their will. That many of these people may show psychiatric "symptoms" is beside the point. First, being homeless can make a person seem crazy. Second, people who are more helpless or less competent (including people who seem mad) are the first to suffer from adverse economic conditions. What these unfortunates need is not involuntary incarceration and drugs, but improved economic circumstances, including, if necessary, nonmedical forms of support from society.

Many of those who are now unable to cope with society, including thousands of street people, have been brain damaged by previous psychiatric treatments. Even those who are neurologically impaired and relatively helpless don't need state mental hospitals. They don't need to be declared "biochemically imbalanced," only to have genuine biochemical imbalances inflicted on them by means of highly toxic drugs. What they do need is a safe haven in which they can be free from these abuses (Breggin, 1991; Breggin and Stern, in press; Mosher and Burti, 1989).

A few years ago I interviewed several dozen homeless people at two California drop-in centers. Some were interviewed alone and some in groups. With one exception, all agreed that no matter how hungry or cold they became, they would never voluntarily enter a mental hospital. They preferred the streets to psychiatric incarceration and "treatment." The one exception was an older woman who said that she would go to a hospital before she'd starve, but survivors of psychiatry in the group arose to warn her never to take the risk.

Some of these homeless people had undergone brief counseling, which they recalled as positive, and none were hostile to "talking doctors." All of these people rejected biopsychiatric interventions, often preferring the hazards of the street to those of the mental hospital. They remind us that involuntary hospitalization and treatment are aimed at serving the convenience of a society that does not wish to confront its conflicts with the poor and the disabled.

PSYCHIATRY AND VIOLENCE: THE LATEST INITIATIVE

For a few hundred years, psychiatrists have claimed to be specialists in predicting violence, thereby justifying the involuntary treatment of presumably violent individuals. Thus they intervened in both family disputes and criminal proceedings to suppress conflict by incarcerating one of the members "for his (her) own good."

Then in the 1974 Tarasoff decision in California, a psychiatrist was held responsible for the violent acts of one of his patients on the grounds that he could have warned the patient's potential victim. Psychiatry did an abrupt turnabout and began to claim that it could *not* predict violence.

I became heavily involved in psychiatric reform activities in the early 1970s in a successful effort to stem the resurgence of lobotomy and other forms of psychiatric surgery. A group consisting of two Harvard neurosurgeons and a Harvard psychiatrist had obtained government funds on the grounds that they were developing a form of psychiatric brain surgery that could treat violent ghetto rioters. Thus they exploited the public's fear of racial violence to obtain publicity and federal funds for a psychiatric solution to the most frightening of our national problems during that period. A critical political problem was to be solved by oppressive medical means (see Breggin, 1991, pp. 418, 426, 427).

The suggested use of psychosurgery for the control of violence was one aspect of larger federal strategy aimed at establishing a series of violence centers in association with well-known urban psychiatric centers. The thrust was biological and genetic with reliance on involuntary treatment, behavior modification, and physical interventions. Psychosurgery for the control of violence was stopped largely as a result of efforts organized through the Center for the Study of Psychiatry and the funding of the violence centers was prevented by a larger coalition.

Twenty years later—at the moment this book is being completed—the federal mental health establishment is again planning a national biomedical program for violence control, and with a decidedly racist thrust. Frederick Goodwin, a biological psychiatrist and the highest ranking federal mental health official, had stepped into a controversy when he compared the inner city to a "jungle" and further compared inner city young men to Rhesus monkeys who are preoccupied with killing each other, having sex, and reproducing. As a result of the furor, I wrote a letter to the *New York Times* and consulted with an aide to U.S. Congressman John Conyers. I received the transcript of Goodwin's remarks as he delivered them to a meeting of the National Mental Health Council. It discloses the "violence initiative," the hitherto unpublicized *top priority* for federal mental health funding starting in 1994. The aim of the violence initiative is the early identification of genetically and biochemically defective young inner city men who will be studied and subjected to involuntary incarceration, behavior modification, and/or drug treatment.

The violence initiative specifically rejects any attempt to identify or remedy social, economic, or cultural causes of violence, such as racism, unemployment, and poverty. As a biomedical strategy, it will locate the problem within supposedly defective individuals who presumably suffer from genetic and biochemical disorders.

Not only will the violence initiative distract society from the true causes of inner city violence, it poses a monstrous threat to civil liberties and to the well-being of those at whom the program is aimed. Goodwin initially estimates that 100,000 children and young people will be targeted. Inevitably, most will be black and inevitably the numbers will grow.

On March 19, 1992, I sent out "An Urgent Message from the Center for the Study of Psychiatry," accompanied by a review of A Dangerous New Biomedical Program for Social Control: The Federal "Violence Initiative." It is the opening round of an educational campaign to alert the nation to this latest biomedical attempt at social control. By the time this book comes out, that educational effort will hopefully be in full swing.

PSYCHIATRY AND THE PSYCHOTIC PERSON

Psychiatry derives much of its power from the claim that it offers special understanding and indispensable medical approaches to people labeled psychotic, such as so-called "schizophrenics." In fact, it offers patients little more than chemical lobotomy and involuntary confinement.

On the other hand, there is ample evidence for the efficacy of more humane, nonmedical approaches. These caring, psychosocial alternatives have been described in a number of places (Karon, 1989; Mosher and Burti, 1988; Breggin, 1991; Breggin and Stern, in production). The superiority of the psychosocial approach for very disturbed people labeled "schizophrenic" has been demonstrated in controlled studies (Mosher and Burti, 1989; Karon, 1989).

My career in mental health began as a college student when I worked in a student-run treatment program for state mental hospital inmates. As untrained college sophomores and juniors working with individual inmates of the institutions, we were able to get the vast majority out of the hospital in less than a year (Breggin, 1991).

People who are so fragile that they distort or withdraw from reality are in special need of tender, caring approaches. These injured persons are less able than stronger people to survive the assault of authoritarian, coercive, and toxic treatments. Anyone who feels sufficiently worthless and humiliated to imagine being Jesus Christ will be especially demoralized by being told that he or she is in reality "a schizophrenic" who is biologically and genetically defective.

People who are drastically impaired in their capacity for social relationships need supportive social relationships from friends, family, rehabilitation workers, or psychotherapists. Often they need help with supervised housing or employment. It would be more helpful, more humane, and in the long run less expensive if society offered them what they need—safe havens staffed by nonprofessional, caring people. Because nonprofessional, nonpsychiatric interventions are less expensive, the overall cost to society would be reduced.

PSYCHIATRY REINFORCES THINGNESS

Modern biobehavioral psychiatry falls almost wholly into Dynamic III: coercion (see the Three Dynamic Table, p. 261). Dynamic III: coercion describes the conditions created by any authoritarian and totalitarian institution, such as a mental hospital or prison. In *Asylums* (1961), Erving Goffman showed how state mental hospitals turn patients into docile inmates devoid of self-respect or self-determination. The same dismal results were achieved in the USSR and Eastern Bloc countries through decades of political totalitarianism (see chapter 10). Thus, the values imposed on patients in almost any Western mental hospital parallel those inflicted on the citizens of the Russia, Poland, Hungary, and many other European nations a few years ago. Carrying our comparison still further, the problem of "deinstitutionalizing" a long-term psychiatric inmate is not different in kind from the problem of bringing a middle-aged Soviet citizen into the era of *perestroika* and *glasnost.*

The philosophies of European communism and American biobehavioral and institutional psychiatry have much in common both in principle and outcome. Both are authoritarian, materialistic, and reductionist; both demean their victims and render them more helpless. Thus, it is no coincidence that nearly all of the descriptive phrases listed as Dynamic III: coercion in the table can be applied equally to both totalitarianism and to biological, institutional psychiatry.

When humans are most irrational and oppressed, they tend to view themselves as "things," as summarized in the Three Dynamics of Human Progress table in the column entitled "Thingness." For example, patients labeled psychotic often believe they are being controlled by outside forces, from extraterrestrials or people who don't really know them, to farfetched energy waves and remote control devices.

As I describe in an article in *The Journal of Existential Psychology and Psychiatry* (in production), psychiatry is likely to view irrational and oppressed human beings in the way they view themselves—as defective, disabled devices, rather than as struggling human beings. When the patient says, "I am controlled by radio waves," the psychiatrist answers, "In fact, you are controlled by genetic defects and biochemical imbalances." When the patient says, "People want to control me," the psychiatrist responds, "If you really believe that then you should be controlled." The psychiatrist then fulfills the patient's worst fears by locking her up "for her own good." Psychiatry reinforces the mental patient's worst self-image as lacking in autonomy and self-determination, unworthy of human love, and deserving of coercion.

Too often, the psychiatrist actually pushes the patient further into mental helplessness by giving suppressive drugs and electroshock. Already feeling like a defective objective, the patient is made neurologically dysfunctional by the treatment. I suggested the term *iatrogenic helplessness* to describe the biopsychiatric principle of maintaining authority and control by damaging the patient's brain (Breggin, 1983). The production of brain dysfunction encourages the patient and doctor alike to view the patient as a defective mechanism lacking in free will, autonomy, or higher spiritual aspirations.

THE OVERALL FAILURE OF THE MENTAL HEALTH PROFESSIONS

As a profession born of involuntary treatment and state mental hospitals, psychiatry is historically rooted in coercion. Its original mandate, still in force, was to suppress conflicts between the homeless poor and the remainder of society by locking up the homeless (Foucault, 1965).

Often psychiatry uses outright force in the form of incarceration and involuntary drugging, and sometimes even involuntary electroshock. More often it uses the *threat* of force, plus moral authority, to control and manipulate people (Breggin, 1964). Seemingly voluntary psychiatric patients frequently remain in treatment out of fear of being coerced if they attempted to quit.

When patients are legally voluntary, psychiatry's approach too often remains Dynamic III: coercion—the dehumanizing of the individual into a defective object or thing by means of biochemical and genetic theories, psychiatric diagnoses, and brain-disabling treatments.

Even more psychologically oriented mental health interventions frequently end up dehumanizing the recipient of the services by diagnosing and manipulating them (Masson, 1988; Cohen, 1990). Since biobehavioral psychiatry tends to set the official standard for mental health practices—for example, through its textbooks and diagnostic manuals—much of what passes for mental health treatment does more harm than good.

Despite its vast opportunity to do so, the mental health profession has not spearheaded our understanding of the damaging effects of childhood abuse. Despite the public's view of psychoanalysis as focusing on the harm done to children by their parents, Freud actually helped delay recognition of the widespread extent of childhood abuse. As a result, his life's work encouraged the oppression of children and the discrediting of adult clients who had been abused as children (Miller, 1984; Masson, 1984).

As Jeffrey Masson has documented in *The Assault on Truth* (1982), Freud used his theory of the Oedipus complex to cover up the sexual abuse of young women and children. When he was rejected by his colleagues for making known that his female patients had been sexually abused as children, he instead made up the Oedipal theory, which claims that patients imagine, desire, and invent the abuse.

Most of the advances in understanding child abuse have come from renegades within the mental health profession, such as Alice Miller (1984), or from those wholly outside the profession, often in the field of social psychology or sociology (see chapter 5). The profession has been especially remiss in its failure to raise issues about patriarchy and the male abuse of women and children. Many psychiatric textbooks, for example, fail to mention these critical issues and also continue to use blatantly sexist diagnoses.

BRINGING TOGETHER PSYCHOTHERAPY AND CONFLICT RESOLUTION

Chapter 6 outlined some of the basic principles of psychotherapy from a conflict resolution viewpoint. Psychotherapy or "talking therapy" can be provided by a variety of professionals, including psychiatrists, psychologists, social workers, and counselers, and also by volunteers and noncredentialed individuals (Breggin, 1991). Attitude is more than any technique. A loving, empathic, enthusiastic approach on the part of the therapist will influence the outcome positively for the client (see chapter 6).

When psychotherapists help people, often they do so despite their training. The best psychotherapists, without necessarily realizing it, utilize a conflict analysis and resolution model rather than a medical model. They help people overcome both intrapsychic and extrapsychic conflict in order to find more personally free and loving approaches to life. These therapists reject the psychiatrically oriented diagnostic and treatment methods they were taught in school.

Experienced psychotherapists often agree with the thrust of this book, that therapeutic help should not prescribe or direct the individual toward particular outcomes. Rather, psychotherapy provides a healthy relationship that encourages personal growth and it implements principles that facilitate self-realization and human community.

Meanwhile, little or nothing about liberty and love is taught to mental health professionals or discussed in the literature. Because traditional psychiatry so offends the principles of liberty, it simply ignores the issue in its books and teaching programs. Psychologists have proven somewhat more willing to examine questions of personal freedom. Love, the ultimate method of healing the wounded heart and resolving human conflict, is rarely addressed anywhere in the mental health community.

Many psychotherapists do learn about loving approaches through their own experiences in therapy and through sharing their feelings with trusted colleagues. Unfortunately, this is left to chance and personal initiative, and is too often discouraged by formal education or training.

As psychiatry has become increasingly authoritarian and biological, fewer and fewer psychiatrists have even an inkling of these more human approaches. The mantle for offering good psychotherapy has fallen to nonmedical specialists, such as psychologists, social workers, and counselors. But the biopsychiatric hegemony tends to corrupt the entire field.

Individual well-being and the good of society is far better served by a conflict-resolution model that emphasizes liberty and love than by the psychiatric model. While there may be little hope in the near future for reforming psychiatry, there is much hope for conflict analysis and resolution, and for psychotherapy; but only if they divorce themselves from traditional psychiatric theory and practice. In the ideal scenario, psychotherapy would eventually become a part of the overall field of conflict analysis and resolution.

▼ ▼

CHAPTER 8

Resolving Conflict within Business Corporations

> *There is an epidemic of disaffection subverting the organizations of America, whether they be public or private. Increasingly more people view their jobs as sentences to be served rather than as opportunities for the realization of their personal dreams. The disaffected are losing any significant belief in their unique worth to their organizations. . . . Too many believe that happiness— however it is defined—is to be found only outside of the job.*
> *David K. Hart, in **The Revitalization of the Public Service** by Robert Denhardt and Edward Jennings, Jr. (1987)*

> *Most people still believe that every kind of large-scale adminis- tration must necessarily be "bureaucratic," i.e., an alienated form of administration. And most people are unaware of how deaden- ing the bureaucratic spirit is and how it pervades all spheres of life. . . . Bureaucrats fear personal responsibility and seek refuge behind their rules; their security and pride lie in their loyalty to the rules, not in their loyalty to the laws of the human heart.*
> *Erich Fromm, **To Have or To Be** (1976)*

Large corporations, as well as Mom-and-Pop corner stores, are supposed to represent the principles of liberty, the free market, and the pursuit of self-interest. Given the potential conflict be- tween liberty and love, capitalism and caring, it is important to explore whether or not corporations can implement the principles of love within the workplace.

CORPORATIONS AND THE FREE MARKET

In reality, of course, corporations rarely if ever compete in any- thing approximating a free market; nor are they run purely for the benefit of profit-hungry shareholders. Large corporations thrive amid innumerable government benefits, from the transportation infrastructure paid for by taxpayers to the innumerable contracts and services provided by government agencies. Tariffs, labor laws, and myriad federal regulations control competition to the advantage of existing corporations. Often corporations engage in monopolistic practices, fixing prices, setting interest rates, and so on. Furthermore, they often fail to pursue the profit of their shareholders. One "golden parachute" scandal after another has testified to how executives place their own self-interest above that of the actual owners of the businesses. Often corporations become rigid bureaucracies with nearly as much automatic tenure as the oldest federal agencies.

Even smaller companies do not function within a free market. Typically they are subjected to government regulation in the form of taxation, building, and health codes, and the regulation of their specific activities, such as home and office construction, food supplies, or health services. Many of these regulations serve more to limit competition than to protect the public.

This chapter cannot provide a thoroughgoing analysis of the complex topic of corporate structure and function, or the limits of free enterprise. Rather, it can illustrate the usefulness of the Three Dynamic Theory in evaluating an important societal institution, the large corporation. In particular, it examines the actual and potential role of love in corporate life.

DYNAMIC I IN MODERN CORPORATE LIFE

In a 1986 conference at Rice University organized by Konstantin Kolenda entitled *Organizations and Ethical Individualism* (1988), psychologists, philosophers, and political scientists addressed the issue of the moral basis of American institutions, especially corporations. Several contributors addressed Dynamic I issues, and there was a remarkable consensus around the need for more caring and loving values throughout society, including the business world.

After proposing a theory of psychological individualism, which closely parallels my own viewpoint, Alan Waterman suggested that corporations provide one avenue for self-realization or self-actualization—the fulfillment of a variety of liberty and love needs, including autonomy, identity, and meaningful relationships. Many theories about enhancing corporate function, he pointed out, support the individual employee's striving for self-fulfillment. As examples that confirm his observations, he cited William Scott and David K. Hart's *Organizational America* (1979), William Ouchi's *Theory Z* (1981), Thomas Peters and Robert H. Waterman, Jr.'s *In Search of Excellence* (1982), and John Naisbitt and Patricia Aburdene's *Reinventing the Corporation* (1985).

Ouchi's book applies Japanese business techniques to America through what he calls the Theory Z approach to management. The aim is to increase productivity. The management style requires Dynamic I qualities, such as trust and intimacy, a "close familiarity" among employees (p. 8). He also emphasizes "subtlety," which in part means sensitivity to individual capabilities. Clearly he believes that the effective corporation provides for many of the basic needs of its employees through what he calls an "industrial clan."

Naisbitt and Aburdene in *Re-inventing the Corporation* emphasize that the economic necessities of the 1970s were responsible for the changing climate of American corporations. These stresses include the "demise of industrial America and stiff competition from global rivals such as Japan," (p. 2). The authors believe that the burgeoning information society will require new values and approaches. Yet these new values themselves are in many ways traditional. Naisbitt and Aburdene observe:

We are entering a dynamic period when the economic imperative for a more competitive, more productive work force is leading us back to the kind of humanistic values expressed in the philosophy of Kollmorgen Corp., "trust, freedom, and respect for the individual." Douglas McGregor's Theory Y, which states, in effect, that people will be more productive if they are treated with respect, was not wrong; it was simply twenty-five years ahead of its time. (p. 2.)

In passing, they acknowledge the potential impact of women in the new corporate world. Women sometimes need to learn from men how to be more "comfortable with power and conflict"; but men in turn have things to learn from women:

*We are re-inventing the corporation into a place where intuition
is respected and where the leader's role is that of a facilitator,
teacher, and nurturer of human potential. This means that
women can transform the workplace by expressing, not by giving
up their personal values. (p. 242.)*

The successful corporation of the future, according to Naisbitt
and Aburdene, will not ignore social problems, such as education
and women's issues. It will respond directly to themes of social
and personal responsibility.

Employees, according to the same authors, will want to "make a
commitment" to their corporations; but to do this, corporations
will have to provide an inspiring vision. They conclude, "The word
will get around which companies have nourishing environments
for personal growth, and those will attract our best and brightest,
thus assuring their survival into the next century," (p. 300).

Peters and Waterman's *In Search of Excellence* provides similar
lessons. The authors focus on the need to stand out, and quote
existential sociologist Ernest Becker: "Society . . . is a vehicle for
earthly heroism. . . . It is the burning desire for the creature to
count. . . . What man really fears is not so much extinction, but
extinction with *insignificance*." On the other hand, they realize, the
desire for distinction can conflict with the desire to belong.

Successful companies inspire a belief in the individual, Peters
and Waterman observe; but their book lacks any inspiring set of
values of its own. We have a call for inspiration without any in-
spirational content.

Scott and Hart, the authors of *Organizational America*, were themselves at the 1986 Rice conference with which this discussion began. Scott presented a paper he wrote with Terence Mitchell,
entitled "The Problem or Mystery of Evil and Virtue in Organizations." It describes the usually unspoken aim of management to
"exist in a mutually satisfying, harmonious condition of virtue,"
(p. 48).

Scott and Mitchell assert that individuals have the potential for
evil and for virtue, and cite contemporary corporate acts to support
both conclusions. Their thrust is to "reduce the venom in organizations" and to "cultivate in organizations, like the woman in the
garden, a certain tenderness and compassion toward others without which we cannot flourish as individuals," (p. 69).

Another of the Rice presentations even more directly addressed what I call Dynamic I: love. David Hart discussed "Management and Benevolence: The Fatal Flaw in Theory Y." Hart believes that caricatures of corporate organizations as inducing either good or evil are too shallow. Life in corporate America "might be mundane, but it is scarcely hideous," (p. 74). The main problem is to help corporations become more conscious of "the complete person," and his or her needs. This requires a shift away from viewing the worker strictly as a producer.

Hart too cites Douglas McGregor's Theory Y management as an attempt to introduce humanistic psychology into business, but concludes that the results have not been encouraging. Criticizing many of the authors who promote humanistic values, Hart concludes that they have a "fatal flaw: the failure to take seriously, and to incorporate, the concept of *benevolence* into Theory Y theory and practice," (p. 75).

Hart sets the problem in its historical context—the Seventeenth and Eighteenth centuries, with Thomas Hobbes on the one hand denigrating the human being's potential for benevolence, and Adam Smith defending it (see chapter 2).

According to Hart, it is a fundamental mistake for corporations to aim at *control* over employees in the interest of productivity. He rejects as immoral the notion that "leaders should use the self-esteem needs of followers to better control them, and thus, to more effectively achieve organizational goals," (p. 83). But even humanistic approaches to management, he observes, act as if self-interest rather than self-actualization primarily motivates human activity. As a result, the corporation does not value individual employees for their intrinsic worth as human beings, but merely for their productivity.

Hart cites benevolence as the missing factor in the equation. By benevolence, he means "the noninstrumental love of others; a love that is complete in and of itself," (p. 87). Here Hart seems in full accord with the Dynamic I concept of unconditional or noncontingent love. In my own words, love is not an exchange but a gift. Hart agrees that, consistent with human nature, organizations and society must raise love for others onto a par with self-love, that love and self-love are in fact inseparable.

Hart says, "To be fully benevolent, the principle of love for others must be clearly understood as fundamental to human nature and its entailments clearly understood," (p. 95). Among the entailments, Hart believes, "The key aspect must be the intention to be benevolent because one loves others" not because one wishes to gain something from them in exchange. Thus he clearly distinguished between Dynamic II: voluntary exchange and Dynamic I: gifting.

In concluding, Hart believes that "until we return benevolence to its right place, our organizational reforms will be both incomplete and insubstantial," (p. 96).

All management theory and practice must be derived from the dual aspects of human nature: the love of self and the love of others. In the workplace or in all society, according to Hart (1988), love leads us to respect the needs and the rights of others:

I must call every man "brother" and every woman "sister"—and be called "brother" by them. . . . It means that any unjustice done to another is intolerable, because one cannot endure the thought of hurt coming to the loved brother or sister. The assumption of moral obligations of brotherhood and sisterhood is the ultimate guarantee that the rights of all will be preserved. (p. 90.)

Hart's viewpoint closely approximates the basic theme of this book: that love is the source of human rights and conflict resolution (see chapter 1). Again consistent with my viewpoint, Hart finds that the persistent denial of love and the reliance on coercion leads to psychological numbing. In another paper (1987), Hart describes "the feelingless functionary" who submerges himself or herself in the larger institution without concern for moral principles or human outcomes.

Corporate management is obviously not alone in its numbing attempt at moral neutrality. It is a problem for society and "moral philosophy must be made accessible to scholars, practitioners, and ordinary citizens alike," (p. 96). Consistent with the growing movement away from the use of technical and academic language (see chapter 11), Hart calls for the reform of philosophy to make it comprehensible and relevant to the ordinary person. He believes, much as I do, that moral philosophy, including specifically benevolent ideals, should be a part of public discussion—just as

Emerson, James, and Dewey, among others, made much of their idealistic writing available to the public.

At the same Rice conference on ethical individualism, in a presentation entitled "Social Organization and Individual Initiative: A Eudaimonistic Model," David Norton sought to unite the concepts of individualism with the good and happy (eudaimic) life. In his initial paper, he did not directly address issues of benevolence and love for others; but in response to criticism on this point from Hart, he appended an enlightening "Afterword," discussing the connection between egoism and altruism, self-love, and love for others. He declares that self-love matures into love for others, and that "a life that does not include unselfish love for others is significantly incomplete. Indeed, love by definition *is*, I think, unselfish," (p. 125).

Norton supports the Dynamic I principle that love transcends distinctions between self and other, making individual interests into mutual ones. He seems to conclude that self-love is the primary or ultimate motivation behind self-actualization, of which love for others is a part. However, I am not inclined to spend too much time making distinctions between Norton's view on the one hand or Hart's or mine on the other. In each case, love is acknowledged as playing a central role in human life.

My own presentation at the Rice conference was entitled "Evaluating Human Progress: A Unified Approach to Psychology, Economics, and Politics." It was gratifying to see that most of the participants, including those with the greatest experience in the field of business management (Scott and Hart), were converging on the same values and themes. My presentation concluded:

Liberty and love generate each other. Love, a joyful awareness of others, encourages us to value the freedom of others as we value our own. Liberty, the absence of arbitrary force, gives us the best opportunity to become aware of others and hence to love them. (p. 157.)

WOMEN'S VALUES

More recently there has been a growing awareness of the values that women can and do bring into the workplace. Sally Helgesen has made them the subject of her book, *The Female Advantage* (1990). Helgesen notes the same Dynamic I trends as I have summarized in this chapter and calls them "feminine principles":

We feel, many of us, that women are more caring and intuitive, better at seeing the human side, quicker to cut through competitive distinctions of hierarchy and ranking, impatient with cumbersome protocols. Our belief in these notions is intuitive rather than articulated; we back it up with anecdotes instead of argument. Some women feel ashamed of their belief in feminine principles; some are scoffing, others proud, even defiant. (pp. 4–5.)

Helgesen's book is written in a readable, popular style, and perhaps of necessity lacks some of the depth of a more thorough feminist analysis, such as Marilyn French's *Beyond Power*. But she draws upon relevant background literature and observes "female values of responsibility, connection, and inclusion have been devaluated in our culture, which tends to celebrate the lone hero, the rugged individual," (p. 233). (See also Gilligan, 1982.)

Helgesen believes times are changing: "the female view that one strengthens oneself by strengthening others is finding greater acceptance, and female values of inclusion and connection are emerging as valuable leadership qualities," (p. 233). Her hope is:

As women's leadership qualities come to play a more dominant role in the public sphere, their particular aptitudes for long-term negotiating, analytic listening, and creating an ambience in which people work with zest and spirit will help reconcile the split between the ideas of being efficient and being humane. (p. 249.)

FROM KARL MARX TO SMILEY BLANTON

The idea that human beings need to approach labor in a loving manner is not new. It can be extracted from the concept of "estranged labor" as presented in Karl Marx's early work, *The Economic and Philosophic Manuscripts of 1844.*

Marx's writing can be difficult to decipher, and I fear that his supporters may be overly generous in describing his attitude toward humanity as basically loving. At times, however, he does say that when labor becomes an involuntary necessity under the control of others, the individual loses his or her personal connection to the experience. Laboring thus loses its intrinsically joyful quality, as well as its direct connection with the individual's personal life. As a result, the individual becomes alienated from his or her labor. Since the process of work is central to one's personal and social experience, the individual becomes self-alienated and alienated from society.

From Karl Marx to Smiley Blanton is a great leap, but one worth taking. Chapter 2 introduced psychiatrist Blanton, the author of *Love or Perish*. Approaching the problem of work from a hybrid of psychoanalytic and Christian values, Blanton believes that the duality of human nature—love and hate—is especially apparent in work. Work often requires aggressive activity, and yet it must be loving in order to be ultimately satisfying. Like Marx, he laments that work has become coerced and soulless in modern times:

We are no longer personal slaves, but work has increasingly become a kind of soulless tyranny in itself. Under modern industrial conditions, more and more people find that they have little genuine interest in what they do. They are but tiny cogs, as a rule, in a huge machine directed by remote corporate management. (p. 133.)

According to Blanton, people must feel that their work is meaningful, creative, and loving, and they must be rewarded with love as well as money. Despite his sermonizing tone, Blanton's conclusions are similar to those of many social scientists:

No man can win true happiness unless he learns to work with loving hands. No society can endure unless it permits its members to work the miracle of love in their daily tasks, on however small a scale. (p. 148.)

JOY IN THE WORKPLACE?

Interesting observations have been generated by research based on Mihaly Csikszentmihalyi's concept of flow and reported in *Optimal Experience* (Csikszentmilhalyi and Csikszentmilhalyi, 1988). Flow is the positive experience of work or play when people are fully involved in doing what they intrinsically value doing, "something that is worth doing for its own sake," (p. 29).

Csikszentmilhalyi compares the concept of flow to Maslow's self-actualization and "peak experiences"; but he has tried to analyze it into components suitable for scientific research. The concept of flow has many philosophical antecedents, and in a general way, can be viewed as the opposite of what Marx called "alienation."

The person in flow feels confronted with a meaningful challenge that he or she is capable of meeting. Thus, there is a sense of mastery. The tasks are freely chosen, and there is a sense of autonomy and personal freedom. Consciousness becomes wholly focused, there is "total absorption" with a diminished awareness of the passage of time. Awareness and action become one. The individual finds the process intrinsically enjoyable and worthwhile, and is satisfied with the result.

Models for the flow experience have come from athletes, artists, scientists, professionals, and others who become deeply involved in their work or play. Those who study flow believe that it is a cross-cultural, universal experience.

Flow is a combination of Dynamics I and II. It designates the experience summed up in "I love what I'm doing." Consistent with Dynamic I, the sense of self and other is diminished, there is no sense of sacrifice in exerting energy and spending time, and the process is enjoyed for itself. Research in *Optimal Experience* also confirms that flow tends to require a Dynamic II context of freedom and autonomy. Conversely, when people are subjected to Dynamic III: coercion, flow is disrupted.

Is flow possible on the typical job? Studies reported in *Optimal Experience* show that it is possible, but only under relatively ideal conditions. Even in professional roles that seem to offer many creative opportunities, people frequently feel frustrated and unfulfilled, and must seek flow elsewhere in their lives. Meanwhile, working class people often give up the hope for anything better and succumb to a life with little flow (e.g., see pp. 47–49).

Not surprisingly, flow advocates believe that it not only enhances enjoyment but also work productivity. In *Optimal Flow,* Judith LeFevre concludes:

Since flow enhances activation, concentration, and creativity, it is likely that performance would improve by increasing the amount of time spent in flow. In addition, increases in flow may improve morale and prevent burnout, since motivation and satisfaction are also enhanced. (p. 318.)

COUNTER-CURRENTS

Not everyone agrees that employees can or should get "in the flow." Indeed, values associated with self-actualization may be losing out in the workplace. In *The New Individualists* (1991), Paul Leinberger and Bruce Tucker forecast the eminent demise of individualism. The search for the "authentic self" is becoming outmoded. It will be replaced by "the artificial person," an identity that is a nonidentity, a self that is embedded in and a reflection of the complex network of relationships characteristic of the modern corporation. The authors suggest, with seeming ambivalence, that the "artificial person" may be necessary in America's postindustrial era.

There are other signs that self-actualization and other higher values have a diminishing place in the modern business world. None of us can help but be shocked by the flood of corporate greed unleashed by the Reagan-Bush era. We can only hope that the seemingly endless disclosures of scandals are having a salutary effect. Nor are we unaware of the materialistic values summed up in the word Yuppie.

AN INHERENT CONTRADICTION?

There is a built-in obstacle to the humanizing of corporate life that few of its advocates seem to take into consideration. It is the same problem we found in psychotherapy (see chapter 6) as the conflict between capitalism and caring.

The purpose of the corporation is profit-making and its function is to compete in the supposedly free market. The values inherent in profit-making and competition must be modified or ameliorated in order to facilitate a more loving, open, and trusting environment.

Consider, for example, Paul H. Weaver's analysis of *The Suicidal Corporation* (1988). As a free-market advocate, Weaver envisions corporations moving toward a more honest affirmation of self-interest, the profit motive, and a competitive free market. While Weaver acknowledges that the Reagan years fell short of promoting a consistent set of free-market standards, he believes that Reaganomics did to a limited extent create an environment more conducive to the free market. He also believes that the younger generation of corporate executives is much more free-market oriented than the previous one.

When Weaver describes the ideal free-market corporation, he says nothing about the "self-actualization" or "self-realization" of individual employees. He does favor a strong code of ethics and believes that "A scrupulously honorable, customer-oriented, product-honoring ethos should prevail," (p. 241). Consistent with the highest free-market standards, he presses corporations "to strengthen the shareholder and customer interests in the corporation, and to subordinate the management interest in them," (p. 244). Corporations, according to Weaver's free-market philosophy, should have a "mission that transcends the career interests of the executives."

Weaver's ideal employee pursues neither self-actualization nor self-aggrandizing careerism; he or she is dedicated to the interests of the shareholders, which includes the needs of the customer and the principles of the free market. Consistent with Dynamic II: liberty, Weaver believes that working within a genuinely capitalistic corporation will give employees a sense of pride or self-esteem.

Weaver's analysis is totally consistent with Dynamic II: liberty, and probably represents the best we can expect from the promotion of free-market values. Unless the views of free-market advocates are drastically modified along the lines suggested by David Hart and myself, there is little hope that the coming years will see a substantially more loving workplace for many or most Americans.

THE FUTURE

As big business encounters increasing difficulties competing in a global marketplace and adjusting to the nation's persistently sluggish economy, what direction will it take in regard to caring values in the workplace? Will it become more efficient and streamlined at the expense of individual self-development and even individual jobs? Or will it find a way to implement more caring and joyful values among its employees? Will the influx of women help to humanize the corporation, or will women ultimately be swept along by the competitive values that are seemingly inherent in corporate functioning?

I doubt that loving values can be thoroughly integrated into an institution whose *mandate* is profit-making, and whose *survival* and *prosperity* depend on outdoing the competition. Without a drastic change in the fabric of American values and social institutions, the corporation will reject those employees who fail to perform competitively. As long as productivity in the interest of profit is the measure of an employee's value, it seems unlikely that many corporations will be able to transform themselves into more caring communities. Indeed, since management must hire and fire on the basis of productivity and profit, management would be hypocritical to speak too loudly of unconditional love or benevolence toward its employees.

Are these conclusions an indictment of capitalism? They do reflect a realistic appraisal of the more or less inevitable results of relating through Dynamic II. Liberty can become the optimal context for love; but when liberty is the be-all and end-all of institutional values, progress toward a more loving environment seems gravely limited and to some extent futile.

While corporations can make a greater effort to take the edge off internal competition and to otherwise "tenderize" the workplace, there may be inherent limits to the process. Different corporations in a variety of Western countries continue to experiment with these limits. It will be interesting to see how the Soviet Union and the Eastern Bloc nations try to solve these conflicts (see chapter 9).

Some unethical business practices are in fact due to a lack of free-market principles. Multimillion-dollar golden parachutes for executives of failing companies result from the personal greed of those executives at the expense of the shareholders. Corporations should function more honestly, and hence efficiently and more honorably, by devoting themselves to shareholder profits and other free-market ideals, and by rejecting government subsidies and special privileges. People will generate self-esteem and respect for others in a more ideal free market environment; but it is hard to see how they will gain in self-love and love for others, and genuinely experience "flow."

Modern society desperately needs a multiplicity of institutional opportunities for people to find loving relationships and community, but large corporations will probably at best make a small contribution in that direction. Society will have to provide a variety of alternative institutions offering better opportunities for joyful activity, self-development, and community.

Meanwhile, corporations can try to provide community and personal opportunities for self-development consistent with the overall aim of profit-making. If a corporation can create a more satisfying community experience, its employees will function with less stress and with more genuine enthusiasm. Good morale will help almost any organization perform better; and while good morale is not nearly so profound as love, it is a step in the right direction.

There is little or no danger that corporations will be injured by introducing more loving and community-oriented values. The competitiveness inherent in the free-enterprise system will prevent a corporation from going overboard. "Bankrupted by love" seems an unlikely epitaph. Without fear of ruining American capitalism, we can urge corporations to try harder to meet their employees' needs for love and community.

LIBERTY VERSUS LOVE IN SOCIETY

In the meantime, even more radical questions will continue to be asked about the free-enterprise system. As both Marxist and antistate critiques have documented, the so-called free-enterprise system quickly learned to provide security for itself through a broad web of state support. Since the beginning of the industrial revolution, as John Kenneth Galbraith has described (1958, 1980), capitalists have used government to build their own safety net to protect them from competition, economic downturns, and failure. Big business has sought much more than a safety net from government; it thrives on government largess of all kinds, from public support of the transportation infrastructure to defense spending, subsidies, research funding, monetary policy, and protectionist tariffs. Capitalism, as it now exists, is dependent upon and is inseparable from the state.

Whether we will ever see a genuine free market implemented on a large scale remains speculative. Whether we would *want* to see such a radical experiment remains controversial. It would be almost impossible to predict its overall effects, but it might quickly degenerate into monopolistic coercion.

The size and power of the state requires limits in order to reduce coercion within society. But in reducing government intervention, it would be cruel and unjust to take away the safety net from the poor before seeing if the rich can do without theirs. Chapter 10 will focus on the plight of the poor in modern society, as well as the overall balance between coercion, liberty, and love in society.

CHAPTER 9

▼ ▼

Resolving Societal Conflict: Eastern Europe in Transition; Poverty, Hunger, Redistributive Justice, and the Environment

Free individuals, able to render relatively rational decision-making, are found only within communities, because only in such communities do people find the psychic and social support that is required to sustain decisions free of pressures from the authorities, demagogues, or the mass media. Individuality does exist, but only within these social contexts.
                Amitai Etzioni, **The Moral Dimension: Toward a New Economics** *(1988)*

Our economic system and our relation with nature have gone haywire because we have lost track of what we really need. . . . So long as we persist in defining well-being predominantly in economic terms and in relying on economic considerations to provide us with our primary frame of reference for personal and social policy decisions, we will remain unsatisfied. . . . To the degree that we measure our lives in terms of social ties, openness to experience, and personal growth instead of in terms of production and accumulation, we are likely to be able to avoid a collision course with our environment without experiencing a sense of deprivation.
                Paul Wachtel, **The Poverty of Affluence** *(1989)*

All the members of human society stand in need of each other's assistance. . . . Where the necessary assistance is reciprocally afforded from love, from gratitude, from friendship, from esteem, the society flourishes and is happy. All the different members are bound together by the agreeable bands of love and affection. . . .
                Adam Smith, **The Theory of Moral Sentiments** *(1759)*

The activities of individuals easily become obscured when the focus is on society; but individual persons are the only source of human activity. There are no "social forces" except those that are generated by persons, and no collective will separate from the impact of the many individual wills expressed within society. There is no great collective ghost or spiritual cloud that emanates from individuals and then looms over them with a life and power of its own. Social conflict is the product of multiple individual conflicts. Even when the conflicts become embodied in institutions, such as political parties or governments, individual persons are the source of everything that is done in the name of the institutions.

Of necessity, needs and values such as patriotism and religion may lead us to speak as if society is a being with a life of its own separate from and acting upon its members. In part this also reflects the reality that institutions and ideologies, although created by people, end up influencing how people think, feel, and act. And so we speak of how schools, religions, songs, movies, and political doctrines stir up patriotic feelings; but the actual feelings exist and are processed in individual people.

Leaders of society, for better or worse, may influence many individuals at once, reinforcing the mistaken perception that "social forces" rather than individual human actions are at work. Indeed, oppressive leaders want their subjects to believe that they are being carried along by something greater than their own willingness to submit. Writing in the Sixteenth century, la Boetie eloquently described how the dictator and the oppressive state depend ultimately on the submission of individuals. Speaking of tyrants, he declares:

But if not one thing is yielded to them, if without any violence they are simply not obeyed, they become naked and undone and as nothing, just as, when the root receives no nourishment, the branch withers and dies. . . . Resolve to serve no more, and you are at once freed. I do not ask that you place hands upon the tyrant to topple him over, but simply that you support him no longer; then you will behold him, like a great Colossus whose pedestal has been pulled away, fall of his own weight and break into pieces. (pp. 51–53.)

That individuals create society is a potentially radical concept. In la Boetie's hands, it became a clarion call for nonviolent civil disobedience (see chapter 11).

While individuals remain the source of all action, we can examine the ideologies, philosophies, and religions that they have created, and how these in turn affect the basic needs, thoughts, and feelings of members of the society.

BASIC PREMISES

Two basic premises are worth recalling:

First, conflict resolution does not prescribe specific outcomes. It enables people to seek out the best possible solutions for themselves as individuals and a group, consistent with the principles of liberty and love.

Second, the conflict-tree metaphor reminds us that conflict resolution requires the recognition of our shared humanity. Even within families and among friends, viewing the other person as a different and lesser human being raises an impenetrable barrier to conflict resolution. In racial, religious, and class conflicts, the antagonists may never become intimate with any of the people seen as our adversaries; and so they find it especially easy to declare others alien to themselves and to humanity.

While it seems more difficult to love people from different races, religions, or socioeconomic classes, to resolve conflict, we must bring down the psychospiritual barriers that divide us. We must "climb back down" the conflict tree to our common root of shared human needs and aspirations (see chapter 1). Ultimately, we must make peace with the "tree" itself—with nature.

The reader might wish to review the table in chapter 1 that summarizes the principles of love, liberty, and coercion, as well as the simplified Three Dynamics Table (see p. 261).

THE STATE AND COERCION

As we begin to look more broadly at society, we immediately come face to face with the state. The state or national government is not the same as society or community, which may be viewed as an affiliation or bonding of people through shared resources and land, common interests and values, or culture and history. The state, as a political entity, holds people together through coercion. Risking a certain amount of oversimplifying, the state is based on coercion, the community on love.

State and local governments do not necessarily represent the values of the various groups or individuals within their boundaries. The recent collapse of the Soviet Union has made that abundantly clear. Government is a central organization with a monopoly over the use of force, backed up by armed forces and police (Hayek, 1944; Nozick, 1974; Oppenheimer, 1975; Nock, 1973). The degree of coercion it exerts varies from nation to nation, but the basic principle remains. The state is founded on coercion. If this were not so, government, and functions such as taxation, would be replaced by voluntary community association and charity.

The state can, of course, roughly coincide with community. Unlike the citizens of the former Soviet Union, most Americans identify themselves with the federal government. Society and state are often viewed more or less as one. Nonetheless, the state, unlike the actual community, ultimately depends on force, and must frequently resort to coercion to enforce its laws. Imagine, for example, if the U.S. government stopped using the threat of force to collect taxes. How many citizens would freely pay the full amount demanded each year by Congress and the Internal Revenue Service? Even with its monopoly on coercion, and with general agreement among citizens on the need for some taxation, the federal government is unable to collect all the taxes it imposes. Most other nations have even more difficulty getting their citizens to pay up.

To illustrate the importance of state coercion, imagine if couples in conflict with each other could routinely resort to government intervention, including the police, to solve their problems. Instead of working out their differences, they would resort to lobbying the state legislature to get their interests enforced. Nowadays, married couples can seek state intervention only on rare occasion, such as contested divorces or physical abuse.

In general, when people or institutions can resort to force, they will not develop more creative methods of conflict resolution. Chapter 8 described how psychiatry relies upon state power to accomplish many of its aims, with the result that psychiatry offers few genuinely valuable alternatives. Similarly, in the former USSR, coercion was the overriding method of dealing with conflict, with disastrous results. Conflict, long suppressed, finally erupted and brought about the destruction of the system. Since nearly all conflicts had been subject to Communist party and state intervention, methods of voluntary conflict resolution did not develop or atrophied. With the collapse of the totalitarian state, people had no institutional mechanisms for dealing with their ethnic, economic, and other societal conflicts.

Under a more democratic and constitutional government, force tends to be less obtrusive. Most U.S. citizens do not become preoccupied with the jails and guns that back up the law, until they come into conflict it. Only a rare social critic challenges submission to democratic state authority (Rothbard, 1973, 1982; Von Mises, 1966, 1969; and others cited earlier in this section).

That coercion is such an accepted part of each citizen's life should not blunt our awareness of its consequences. The lack of awareness makes the effects of coercion more insidious and potentially injurious.

THE STATE AND CONFLICT RESOLUTION

Because coercion is so central to government activities, it vastly encumbers the state's attempts to resolve conflict. Coercion, as emphasized throughout this book, is largely incompatible with conflict resolution. When the state attempts to resolve conflict, it enters into the dispute as both a source of power and money, and as a source of outright coercion; and in these capacities, the state tends to generate increasing conflict.

In modern society, interest groups vie for control of the state apparatus in order to coerce others into meeting their needs. First one lobby and then another wants more of whatever it seeks through government intervention. Since one group's claim is inevitably at the expense of at least one other's—or there would be no need for coercive state intervention—other interest groups feel compelled to escalate their own demands merely to keep up. A cycle of competition and conflict over the control of state power is inevitable.

Interest groups seek to fulfill myriad needs through the state. Some of the motivation is at least partly altruistic, as in promoting health care and welfare for the poor, public education, and civil liberties. Other aims are more obviously selfish. Meanwhile, everyone in the society ends up competing for government largess and government power: individuals, religious and cultural groups, labor, business, various professions, different age groups, towns, cities, states, and so on. Any one citizen may be benefitting from and suffering from the effects of a multitude of competing lobbies.

What if, instead, the state became an institution devoted to conflict resolution—a place to turn for help in resolving conflicts without resort to force? Suppose the state helped groups to assess the cost of coercion and unrelenting conflict, and worked to bring them together in more mutually satisfying ways?

The concept of the state as an institution of conflict resolution is at present visionary; but the fulfillment of that vision might become possible as the principles of conflict resolution become better understood and as people gain faith in the possibility of less coercive, less conflicted community. As the state evolved into an instrument of conflict resolution, it would eventually cease to be a state. It would become a true community—a place where people solve their problems through collaboration and without resort to force.

THE FORMAT OF THE CHAPTER

Because of the variety of issues, this chapter is divided into four parts. Each deals with the potential conflict between state and community, between coercion and love.

PART I: Liberty and Love in the Former USSR

PART II: The Cost of Coercing Good Deeds

PART III: Hunger, Poverty, and Redistributive Justice

PART IV: Liberty, Love, and the Environment

To provide continuity, many examples will be drawn from two regions of the world, the former USSR and the United States.

Part I: Liberty and Love in the Former USSR

The transformations taking place in the former communist societies make it easier to examine the interaction between psychological and political factors, as well as the effects of coercion, liberty, and love.

BASIC STRESS PARADIGMS BEHIND THE IRON CURTAIN

Nearly everyone who visits or reports from the former USSR and former Eastern Bloc nations describes learned helplessness as an endemic impediment to growth in these societies. In many ways, life in these closed, totalitarian societies was one neverending Basic Stress Paradigm of hurt, fear, and debilitating helplessness.

The imprinting of fear and helplessness was not complete, however, especially within the younger generation. A Czechoslovakian professor explained to me that the teaching of communist ideology in the schools was so bumbling that it failed to crush the spirit of young people. On the other hand, after a lifetime of indoctrination, most older people have been unable to adjust to a more self-determined way of life.

Conflicts between people both restimulate and draw upon the painful emotions associated with Basic Stress Paradigms. The same is true in regard to race, gender, ethnic, class, and other societal conflicts. While racism and sexism, for example, exist in their own right, they are also fueled by Basic Stress Paradigms of hurt, fear, and helplessness. And they initially bring them about as well.

In *Escape From Freedom* (1941) Erich Fromm showed how the suppressive nature of German parenting contributed to the development of Nazism. Alice Miller has more recently made similar observations. It is now generally accepted that personal frustration feeds racism, sexism, and other forms of prejudice. It also feeds submission to totalitarian regimes. Totalitarian regimes in turn create the conditions under which especially severe Basic Stress Paradigms are caused or reinforced.

A DOSE OF LIBERTY IN UNEXPECTED PLACES

To nations floundering economically, liberty—meaning individualism and capitalism—now seems like the only road to progress. Even the acme of hatred for Western ideals, Iran, sees the practical necessity of creating a capitalist enclave to lead the nation out of its economic quagmire. The government has created an "Islamic glasnost," an offshore island, Qeshm, based on a market economy. Vietnam as well has been encouraging capitalism and seeking an infusion of U.S. investments.

In China, where totalitarianism has once again suppressed much of the overt spirit of political liberty, the economy is continuing to improve. In a recent analysis in the August 25, 1991 *Washington Post*, Daniel Southerland points out that the Chinese have found ways to continue to encourage the spirit of capitalism despite their politically oppressive regime. Large foreign investors find it increasingly easy to prosper in China, and many small businesses have moved in. Decentralization of the economy is progressing and the nongovernmental sector is growing, including both private businesses and collectives. Even the collectives increasingly pursue self-interested, capitalistic policies, while continuing to call themselves socialistic. Individual Chinese have found a way to "pursue their own self-interest in a practical way" and an "entrepreneurial class" is prospering.

That all this is happening in China serves to remind us that liberty is everywhere connected to what most people consider economic progress. Too many well-intentioned social critics and idealists try to envision a world devoid of self-interest, competition, and free-market economics—without realizing that liberty is rooted in our basic needs and inspires much of what human beings accomplish. What is needed is not the abolition of freedom, but the development of a stronger context of love.

THE NEW INDIVIDUALISM IN THE
EASTERN BLOC AND RUSSIA

In Russia and the former Eastern Bloc nations, anarchistic extremes of capitalism are coming alive, although as of yet in a relatively stumbling and ineffective manner. Ayn Rand fled the Soviet Union as a young woman and went on to write *The Fountainhead* (1943) and *Atlas Shrugged* (1957), two fiercely individualistic, pro-capitalist novels. Now the often heartless and rapacious heroes of her novels are coming alive in her rejected homeland. This is not surprising. The totalitarian outrages that inspired Rand's extreme individualism are also motivating the newly liberated generation.

In a July 7, 1991 *Washington Post* article entitled "Brash New Breed 'Building Empires, Not Evil Ones,' " David Remnick describes what may be called the "Russian Randians." In an interview, twenty-four-year-old entrepreneur German Sterligov declares:

Why should I pity the poor and the lazy. Pity the sick and the weak, okay, but if the rest want to live in poverty—God help them. If they want to be slaves—well, then every slave has dignity before God. But history is made by the individual, not the crowd. It is only when the ignorant crowd takes part in the historical process that it turns into a mess.

My generation despises the system. It killed everyone and everything it touched. This was the richest state in the world and they destroyed it all down to the bone! But older people don't understand us. Their psychology is all screwed up. They are used to being equal in poverty and they assume if you have any money, you are a crook. (p. A 22.)

With the exception of the references to God, which are probably ironic, and with the exception of pity for the "sick and the weak," these statements rival those of the most ideological Randian. This new breed of extreme individualists, generally considered anachronistic in the United States, is playing an increasing role in Russia and elsewhere.

Further on in Remnick's article we hear contrasting views from the father of one of these fledgling capitalists. He laments:

Social ideals of equality, social security and a simple love for other people *play a much greater role for me than for [my son].* Maybe he is right. *Maybe to talk about social justice, you have to make society rich first. . . . But still, I can't be indifferent if I see the rise of millionaires who live on other people's labor. I can't bear that.* (*p. A 22,* emphasis added.)

Of course, neither side is without fault or flaw. The young entrepreneur is callous to the plight of the older generation that was victimized by the communist regime. The new capitalism that the younger generation reveres is already spawning widespread fraud and degrading the lives of many people less able to compete in the new system. Nor is the father's lament for lost love wholly convincing. He longs for a "simple love for other people," which in reality was used to justify one of the most oppressive systems in the history of the world.

A NEW ENTHUSIASM FOR LIBERTY

At psychology and conflict-resolution conferences I attended in the United States in the early 1990s, the group that most consistently spoke enthusiastically about the values of freedom were visitors from Eastern Europe. Some of the professors talked specifically about overcoming the "learned helplessness" developed over years of communist indoctrination and about how to stimulate "human agency" and "individualistic democratic" political processes.

During my lecture on the Three Dynamic Theory at one of the conflict-resolution conferences, I suggested, "Communism at its best is an attempt to implement love through coercion. There's a built-in contradiction." It seemed to me that the newly liberated Eastern Bloc members of the audience most fully appreciated my remarks.

One East European professor described the innovations she and her colleagues had made on T-Groups, one of the original sensitivity training methods popular in America in the late 1960s. With information on newer group techniques unavailable behind the Iron Curtain, they had developed their own innovations to encourage communication and negotiation, as well as personal assertiveness and autonomy. Thus they tried to help people overcome the effects of a state that had thwarted all such aspirations.

Polish social scientists described how Polish youth have, in a mere few years, progressed from attitudes of apathy and indifference to those of initiative and competition. Recently, I spent time with two sisters from a former Eastern Bloc nation. One had bravely fled many years ago, the other was now on vacation from her homeland, urging her sister to return to the new "land of opportunity" for daring entrepreneurs.

Some older social scientists from Poland and Czechoslovakia are wary of too strong an "individualistic" and "anarchistic" influence among some of their youth. The nearly overnight blossoming of these sentiments among the young suggests that the spirit of liberty is embedded in human nature. Ironically, the newly liberated youth sometimes fail to appreciate that America's much admired capitalism is modified by a complex safety net funded by government.

Rarely do Americans so consciously examine the values of individualism, autonomy, and freedom that are implicit in our legal, economic, and political system. Among academicians and intellectuals, these values are frequently denigrated in favor of social justice. But Eastern Bloc leaders are now keenly aware of the importance of liberty in their personal lives and they hold out the hope that American-inspired capitalism will rescue their collapsing economies as well. Yet they, along with most citizens, also display skepticism, fear, and confusion in dealing with these new ideals. They now favor everything from private property to freedom of speech, while nonetheless feeling frightened over the potential havoc wreaked upon older cultural values and a caring community. In their inner conflicts and in their real life dilemmas, these people embody the contrasting and sometimes incompatible values of liberty and love.

THE FAILURE OF SOME AMERICAN INTELLECTUALS AND SCHOLARS

On August 19, 1991, like many other Americans, I awoke to the dismaying and depressing news that a hard-line communist coup had taken place the night before in the USSR. I was attending the annual convention of the American Psychological Association in San Francisco at the time, and had the opportunity to attend a workshop quickly convened in response to these events. It was led by peace activists, including psychologists, social psychologists, and related professionals.

I expected an outpouring of loving support for the brave Russian souls who were risking their lives by opposing the coup, even by lying down in front of tanks. I also anticipated many expressions of sadness over the looming danger that the bravest and most freedom-loving Russians might soon be slaughtered in the coming days. Since the Russian resistance fighters were risking their lives for values we had helped inspire in them, the least we could do was to empathize with them.

I heard no such empathic, freedom-loving themes from the professionals who had hastily gathered in response to the coup. Instead, I heard the following:

1. *We shouldn't judge Russians by American standards; they are "different" because they are starving to death and might need a more authoritarian leadership, such as that provided by the coup.* The shocking "they are different" theme was repeated without a voice being raised in protest.

2. *Americans must do nothing to upset the coup leaders, such as showing solidarity with the freedom fighters or with the rebellious national groups in the Balkans and Eastern Europe.* In effect, the group identified with the aggressors and sought to placate them, while immediately giving up hope for the victims.

3. *We must find ways to help people like the coup leaders overcome their fear of reform, so they can realize that progress will improve their lives as well as everyone else's.* This hope seemed incredibly naive. The coup leaders, their associates, and their families of course had an enormous personal stake in resisting change and in maintaining the old order.

4. *America had its own civil war, and we would have resented interference, and so we should mind our own business during the coup.* The Russian coup and U.S. Civil War hardly seem comparable. It would have been more appropriate to compare the coup to a potential military takeover in the United States.

5. *The Russian reformers want to implement an American-style free market, and that is one reason not to support them against the coup.* This statement was greeted with widespread approval.

6. *America's leadership tries to create enemies to distract us from our own domestic problems, such as racism and poverty, and we must therefore discourage the American people from hating the coup leaders.* All governments, including ours, tend to create enemies in order to distract their citizens from domestic problems. On the other hand, on the day of the coup there seemed many good reasons for strongly favoring the reformers over the coup leaders.

7. *Avoiding nuclear holocaust is more important than who happens to lead the USSR at any given time, so we must not do anything to antagonize the coup leaders.* This seemed a widely held feeling in the workshop, even though the coup had been in power for less than twenty-four hours. Peace at any price became temporary peace at the cost of possible future war, since the coup leaders were known to be far more militaristic than the reformers.

8. *It is sad to witness the decline of a "great nation" like the Soviet Union.* This nationalistic sentiment, perhaps appropriate toward a country like Canada or the United States, seemed inappropriate to an empire made up of so many captive states, cultures, and citizens.

No one at the meeting protested these pronouncements, yet rightly or wrongly, they would have struck the average American as outrageous. They would probably enrage the average Russian as well, and most certainly the average Hungarian, Pole, Czech, or Balkan citizen. While some of the concerns being shown did have a kernel of truth to them, the overall thrust was devoid of empathy for or identification with the Russian victims of oppression. Instead, sympathy and some overt support went toward the coup leaders.

What motivated these highly educated, psychologically sophisticated professional people to take such positions? As a group they were probably not more devoid of sympathy and caring than other people. As people especially devoted to peace, they probably had considerable empathy for others.

Perhaps because of their own institutional privileges as professors and professionals, they tended to side with authority and hence with the coup; but that did not seem to explain the extent of their rejection of the reformers and freedom fighters. While their reactions undoubtedly reflect more complex motives, two factors seem especially important:

First, many reform-minded "liberal" academics and intellectuals have little appreciation of the principles of either liberty or love. They experience themselves as alienated from American values, but do not possess a sustainable set of alternative principles of their own. They equate liberty with all the failings of American capitalism. They equate love with religion, romance, or other devalued sources. This book is one attempt to remedy this situation by clarifying the values of liberty and love, and their functions in society.

Second, faced with the truly horrible threat of a renewed cold war, the people at the meeting became restimulated on hurt, fear, and helplessness, and thus abandoned the natural human tendency to empathize with and to support victims of blatant oppression. Overcome with feelings of helplessness, they did what so many frightened people do—they identified with the aggressors in the hope of staving off further trouble. Personal Basic Stress Paradigms and learned helplessness took over, blurring their political judgment and their identification with the victims of oppression.

NO MECHANISMS FOR CONFLICT RESOLUTION

While often eager to embrace liberty, members of former communist societies have little or no experience with the peaceful processes for resolving the inevitable conflicts that surface in relative freedom. According to communist ideology, these societies were supposed to be conflict free. As a result, there could be no acknowledged need for mechanisms such as mediation, arbitration, or negotiation. There were no public forums for interest groups to debate or to vie for power. The very existence of contending interest groups was denied in order to perpetuate the myth of solidarity.

Furthermore, there were few community or loving alternatives for conflict resolution. Religion was suppressed and there were few if any other private or voluntary organizations existing outside the government and Communist party realm. Scientific, educational, publishing, artistic, philanthropic, and fraternal institutions were inseparable from the state and the party, bound together more by coercion than by affinity. Whenever people came together for any purpose, they could never be sure they were free of surveillance.

Coercion was the dominant method of conflict resolution in the USSR. Orders came from the top down and resistance was largely passive, taking the form of apathy and resignation. Disputes were handled out of public view within the Communist party apparatus and the outcome was enforced by the state.

Freedom, by contrast, liberates people to express their needs and values, and hence their potential conflicts. Society must provide methods to help resolve conflicts, but liberty *per se* does not seem to adequately do this. Western society itself is grossly lacking in institutions for conflict resolution. In the final chapter we will look at this most difficult problem—how to institutionalize or otherwise make conflict-resolution processes more available.

LIMITS ON THE NEW LIBERTY: INSTITUTIONALIZING FREE ENTERPRISE

Eastern European states are already running into the limits of freedom as a principle. Issues of social justice became apparent from the very earliest attempts to introduce private property and free enterprise. Those in the best position to take advantage of the new freedoms are often the very same people who have a head start by virtue of their connections with Communist party leadership and government *apparatchiks*. In a society suddenly "made free," the original perpetrators are likely to come out on top again. Nothing so clearly illustrates how liberty can degenerate into renewed oppression.

One possible approach involves providing each citizen an equal share in what the government once owned, perhaps through a distribution of cash or vouchers that can be sold, traded, or used to purchase former government property, such as factories, automobiles, and apartments. Efforts are being made in these directions. But a distribution of cash or vouchers will not prevent the rapid reaccumulation of that wealth in the hands of those few who already have the advantages of relative wealth, old-buddy connections, and know-how.

LOVE IN THE SOVIET UNION AND THE EASTERN BLOC

The victims of these totalitarian regimes often managed to maintain close family ties and friendships. Faced with chronic deprivation, generosity became more valued, as individuals shared their limited resources with each other. Family conflict between the generations was considerably muted compared to Western society. People needed each other to survive. In addition, as the churches were suppressed, many people turned more fervently to their spiritual roots. Thus theories that promote a rigid hierarchy of values fail to realize that love often thrives at precisely those moments that people are feeling insecure and deprived of their liberties. The formerly communist societies have a wellspring of love and caring from which they can draw in creating a new community. Their future will be determined in part by their willingness and ability to transform their political system without rejecting their commitment to loving relationships.

Part II: The Cost of Coercing Good Deeds

According to a news report on a verbal exchange between Nikita Khrushchev and Dwight Eisenhower, the Soviet dictator challenged the American president by observing that communism more than capitalism was attempting to implement the Christian values of altruism and sharing. There was some truth to his remarks. Communism, at its most ideal, attempts to enforce love. But so do all forms of modern liberalism and socialism, as well as conservatism. Each has different moral values; but each uses the state to impose its ideals on the society.

DENYING MORE SUBTLE COSTS

The cost of state coercion against its own citizens for supposedly good purposes rarely receives sufficient attention. Most Americans assume that a great deal of government enforcement is necessary not only to suppress crime and maintain defense, but to implement programs for the general good. They want to tax people to pay for public transportation, education, welfare, health services, and the military. They want to control the prices of vital services and to stimulate the economy with various incentives. People may argue about the best approaches and optimal degree of such coercion, but few challenge the principle of coercion itself or look at its negative consequences in any depth.

In their relationships with friends and family, many people more readily accept the need to respect each other's freedom. They wish to develop wholly noncoercive personal relationships. In regard to love, for example, they readily see that it is wrong and self-defeating to try to force their partners to love them. Yet these same people see no potential harm or ethical problem with coercing people for every imaginable "good purpose" in the political arena.

But as already discussed, any use of force in any arena, personal or political, will have negative consequences on the victim and the perpetrator (see chapters 4–6). This means that policing people for their own good—such as preventing them from smoking, drinking, or eating anything they want—has its cost. Similarly, taxing people for their presumed good or the good of others—even for the building of roads, dams, schools, and hospitals—constitutes coercion and has its cost.

Imagine a society in which people feel no financial incentive to work, no pressing need to provide for themselves or their families, and no ability to benefit from their own property and labor. In the USSR and Eastern Bloc nations, years of statism deprived many people of their belief in self-determination. While the widespread lethargy was in part inspired by state terror, it was also produced by crushing individual initiative and the pursuit of self-interest. The former communist societies themselves have, to a great extent, come to this conclusion. While there are differences within regions and cultures, and a considerable amount of skepticism on the part of almost everyone, surveys have shown that most Soviets favor increasing private property and free enterprise. At this moment,

Russia is embarking on radical experimentation with capitalism. Some of the former Eastern Bloc nations are already moving along the free market road with some degree of success.

Of course, the citizens of formerly communist countries are also fearful of these new ideas, but as already noted, freedom must have profound appeal to human nature if they are so willing to consider it after so many years of wholesale indoctrination to the contrary.

CHARITY VERSUS WELFARE

The untoward results of state intervention and coercive social policy are not limited to the extreme example provided by the USSR. At least in the modern industrial society, state centralization of planning has a stultifying effect on individual initiative. Similarly, it is difficult to plan a safety net that does not have some negative consequences on personal responsibility. During a recent trip to Scandinavia, I heard many concerns that young people were no longer willing to work because unemployment insurance paid so well.

On the other hand, the tendency for "government handouts" to make people slothful has been vastly exaggerated. In the United States, where the safety net is much more porous than in Scandinavia, Aid to Families with Dependent Children (AFDC) is the main "welfare" program. It mostly affects families made up of very poor mothers with small children. The malingerers among these mothers appear to be small in number. Mostly, they have their hands full trying to raise children at a poverty level in socially disorganized communities without the help of fathers. Often they work when they can, and most remain on AFDC for short periods of time (Trattner, 1984).

Piven and Cloward observe (1985):

What remains, then, is the minority of AFDC mothers whose life situation has demoralized them, whose experience of unemployment and social disorganization has made them "dependent," whose children may, if these conditions persist, grow up to be "dependent" as well. Welfare is not a good solution for these

*people. It may keep them from starving, but it does not enable
them to reconstruct their self-respect. Eliminating welfare pay-
ments in the absence of other economic and social opportunities
is, however, a worse solution. (p. 4.)*

Unemployment, culturally deprived family life, crime, racism,
inadequate education, and other factors create involuntary poverty
in the larger industrial societies. It is no secret that the inner cities
of America are in many respects like, or even worse than, "Third
World Nations" in regard to poverty, homelessness, violent crime,
infant mortality, inadequate health care, and other measures of
social disintegration.

The problem of poverty cannot be dismissed as laziness, malin-
gering, or the like. Increasing numbers of poor in the United States
cannot keep up no matter how hard they work. Many children are
growing up without the physical health, education, or viewpoints
required for survival or success in modern society. A realistic, loving attitude toward the poor does not allow us to dismiss them as
deserving of their fate.

The great misfortune of modern society is the failure to understand that liberty and love, and not state coercion, is the best
approach to solving problems such as poverty. We would be far
better off if the community could provide charity to its less fortunate members without resort to taxation and government intervention. Then the poor could benefit from both the opportunities
inherent in liberty and the resources of loving community.

The argument is made that the receipt of charity is humiliating,
but it could hardly be as humiliating as the typical experience of
"welfare mothers." Furthermore, charity suggests that someone
actually cares about the individual in trouble. And charity, unlike
government relief, might inspire the recipient to "pay back" by
giving charity to others at a later date. But most important, charity
eliminates coercion, and expresses love.

I am not arguing for an end to the already shredded safety net.
Given the plight of the poor in our callous society, that would be
unspeakably cruel. I am suggesting that we begin to reconsider the
community rather than the state as our source of human kindness.
It would be inhumane to further diminish current levels of aid to
the poor, but we can begin to think about a greater role for love in

the future of society. I will deal further with this issue in chapter 11, but now want to emphasize that liberty and love always provide far better solutions than coercion. Sadly, we seem, as a society, a long way from such a realization. We are becoming an increasingly coercive and loveless nation.

PERPETRATOR OF INVOLUNTARY GOOD DEEDS

Coercion tends to encourage alienation and unrealistic self-evaluations in the perpetrators. Consistent with the perpetrator syndrome discussed in chapter 4, perpetrators, including political leaders and government bureaucrats, become increasingly more grandiose and less sensitive to those whom they are controlling. In a recent public discussion (see chapter 10), former president Jimmy Carter described how dictators frequently, and unrealistically, imagine that they will win popular elections. They consent to the democratic process, only to find that the vote goes against them.

Even democratic leaders exaggerate their public support. In the United States, as confirmed by the small voter turnouts, there is general frustration and apathy about the whole electoral process. Democratic leaders also overestimate their ability to do good. Projects are invented and implemented without regard for their actual outcome or usefulness. Motivated by righteous impulses or the desire to impress the electorate, the benevolent perpetrator is rarely in direct contact with the needs of those he or she seeks to help, and too often, the impact is anything but good.

In order to wield coercive power for the supposed benefit of others, politicians or government agents must first *possess* coercive power. The implications of this are too rarely considered by those who promote the use of force for benevolent purposes. But how do people conduct themselves when they possess coercive power? Are they likely to be more pure than the rest of us—more able to exercise that power in the interest of the relatively powerless electorate rather than in the interest of themselves and their more potent supporters? Or are they likely to be corrupted even beyond the norm by their power and their need to maintain it? The poor and the disenfranchised benefit so little from do-good programs in part because the leaders are first and foremost taking care of themselves, for example, by steadily increasing the strength and scope of their own positions and programs, and their bureaucratic empire. Thus federal projects to feed the poor are more likely to end up feeding an ever more bloated government power structure. State-inspired "conflict resolution" too often leads to conflict generation.

VICTIMS OF STATE COERCION

Victims of state coercion—those who feel oppressed by taxes or government regulations—tend to lose their initiative. We have seen that dramatically displayed in the former communist nations.

The supposed beneficiaries, typical of the coercive dynamic, also tend to become victims. Welfare with its humiliating rules and regulations can discourage people from becoming more autonomous and competent.

As already noted, well-intentioned state activities can be viewed as attempts to coerce love, with all the inherent hazards and contradictions involved in imposing Dynamic III on Dynamic I. We must always beware of attempts to accomplish good ends by means of force. We must move the state from being an institution of conflict generation to one of conflict resolution. Instead of fighting for control over state power in order to enforce their own solutions, people must learn to participate in community—to seek collaborative problem solving without the use of force.

Part III. Hunger, Poverty, and Redistributive Justice

Can the Three Dynamic Theory clarify the issues surrounding specific good intentions, such as the desire to relieve poverty and hunger through redistributions of wealth?

COMPENSATING FOR INJUSTICE BY REDISTRIBUTING WEALTH

Redistributive justice is the attempt to correct earlier injustices and unfair imbalances of wealth. Typically, it motivates taking from the rich in order to give to the poor, for example, to provide special help to the underprivileged in finding employment or seeking education. It epitomizes both the pitfalls and the necessity of coercion in modern society.

Redistributive justice is, by almost any definition, a form of coercion. One group is forced to help another. These implications are rarely considered outside of free market analyses (Von Mises, 1966). Within John Burton's viewpoint (1990), for example, redistributive justice is considered a benign basic need.

At its worst, the impulse to redistribute is motivated by envy. Even if *everyone* ends up worse off, some resentful people want to see society leveled. This is not mere jealousy—the wish to have what someone else has; it is envy—the wish to take away from others. It is born of psychological helplessness: "If I cannot get what I want, no one else will either." In Remnick's article, the young entrepreneur Sterligov identified envy when he said, "Their psychology is all screwed up. They are so used to being equal in poverty that they assume if you have any money, you are a crook." In *Envy* (1966), Helmut Schoeck describes this motivation as the root of socialist and communist programs—the impulse to level anyone who tries to rise above the crowd, even if it means less for everyone.

On the other hand, redistributive justice can be motivated by a very different interpretation of the principles of liberty. Those who have previously been *robbed*—for example, former slaves who were robbed of their freedom and the products of their labor—are now to be compensated by the society that benefitted from the crime. Similarly, Native Americans were exterminated in large numbers, robbed of their lands, and systematically persecuted. Furthermore, both the former slaves and the Native Americans continue to suffer from government policies and social prejudices that suppress their opportunities.

The principle of liberty, which is based on the rejection of force except in self-defense, can thus be used to defend force aimed at redressing past injustices. It is a matter of returning stolen goods and making restitution for past oppression.

Of course, the people compensating former slaves or Native Americans are not the ones who stole from them. Contemporary white people did not use black slaves to earn their wealth. Nor did they steal Native American lands. But Americans in general have benefitted from the capital and other advantages accrued through slavery and the abuse of Native Americans; and, due to continuing racism and prejudice, white Americans continue to benefit disproportionately.

Love also motivates redistributive justice. Through taxation we are made to act charitably (lovingly) toward those who have been disadvantaged. Thus the welfare state can be looked upon as coerced love. Where charity would fail to meet the needs of people, the state enforces giving. But whatever this is, it is hard to call it genuine love or "gifting," or individuals would do it without the threat of the IRS.

CHILDREN AND SHARING

Consider the problem of redistributive justice in regard to teaching fairness to children. If Johnny does not wish to share his toys with Jane, we may encourage him by pointing out that he loves Jane. Or we may explain the practicality of gaining future exchanges in kind from her. Best of all, I believe, we may try to teach him to share through the example of our own generosity toward him and toward others. But only as a last resort would we force Johnny to share his toys. Forcing him to share would, in all likelihood, backfire. It might instead teach him to resent sharing. It may even make him hate Jane. Common sense and empirical research indicate the futility of coercing children in order to make them more generous.

On the other hand, if a child steals from another child, the property must be returned. Redistributive justice, it seems to me, is best formulated in terms of restoring rights and especially returning stolen property. In modern society, where the rich and powerful systematically steal from the poor and disempowered, concern for human welfare supports redistributive justice. But we must set limits on it, and never lose sight of the shortcomings and negative consequences of trying to coerce charity.

Again, what is really needed is a more loving society. Those of us who are more successful must find ways of making the community more livable for those who are not. Ironically, it would be in our best interest to do so. It would require much less financial expenditure to provide charity through private agencies rather than through the government bureaucracy, and even through personal volunteer services rather than through paid bureaucrats. Much more could be done with much less financial burden.

But self-interest is not a sufficient motivation for helping others. In the short run, it is too tempting to grab what one can for oneself. People must, through empathic love, care about the well-being of all members of the community, including those generations who will follow us.

FURTHER JUSTIFICATIONS FOR REDISTRIBUTING WEALTH

As already noted in chapter 3, in order to participate in a competitive, relatively free society, individuals must bring to adulthood a large measure of autonomy and self-determination. This requires certain optimal conditions. Hapless children—raised amid racism, sexism, poverty, starvation, ill-health, and abuse, and without a decent education—have little chance to develop autonomy and to benefit from economic freedom. Similarly, older citizens of Eastern Bloc societies have little psychological capacity to take advantage of the new opportunities. Their more self-determined fellow citizens describe them as lost causes and say in effect, "We can't expect anything from them and we will have to take care of them." If not provided for in their old age by a safety net, they would suffer enormously.

Furthermore, even if all people could reach adulthood more or less autonomous and self-determining, some would still possess overriding advantages. In the United States, for example, those born white, male, wealthy, and in the cultural mainstream are vastly advantaged in competition with equally competent persons born without those attributes. Given the tendency of advantaged people to cooperate with each other to maintain their advantages, the unfair accrual of further advantages seems inevitable. Nor are minority attempts to cooperate with each other an effective counterbalance. Disadvantaged demoralized people are less able to cooperate or conspire on their own behalf, and those in power are often able to thwart their ambitions.

Redistribution of wealth again seems a just policy from this view-point, especially if it is used to support the development of auton-omy and self-determination among disadvantaged children.

Liberty does include the possibility of redistributive justice, but notice that cogent arguments can be made for and *against* it. What tilts the scales? I believe that the balance of liberty and love is critical. For those who empathize with the poor or disadvantaged, the balance will favor helping them out, even if it bends the prin-ciples of liberty.

By contrast, love has *nothing* weighing against it, except the difficulty contemporary humans beings have in feeling it for others less fortunate than themselves. Yet human beings are in-herently loving, and human beings flourish best in loving commu-nity. The problem is twofold: to awaken the idea of love within the hearts of individuals and to find better ways to build loving com-munity.

HUNGER AND POVERTY: DIFFERING ISSUES IN THE U.S.A. AND EMERGING CAPITALISTIC SOCIETIES

Will the poor and the hungry always be with us in our larger industrial societies? Are we doomed to this unfortunate reality? The problem has of course been discussed since the earliest cri-tiques of capitalism and the industrial revolution. The cynicism of Malthus is well-known, as is the greater optimism of Adam Smith. These issues will be framed in terms of the Three Dynamics.

One approach to hunger and poverty is to ask, "How can we resolve the conflict between the rich and the poor, the well-fed and the hungry?" But even though disparities do exist, this is not the central problem in the former communist nations. They don't have enough to go around. For them, the challenge is how to generate wealth. Therefore, the moment freedom blossomed but a little, they became preoccupied with implementing capitalism. In the process, as the press reports quickly indicated, the "rugged indi-vidualist" entrepreneurs initially accumulate their wealth partly at the expense of others who do not know how to compete. That is the price these societies seem willing to pay for Western-style progress.

The problem is not the same in the more successful capitalist countries. In the United States, for example, we already have more than enough *material* resources to eradicate poverty and hunger among our own citizens, and probably enough additional resources to help much of the remaining world as well. My own Montgomery County has for many years been ranked at or near the top in the nation for average family income; and yet we have a growing problem of hunger and poverty. That we do not eradicate poverty and hunger in America—that it seems as if we *cannot*—is not a matter of material or technical capacity.

The extreme free-market position warns that the great engine of economic progress will grind to a halt if some people get a free ride or a free lunch. It is also argued that it is morally wrong to tax one person to take care of another. The "no free lunch for the poor" argument falls apart when the state is already lavishing support on big business and other privileged groups, often to the detriment of the poor (see chapter 8).

There are many other reasons why we have no national mandate to help the poor and hungry. The major liberal attempts to end poverty have not succeeded. Why fail again? Often it seems like a matter of priorities. We consider other problems more important. Class and racial conflict also interfere. The wealthiest among us use their power and influence to maintain their status at the expense of others; and in general the white majority resents helping the underclass, whom it perceives as "different" from them. Sexism plays a role: the poorest and most hungry among us are families with single mothers and children. Clearly, our shameful disregard for the needs of children also plays a role. Patriarchal concepts of superiority, rugged individualism, and competitiveness leave little room for generosity, charity, and empathy for those who are less fortunate.

But whatever conflicts prevent us from eradicating poverty and hunger within America, solving the problem is materially within our grasp, requiring but a fraction of each year's gross national product.

In the Three Dynamic Theory, poverty and hunger can be viewed as a conflict between American society and its large underclass of poor and hungry people. Solving these problems requires a different attitude toward the poor and hungry in America. It means much less coercion, and much more liberty and love. It entails identifying with and empathizing with the less fortunate, helping them to find the means to survive in the short run, and empowering them in the longer run to join as full members of society. In the case of a relatively small number of disabled people, it means being loving enough to take care of those who cannot take care of themselves.

Part IV: Liberty, Love, and the Environment

Liberty is usually considered the enemy of environmentalism. When defenders of the environment look for the chief culprit, it almost always is identified as free-market activities based on self-interest, the profit motive, individual rights, private property, and capitalism. When the lifting of the Iron Curtain disclosed some of the most tragic pollution on earth, pointing the finger exclusively at the free-enterprise system became a little more difficult. Libertarians and anarchists had always pointed *their* finger at the state, and that would have predicted exactly what was found in the totalitarian nations of Eastern Europe and Russia. Now the problem remains: how to revive industry without asphyxiating Eastern Europe.

INDUSTRIAL POLLUTION BEHIND THE IRON CURTAIN

Industrial pollution is so bad in some parts of Eastern Europe and the Soviet Union that the population ages and dies prematurely. But if these industries are shut down in order to protect the public health, the already precarious economies could be tipped over the edge. Meanwhile, the environment and the health of citizens deteriorate with every day that the industries spew forth their toxins. No abstract principle of liberty is sufficient. No general principle of love solves the problem.

Few people realize that the principles of liberty do not support pollution. The principle of self-defense gives every individual the right to prevent his or her body from being exposed to toxin. The offending plants would be closed on the grounds that they were committing aggression against others by polluting their environment and their bodies. Thus, if the right to self-defense were upheld by the state, it would become almost impossible for polluters to exist. Liberty, if properly understood, can become a sword wielded on behalf of the environment.

While escalating the economic crisis, the prohibition of pollution would wipe the industrial slate clean and open the way to a complete overhaul of industry. This could result in a dramatically different kind of society than now exists in the Western world. It could be a step in the direction of smaller, more ecologically sound industrial development. Thus free-market principles provide unexpected support for putting environmental values ahead of industrial development.

INDIVIDUAL AND PROPERTY RIGHTS IN DEFENSE OF THE ENVIRONMENT

The results of applying Dynamic II: liberty to industrial pollution are somewhat startling. Instead of fostering big industry, as free marketeers so often favor, an uncompromising application of free-market principles would close down poisoners of the environment.

In *For a New Liberty* (1973), Rothbard writes, "Government ownership, even socialism, has proved to be no solution to the problem of pollution," (p. 269). He goes on to say: "Note, for example, the two crucial areas in which pollution has become an important problem: the air and the waterways, particularly the rivers. But these are precisely two of the vital areas in society in which private property has not been permitted to function." That is, some of the worst pollution problems involve air and large bodies of water, resources controlled by the state rather than by the free market.

From Rothbard's perspective, if property rights had been recognized, air and water pollution could not have started and could still be brought to a halt. Whenever an industry pollutes the air or any large body of water or any underlying aquifer, the industry offends the rights of *other people*—their bodies or their property. If individuals could sue for damages from air or water pollution, perpetrators would be quickly forced to mend their ways.

However, allying themselves with the industrial revolution, every state in the world has limited the rights of individuals to sue polluters. To protect industry, the state sets the basic standards of *allowable* pollution.

Similarly, if individuals rights were strictly adhered to, there would be little or no danger from nuclear power plants. Until they were safe, there simply wouldn't be any. When the U.S. government first sought to encourage the development of atomic power plants, it became clear that the plants would never be able to obtain private insurance coverage against disasters, because one calamity would bankrupt even a consortium of insurers. So the government intervened and passed legislation to limit the liability of these public utilities. No matter how much damage they might do in the future, the victims will be able to collect only a limited amount.

Without the government setting limits on their liability, nuclear power plants would not have been built until private insurers thought them safe to insure. Perhaps this would never have taken place. Small atomic energy sources might have been safe enough to be insured. Perhaps larger plants might have become safe enough to insure in the distant future; perhaps not. . . . But the landscape would not now be dotted with these behemoths, and the public would not live in fear of them.

Thus, in some cases at least, free-market principles can protect the environment. They are especially effective when individuals can sue to protect themselves from actual or potential hazards. In the arena of pollution, liberty turns out to be a surprising ally. But will Dynamic II principles work when animals and nature, rather than persons, are being exploited and endangered?

CAN THE FREE MARKET PRESERVE NATURE?

Terry L. Anderson and Donald R. Leal have tried to make the case for liberty in *Free Market Environmentalism* (1991) in which they equate the free market with individualism and the pursuit of self-interest. Anderson and Leal are sophisticated enough to add the caveat that self-interest can be modified by concern for "close relatives and friends" and "conditioned by moral principles," (p. 4). But for them, plain old selfishness motivates the world: "Most scientific approaches have implicitly assumed that self-interest dominates behavior for higher as well as lower forms of life," (p. 5).

How can self-interest produce environmentally sound policies? The key, according to free-market advocates, is the desire of people to protect the environment—how much they will pay to accomplish their end. When people becoming willing to spend on behalf of environmental preservation, creative entrepreneurs will find a way to meet their needs, for example, through selling and managing environmental preservations. The Nature Conservancy is a nonprofit organization that identifies and purchases environmentally significant land for preservation. To date, they have saved over three million acres of land (Scheffer, 1991). But as the Nature Conservancy would readily admit, it has thus far been able to save less than a drop in nature's endangered bucket.

Without Anderson and Leal explicitly saying so, it comes down to this: When people care as much about wilderness as about Disneyland, they will pay for the preservation of wilderness the way they pay for Disneyland. This observation has appeal; but it also has shortcomings. Sportsmen pay large sums to preserve game for hunting, but their particular use and enjoyment of nature itself raises moral questions and tends to abuse the environment in other ways. The lead shot used in duck hunting was deadly to the ducks and other birds who ingested the pellets, and by no means all hunters were willing to forsake using it. By contrast, those true "outdoorsmen," the Native Americans, thought of themselves as stewards of the land and its creatures for future generations (see p. 204). Too often contemporary users of the outdoors do not share their reverence toward nature.

Ironically, free-market environmentalism must depend upon love. It must hope that enough people will grow to treasure the environment sufficiently to pay for preserving it, without hope of financial profit from the expenditure. Vast numbers of people would have to love the earth sufficiently to spend large sums of money on its behalf. But the competitive values generated by the free market often mitigate against loving anything for its own sake, especially usable "natural resources."

People will resent paying to save vast areas of air, land, and water, when other people who do not share the cost will nonetheless share the benefits. People generally become willing to sacrifice for a public good only when assured that everyone will be joining in, and that requires coercive state interventions.

Furthermore, not enough people seem willing to take a long-range and even transgenerational view. We must preserve nature not only for ourselves, but for future generations who have no say in what we are now doing. Future generations may not feel very forgiving toward us when told that nature simply had to go because its preservation wasn't consistent with liberty and the free market.

PRIVATE OWNERSHIP OF THE WHALES?

If an animal, piece of land, or other aspect of nature is not owned by anyone, the free market cannot protect or conserve it. Whales and migrating birds, for example, cannot easily be made into property. Furthermore, in a society that promotes free-market values, people are not likely to have an interest in saving anything that they do not own. Yet it is difficult or impossible, and perhaps morally wrong, to establish individual ownership of many natural resources, such as endangered species of whales or migrating birds.

Anderson and Leal look forward to a day when some animals may be electronically tagged and/or fenced in, thereby making it possible to own and preserve them. But this hope is based on a naively atomistic conception of nature. Accustomed to thinking of society purely in terms of isolated individuals, Anderson and Leal tend to think of animals in the same way. The suggestion for tagging endangered species for ownership smacks more of desperation than rationality. We cannot begin to identify every form of life (insects, plants, small mammals, etc.), let alone tag it. As the authors note, even our largest animals, the whales, cannot be easily "owned" and hence protected by the free market.

LESSONS FROM NATIVE AMERICANS

What is needed is not the preservation of individual creatures but of entire ecosystems. In the case of the whale, the ecosystem is the oceans of the world, not to mention their shorelines, the rivers that empty into them, and the air that surrounds them. An individual whale or wolf cannot be saved without saving its habitat, and that habitat can sometimes span across the face of the earth and into the depths of the earth, the air, and the ocean.

Not individual creatures, but whole oceans, vast air spaces, expansive wetlands, great mountain ranges, and immense rain forests must preserved. Even dividing up the earth into "ecosystems" will not ultimately work. Our plans must encompass the whole planet.

Like the Native Americans, we must see ourselves as but a part of a vast, all-encompassing reality (Erdoes, 1989; Weatherford, 1988). This is conveyed by the words of a Hopi, Thomas Benyacya (Erdoes, 1990):

Native Americans have a strong belief that they are responsible for the Earth's well-being. A Hopi elder said in an address to the government: "This land is the sacred home of the Hopi people and all the Indian race in this land. It was given to the Hopi people the task to guard this land, not by force of arms, not by killing, not by confiscation of properties of others, but by humble prayers, by obedience to our traditions and religious instructions, and by being faithful to our creator, Masau'u. (p. 64.)

Wendell Berry (1987) has also expressed sentiments on the spiritual importance of nature:

The survival of wilderness—of places that we do not change, where we allow the existence even of creatures we perceive as dangerous—is necessary. Our sanity probably requires it. Whether we go to those places or not, we need to know that they exist. And I would argue that we do not need just the great public wildernesses, but millions of small private or semiprivate ones. Every farm should have one; wildernesses can occupy corners of factory grounds and city lots—places where nature is given a free hand, where no human work is done, where people go only as guests. These places function, I think, whether we intend

*them to or not, as sacred groves—places we respect and leave
alone, not because we understand well what goes on there, but
because we do not. (p. 17.)*

According to Berry (1987), we not only need to experience nature for our individual spiritual survival and rejuvenation, we must
build communities to a scale that fits within nature:

*If the human economy is to be fitted into the natural economy in
such a way that both may thrive, the human economy must be
built to proper scale. It is possible to talk at great length about
the difference between proper and improper scale. It may be
enough to say here that difference is suggested by the difference
between amplified and unamplified music in the countryside, or
the difference between the sound of a motorboat and the sound of
oarlocks. A proper human sound, we may say, is one that allows
other sounds to be heard. A properly scaled human economy or
technology allows a diversity of other creatures to thrive. (p. 16.)*

From the viewpoint of many environmentally oriented critics of
the free market (Berry, 1972, 1987; Clark, 1989; Ross-Breggin and
Breggin, 1992; Ross-Breggin, 1990), the market is inherently too
human-centered. The environment and its life forms will be exploited and endangered as long as the needs of *people*—even their
individual desires to preserve nature—are the central concern.

Essentially, animals and nature must have their own rights, an
idea that seems preposterous to most free-market advocates.
Whales—and all of nature—must be valued unconditionally. That
means, they must be loved. Perhaps then trees will have "standing" in court, and suits will be brought on the behalf of mountains
and lakes. As Ginger Ross-Breggin has suggested to me, perhaps
the concept of self-defense can be extended to life forms other than
human beings.

A philosophy is needed that focuses on the inherent worth of all
life forms, rather than on the self-interest of individual human
beings as reflected in preserving this or that life form. Consistent
with Native American cultures, humans must live within nature,

and in spiritual awe of it, without attempting to dominate or exploit it.

THE FUTURE OF ENVIRONMENTAL POLICY

Both liberty and love must play a role in the developing attempts to save the environment and the earth itself. It is critical, however, to have clear definitions of the principles of liberty and love in order to understand where each is most appropriate and effective.

Surprising to many environmentalists, greater respect for individual rights and property is one of the keys to saving the air and water in specific locations where people may sue for damages. But when individual rights cannot be so easily defined, we cannot rely on freedom. The profit motive and individual human rights will not protect the inhabitants of the sea or the great rain forests. They require loving interventions by people motivated by their ideals and their identification with nature.

Educating the public and motivating people to take action are crucial to saving the planet. More people must become aware and concerned enough to take action. Every method of public education must be employed, from talking with one's own family and friends, to writing books, lobbying, running for public office, and influencing the mass media.

In my local neighborhood, the county has given official recycling collection boxes to every household. Many people are already recycling on their own. Environmental awareness is growing, but surely not fast enough. There is more hope in a broad-based movement that includes not only environmentalists but those interest in social justice, human rights, peace, and a variety of other closely related reform issues (see chapter 11).

Hopefully the principles of conflict analysis and resolution can help to solve the growing number of clashes between those who would save their jobs and those who would save the environment. On some refrigerators in the United States, there are cartoons depicting the heartless destruction of the spotted owl's habitat by greedy loggers. On others, there are depictions of loggers losing their jobs and their homes because of efforts to save the same creature. Similarly, in the Brazilian rain forests natives struggle to make a marginal living by slash and burn farming techniques that ruin many acres of land. Ironically, the people who want to fight to preserve these rain forests are often the same ones with the most sympathy for poor, indigenous peoples.

It will not be possible to make much progress toward preserving the environment without at the same time meeting the needs of people whose livelihoods depend upon using up those same resources. It is difficult to imagining carrying out such large-scale balancing acts without massive government involvement. Yet government, rooted so deeply in coercion, has seldom been much help in conflict resolution.

Can love be brought to bear on these problems without turning increasingly to coercive state interventions? There is one way, exemplified by Greenpeace and other deep ecology groups who value nature for its own sake and who are willing to risk themselves in its defense, often through civil disobedience.

Recently a sympathetic member of a Congressional staff told me that it was politically dangerous to speak well of Greenpeace on Capitol Hill. Yet the same week, *National Geographic*, an organization known for its conservatism, sponsored a lengthy TV special in support of the environmental group. Clearly, we are in a time of transition. Civil disobedience, with Gandhi's "loving firmness" as the model, may be the ultimate approach to stopping the destruction of nature (see chapter 11).

UTOPIAN SOLUTIONS AND CONFLICT RESOLUTION

Social scientists, especially ecologically oriented ones (Clark, 1989; Sale, 1985; van Andruss, Plant, Plant, and Wright, 1990) are urging us to develop a new concept of community. Mary Clark's book, *Ariadne's Thread* (1989), is particularly well-informed and enlightened about the tragic path humanity is now following, and it offers an alternative consistent with some of the more progressive contemporary movements of deep ecology and social justice (see chapter 11). Her approach allows us to contrast the development of alternative "utopian" models to the *process* of conflict resolution, which is something quite different.

Clark advocates smaller, more tightly knit, and loving communities based on self-sufficient ecological systems. No society, according to this plan, would use more energy than was available to it. Living within nature, we would fit our needs to those of nature instead of trying to force nature into ours. People would be as connected as possible to their work, and their work would be connected as much as possible to the resources of their own ecosystem.

In Clark's vision, each society would express its own sacred meanings. Cultural diversity would not be expressed within large pluralistic societies but through smaller, separate eco-cultural systems. One's spiritual state would replace one's pocketbook as the measure of personal success. Mutuality and sharing, rather than competition, would be the guiding principle of social relationships. Clark's community is at one with itself and with nature, a true Dynamic I vision of life.

How viable or practical is Clark's vision? Could these or similar communities arise out of the ashes of the USSR and Eastern Bloc nations? There is certainly a tendency for the breakdown and decentralization of the former communist states. But it is hard to imagine that trend reaching the proportions required by Clark's vision.

The long-suppressed peoples of Eastern Europe and Russia want to become more like us, and are bent on adopting capitalism. They may ultimately outdo us in their individualism. And the trend in Western Europe is not toward local community but toward international unity. Furthermore, I will suggest that the global village is a necessary condition for successful local communities, and that it requires free-market industrialization, especially modern transportation and communication (see chapter 11).

Those who promote utopian ideals must be prepared to tell us how we get "from here to there" without the use of massive coercion. While a specific social blueprint may inspire a small group of people, it is not likely to be freely adopted by a whole society. People want to go through their own decision-making processes. That is why the force of a totalitarian state is required to impose any predetermined ideal upon a population. That is exactly what happened in the USSR under Lenin and his successors.

A free people need philosophic and social tools—principles and institutions—that facilitate conflict resolution as they plan and evolve their own communities. Ideals must be generated by individuals, so many individuals that whole communities eventually began to change for the better. In the words of Wendell Berry (1977):

The only real, practical, hope-giving way to remedy the fragmentation that is the disease of the modern spirit is a small and humble way—a way that a government or agency or organization or institution will never think of, though a **person** *may think of it: one must begin in one's own life the private solutions that can only* **in turn** *become public solutions. (p. 23.)*

Given freedom and encouragement to love, people are likely to surprise us, and themselves, with their creative solutions. Out of liberty and love springs genuine community.

CHAPTER 10

▼ ▼

Resolving International Conflict: The Middle East

I refuse to accept the cynical notion that nation after nation must spiral down a militaristic stairway into the hell of thermo-nuclear destruction. I believe that unarmed truth and uncondi-tional love will have the final word in reality. This is why right, temporarily defeated, is stronger than evil triumphant.
        Martin Luther King, Jr., **Nobel Peace Prize acceptance address, Oslo, December 11, 1964**

The prophecy of a world moving toward political unity is the light which guides all that is best, most vigorous, most truly alive in the work of our time. It gives sense to what we are do-ing. Nothing else does.
        Walter Lippmann, *"Reflection After Armistice Day,"* **New York Herald Tribune,** *November 12, 1931*

The problem of peace and security is indeed far more important than the conflict between socialism and capitalism. Man must first ensure his survival; only then can he ask himself what type of existence he prefers. . . . The struggle for power is equally re-pulsive, conducted as it is, both here and there, with the tradi-tional dishonesty of the political craft.
        Albert Einstein, **Einstein on Peace (1968)**

As community increases in size, it becomes increasingly difficult to apply any given set of principles to resolving its problems. When large communities themselves come into conflict, the issues be-come complex beyond one person's comprehension. In this chap-ter, the principles of liberty and love will be applied to international conflict, using the Middle East as the main example. Clearly, such a task is daunting, and I hope to shed new light on the subject without pretending to solve the world's most threatening and dif-ficult problems.

The attitude of American citizens toward the Gulf war will be given special attention, since America was largely responsible for the dramatic escalation of the conflict. I'm an American, and by focusing on Americans I hope to begin where conflict resolution should begin, with a better understanding one's own role in the conflict.

BASIC STRESS PARADIGMS
AND INTERNATIONAL POLITICS

We have described how Basic Stress Paradigms—hurt, fear, and helplessness—are caused by stress and trauma, and then go on to energize interpersonal and societal conflicts. The same process takes place on an international level. War provides an example.

Love, with its abhorrence of violence against others, motivates people to reject war. But the frustration, anger, and hate generated by Basic Stress Paradigms provide readily available fuel for murderous conflict. I am reminded of an incident during a visit to Israel in the early 1970s when I strayed from the main streets on the outskirts of Jerusalem. I found myself in an alley between partially demolished buildings where Arab children were playing outside the door to their home. Several youngsters, varying in age from a few years old to nine or ten, were using a sharpened stick to torture a puppy to death. One can only imagine what injuries of their own they were revisiting upon the squealing puppy, and with what ease these same injuries might fuel their adult hatreds in the Arab-Israeli conflict. Nor are Basic Stress Paradigms fueling Arabs to the exclusion of Jews. No culture has a monopoly on benevolent childhoods.

Political ideologues and leaders are able to restimulate painful emotion and to channel it into political conflict. During the recent Gulf war, the Israeli leaders used Holocaust images to motivate their citizens and worldwide Jewry. They did so by repeatedly showing footage of Israelis donning gas masks. Few Jews could be wholly immune to such propagandizing. In order to deal fairly with the Arab-Israeli conflict, I have had to overcome the emotional reactions that began in my childhood when I confronted the Holocaust while watching Movietone News. Handling that Basic Stress Paradigm has enabled me to see the humanity of the Palestinians with whom we Jews must now deal equitably. Thus I had to climb down my own conflict tree (see chapters 1 and 9).

While Israel was busy manipulating Jewish feelings of helplessness during the Gulf war, U.S. leaders were manipulating America's post-Vietnam humiliation by promising an overwhelming use of force aimed at a swift, decisive victory. Still playing on shame over Vietnam, they promised to bring the soldiers home quickly and to welcome them as heroes. Thus the Bush administration successfully exploited the energy of America's post-Vietnam Basic Stress Paradigm to motivate support for a gargantuan military assault.

We Americans also sought to *heal* the hurts of Vietnam through reaffirming our patriotism, winning a great victory, and welcoming home our troops. But the perpetrator syndrome (chapter 4) is the ultimate result. Violent victory inflates our egos and distracts us from our inner selves, as well as from caring about others. We become less aware of ourselves and others, and more inured to their pain and suffering. We substitute bravado for justice and mercy. We feel larger, as we become smaller; we feel omniscient as our vision narrows. Superficially we feel less afflicted with helplessness, but in reality we become more deeply mired in it. Basic Stress Paradigms are restimulated but not healed by violence against others. At best, our violence numbs us.

Recently Republican party leaders have lamented how quickly America's morale once again declined after the war, and how quickly President Bush's popularity slid down hill along with the economy. The war's "uplifting" impact was short-lived indeed. Nor does the military victory continue to seem so complete. Saddam is still in power, perhaps more firmly entrenched than before, and the pain inflicted on his people by the war may inflame them to support future wars of revenge. Americans aren't the only ones who will turn to war in order to "heal" the wounds of earlier lost wars.

Basic Stress Paradigms become even greater impediments to peace when they have been inflicted upon each other by the contending parties. Palestinians and Israelites, America's black and white population, women and men throughout the world: Each has so many Basic Stress Paradigms with the other's name on it; peaceful resolution of the conflicts becomes increasingly difficult.

HEALING BASIC STRESS PARADIGMS

Political, religious, and educational institutions—and their leaders—can lend their weight to destimulating societal hurts. They can call for forgiveness and mercy. There are also more direct approaches to healing Basic Stress Paradigms on a personal level. At the 1991 National Conference on Peacemaking and Conflict Resolution (NCPCR) in Charlotte, North Carolina, one presenter, Cheri Brown, conducted what was billed as a seminar on international conflict. In her hands, it became a psychodynamic workshop in the traditions of individual psychotherapy and psychodrama.

Brown believes that generic "painful emotion" derives from childhood hurts and that "Where we are hurting, we are not thinking." Especially, resentment rather than love can dominate us, fueling cultural, racial, religious, and political conflict.

For Cheri Brown, a workshop on political conflict resolution involves feeling, expressing, and working through the painful emotions of individual persons. In terms of the Three Dynamic Theory, as the participants free themselves from hurt, fear, and learned helplessness, they become better able to resolve conflict through the principles of liberty and love.

Of course international conflicts cannot be resolved by holding encounter-group workshops. But it helps when people in conflict become more aware of how their personal hurts help to drive their political outrage.

THE DENIAL OF EMPATHY BY AMERICANS

In talks during and after Desert Storm, Richard Rubenstein of the Institute for Conflict Analysis and Resolution at George Mason University made a singular observation on the prevention of war. He said, in effect, "We will not prevent wars such as the one in the Gulf until we place as much value on the life of a young Iraqi soldier as on the life of a young American soldier." He challenged the values that led Americans to view a kill ratio of 1:1,000 as something to cheer about. Indeed, as the casualty count mounts, including the Iraqi and Kurdish children who are dying of starvation and public health hazards, our *continually growing* kill ratio may exceed 1:10,000.

The U.S. government seemed worried about the potentially inhibiting effects of empathy on public enthusiasm for the war. The military was determined to avoid what it saw as a disastrous mistake in Vietnam: allowing the war to be conducted on television. Seeing the actual violence had stirred the feelings of many Americans. Empathy toward both the Vietnamese and our own soldiers made many TV viewers less willing to tolerate the war.

In the Gulf war, the government and the military succeeded in imposing censorship on the press. As a result, we saw "smart bombs" finding their way into air shafts; but we saw nothing of the hellish strafing of tens of thousands of helpless Iraqis trapped in the traffic jam while retreating from Kuwait. Films of the actual assault on that road of death have never been seen on U.S. television.

The European press permitted one small photographic window into the human cost of the war. Despite the censorship, photographer Ken Jarecke shot a grim and gripping picture along the road of death leading from Kuwait to Iraq where airplanes bombed and strafed nearly defenseless fleeing soldiers. The photo shows in graphic detail an Iraqi soldier, killed by a bomb blast, blackened and mummified, with a fixed grimace on his face, as he struggles to drag himself upright and through the windshield of his truck. The visual impact of the soldier, forever frozen at the moment of the blast, is as dramatic as a Rodin statue, racked with pain.

When Jarecke's photo was published in a British newspaper, *The Observer*, there was an outburst of public resentment, not against the war, but against the picture. Harold Evans, president and publisher of Random House, wrote a defense of the photograph in *The Observer* and, along with the photograph, it was reprinted in the July/August 1991 *American Photographer*. Evans spoke of the need "to redress the elusive euphoria of a high-tech war":

There is something more significant in the protests to **The Observer** *than a proper reticence. They suggest that even now, at the end of the bloodiest century the world has known, even now after the trenches, and Hiroshima, and My Lai, popular culture is still imbued with a romantic conception of war and resents a grimmer reality.*

Americans were equally willing to deny the "grimmer reality"; the photograph was never published in the United States until that memorable issue of *American Photographer*.

PSYCHIATRY IN THE SERVICE OF WAR PROPAGANDA

We have observed that diagnosing people permits psychiatry and the public to perpetrate coercive, inhumane, and physically destructive treatments against mental patients (see chapter 7). The person labeled mentally ill no longer draws our sympathy and concern. Psychiatric diagnosis was also used to obfuscate our violent actions toward Iraq.

A Washington, D.C. psychiatrist, identified as an expert on Saddam Hussein's personality, was called upon regularly by the media during the war to diagnose the Iraqi leader as a madman. The public, long inured to assaults on the "mentally ill," was lulled into believing that the U.S. was going to stop one insane dictator. The cost to tens of millions of people directly and indirectly involved in the conflict was effectively dimmed by the definition of the "enemy" as a single, solitary madman.

When Saddam was not killed or deposed in the conflict—when the U.S. seemingly decided to accept his existence as a counterbalance to Iran—the psychiatrist disappeared from TV. It was perhaps too much for the psychiatrist to proclaim that the war had provided the "shock treatment" that "cured" the madman.

Mental health experts on child psychology also helped us reject our feelings of empathy. Several psychologists commented in the media on the impact of war-induced stress on American children. These psychologists told parents to remind their children that the war was "far away in a distant land" and that there was no chance that it would directly harm them.

But what about the *healthy* tendency of children to empathize with other children? We know that children begin to empathize with each other from very early in life (see chapter 2). Infants respond contagiously to the pain of others and toddlers sometimes extend gestures of sympathy toward other children who are suffering.

Did American children feel no empathy for their Iraqi counterparts? Did they in no way identify with the American soldiers who were being directly exposed to the war? Was love not a part of their distress? Shouldn't it have been? Or do we wish to raise a generation of children who respond as indifferently to the real victims of war as they do to the mass murders in Rambo movies and Sunday morning cartoons?

There was nothing in itself wrong with reassuring children that the war was being fought far away from their homes. It appears that many adult Americans needed the same reassurance, as they stayed away in droves from flying within the continental United States and from taking vacations in places that seemed possible targets of terrorism, like Washington, D.C. and New York City. But after reassuring our children, shouldn't we have *encouraged* their empathy toward other children around the world? Don't we want them to learn that war is harmful to everyone involved, including the people on both sides, and that modern warfare poses risks for the whole planet?

THE DENIAL OF WAR'S IMPACT

Too many adults, including our national leaders, seem unaware that war always has unforeseen negative consequences. In this brief but violent conflict, the cost to the Iraqi people has been beyond calculation. Millions have suffered terrible personal losses in property and in the lives of their family members, both civilian and military. The country's infrastructure has been destroyed, resulting in starvation and epidemic disease. Their bravest youngsters—those who took the opportunity to rebel against Saddam Hussein—have been slaughtered. The dictator may be more firmly entrenched than ever before. The Kurdish people have been uprooted and sustained enormous injury. So have other cultures within the borders of Iraq. The boycott and the flow of refugees has strained surrounding economies. Within Kuwait, the authoritarian government has been reestablished and revenge has replaced justice. The environment has been catastrophically despoiled by oil and by oil-well fires.

In an address at George Mason University on April 8, 1991, James Laue eloquently confronted the catastrophe in terms of lost lives:

As many as 200,000 of our sisters and brothers are gone forever from their families and their communities. Iraqis, Kuwaitis, Kurds, Saudis, Israelis, Palestinians, Americans, Brits. I'm going to stop for a moment so we all can reflect silently on this incomprehensible loss. (p. 5.)

The public and the press should never again allow censorship to remove them from the realities of war. They should *now* demand that realistic films of the slaughter be released and shown to the public.

A more loving attitude toward all people and a more profound concern for the planet itself would have prevented the American public from accepting the attack on Iraq. So would greater confidence in alternative methods of conflict resolution. We return to the need for the state to become more of an institution for conflict resolution, and less of an instrument for conflict generation.

THE DENIAL OF PERPETRATION BY AMERICANS

The attack on Iraq should have encouraged a more critical examination of the concept of liberty, and especially the principle of self-defense. Instead, typical of the perpetrator syndrome, it led Americans toward a collective denial of responsibility.

Many Americans would not characterize the U.S. attack on Iraq and Kuwait as an act of aggression. We want to believe it was self-defense. We were protecting the Kuwaitis, our own oil supplies, international respect for law and order, and the principle of liberty itself. We made a necessary preemptive strike against a dictator determined to control the Mideast, its oil, and therefore the world's economy. We had to obliterate Hussein's long-range rocket and nuclear weapon potential before it obliterated others.

If we regard this viewpoint to be true, then we must admit, at the least, that this particular act of self-defense was very costly to everyone involved. I've already summarized some of the international costs. At home, we have reinforced our perpetrator syndrome, inuring us further to war, glorifying the results of violence, and denying the destructiveness of our actions. The war drained resources and distracted us from more critical domestic problems, including poverty, hunger, declining health care, a collapsing educational system, continued racism, and catastrophe within the banking system. Instead of encouraging us to conserve energy and to develop alternative sources, the war has bound us even more tightly to Mideast oil. The war brought about the most airtight press censorship in the history of the United States.

It also seems undeniable that the U.S.-led attack on Iraq far exceeded the customary definitions of self-defense. Self-defense is legitimate only if it employs the *minimal* amount of force necessary to prevent further aggression and possibly to coerce just reparations (see chapters 3 and 9). The force used against Iraq far surpassed anything needed to drive Saddam Hussein out of Kuwait and it persisted until the goal of destroying Iraq's military might and overall infrastructure became apparent. The demolition was so thorough that it undermined any hope that the Iraqi economy could generate reparations. Furthermore, it caused incalculable damage to noncombatants, including the earth itself. As in most wars, self-defense became a pretext for a much broader political agenda. Furthermore, it has thus far failed to meet two of its stated goals—getting rid of Saddam Hussein and nullifying Iraq's nuclear capability.

ALTERNATIVES TO THE WAR AGAINST IRAQ

Few people in the West and few governments felt that Iraq's invasion of Kuwait should have gone unanswered. A remarkable worldwide coalition favored sanctions and many observers in the field of conflict analysis and resolution felt such measures were justified. Had the United States intended to prevent further Iraqi aggression and to restore Kuwait, several immediate steps were required, followed by a more long-range solution.

Stopping Iraqi aggression was quickly and relatively easily accomplished by providing military support to Saudi Arabia. This required relatively little military capability and no offensive warfare. Putting pressure on Iraq to leave Kuwait was begun with the United Nation's sanctions. The UN embargo should have been maintained for much longer before turning the Mideast into a war zone.

The problems in the Mideast, including Iraq's attack on Kuwait, have a long history behind them. A glance at the map indicates how carefully the British carved up the area to make sure that Iraq lacked an adequate outlet to the sea. It is well-known that Iraq took the brunt of the war against Iran, while Iraq's backers stayed out of the fighting. It is also clear that the Mideast is too drastically divided into the haves and have-nots.

Serious long-range difficulties stood and continue to stand in the way of peace. Focusing on conflicts among the Arabs, the disparity in wealth in the Middle East is appalling. Countries like Kuwait are rich, while others like Iraq are poor. Within the countries, there are enormous class differences. Any amelioration of conflict would require an increasing generosity on the part of the rich. Dynamic I: love needs more than its customary lip service within the Arab world.

Concern for the well-being of Arab peoples must also play a much greater role in the decision-making of those who are in conflict with them. Unhappily, any increase in Arab unity is seen as a threat to both Israeli and Western interests. A fragmented Arab world seems, on the surface at least, to guarantee Israel's safety and Western access to cheap oil. Thus, the United States was not really interested in ending conflict in the Middle East but rather in preventing Arab unity under Saddam Hussein.

James Laue (1991) has questioned whether this costly war accomplished anything, and urges an approach based on the principles of conflict analysis and resolution:

The situation still cries for real solution: mutually satisfied parties, jointly determined outcomes that are mutually satisfactory to all parties, the addressing of the major underlying issues, meeting the standards of justice and fairness, self-implementation by the parties, improvement of the relationships and a commitment to honor the new arrangements voluntarily and permanently. . . . A viable peace plan comes only from a process developed and owned by the parties. (pp. 5–6.)

ARAB-ISRAELI CONFLICT

The war against Iraq was not caused by the Arab-Israeli conflict. Instead the war was largely the product of conflict between the Arab oil-producing nations and the Western oil-consuming nations, especially the United States. While I am personally grateful for the existence of Israel, it has been too closely tied to U.S. oil diplomacy.

As much as any in the world, the Arab-Israeli conflict exemplifies how coercion breeds and perpetuates conflict. On the one hand, we have the worldwide Jewish community, subject to persecution for more than two thousand years, culminating in the recent Nazi exterminations. Israel, always the spiritual home of the Jews and their religion, became an earthly necessity after the Holocaust. Nor did the threat of extermination wane with the establishment of Israel; it became focused on the population of Israel. Modern Jewish political concerns, including Israeli domestic and foreign policy, is largely governed by the history of persecution and the seemingly ever-present threat of extermination.

But the Arabs, and especially the Palestinians, are themselves the victims of centuries-old oppression, both from indigenous empires and states, and from western exploitation. Since the end of World War II, the Palestinians have been pushed out by uninvited waves of Jews. They have nothing to look forward to but increasing numbers of immigrants into what used to be their country. Nor can they expect any real help from the larger Arab community which is more interested in using them as pawns against Israel and the United States. While Israel has been busy absorbing Jews from the Arab countries, the Arab countries have continually rejected the Palestinians.

Both parties in the Arab-Israeli conflict have legitimate claims. We have a classic example of conflicting claims, each with their own logic and legitimacy. It would be possible to write a seemingly rational treatise justifying either side's position, while vilifying the other's. Indeed, it has been done many times. And so we have two feuding groups, both identifying with the role of victim and both claiming that God, history, and justice are on wholly on their side.

Meanwhile, there is a limited amount of homeland to go around and much of it is sacred to the history of each contesting party. What is to be done?

COERCION IN THE ARAB-ISRAELI CONFLICT

As the Gulf war demonstrated, the Arab-Israeli conflict involves the interests of the entire world. For practical purposes, however, the focus will be on how to approach the conflict between the two most intimate antagonists, the Palestinians and the Israelis. In terms of the three dynamics, what sorts of change in viewpoint do they need to resolve their conflict?

Coercion has of course dominated this stage from the beginning. Even identifying the "beginning" is a matter of dispute, but it is safe to say that both sides feel that the other initiated the use of force. Both sides see the other as the perpetrator and oppressor. Regardless of whoever threw the first stone, after so many years of conflict, both are undoubtedly right about the other. All this is typical of deep-rooted conflict on every level from the personal to the political.

Both sides, or at least the majority of their recognizable leadership, tend to view coercion, including boycotts and military force, as the only solution. The Palestinians want their land back, and believe it will never be relinquished voluntarily. Most Palestinians envision a future in which they will be pushed from the West Bank further into the inhospitable laps of their Arab neighbors. Similarly, the Israelis see their very survival as dependent upon armed might, including an ever-expanding population and land base. From their viewpoint, the surrounding Arab nations, with their enormous superiority in land and population, will attempt to annihilate the entire Israeli nation at the first opportunity. Furthermore, many Israelis believe in a divine mandate to reclaim and settle all those lands awarded by God in the Bible. And so both sides seem almost wholly devoted to coercion as a solution.

Meanwhile, the cost of uncompromising coercion has been devastating to both sides. The Palestinians have lost their homeland and have no place else to go. Some live uneasily in Israel; many are dispersed in exile around the world; and many are penned up with their back against the river Jordan.

How deep is the Palestinian frustration and commitment to violence? In *From Beirut to Jerusalem* (1990), Thomas L. Friedman describes a West Bank toddler walking about carrying a stone, practicing to throw it at the Israelis.

The Israelis too suffer mightily from the cost of their resort to coercion. Their economy is swamped by the cost of the military, their people live in perpetual insecurity, domestic freedoms are compromised, and their coercive tactics against the Palestinians divide them at home and cost them dearly in terms of world-wide support, even among Jews.

TWO PEOPLES UNITED?

The Jews of Israel and the Arabs of Palestine have much in common. They are of course similar in origin, both with their roots in the Mideast. Even their word for "hello" has a similar ring and a common root. In their hearts, both share the same land. In regard to the Jews, it is clear that they are surrounded by a dry sea of hostility. But so are the Palestinians. Palestinians in Israel and on the West Bank (until Intifada) lived better materially than those who fled to Arab nations. Neither Palestinians nor Israelis can expect much help from their immediate neighbors.

THE FIRST PRINCIPLE

The fates of the Palestinians and the Israelis are intertwined. Recognizing this is the first principle for resolving their conflicts.

It seems unlikely that the Jews will expel the great majority of Arabs from Israel and the West Bank. Short of that, Arabs and Jews are going to be intimate enemies for a long time. The alternative of a complete expulsion, while providing momentary security, would only fan still more feverish hatreds. And for ethical reasons, as well as practical political ones, driving out the Palestinians is not a viable alternative. Even in simple economic terms, the continued escalation of hostilities between Israel and the West Bank is too costly to Israel.

Conversely, it seems unlikely that the Palestinians will ever be rid of the Israelis. Driving the Jews into the sea is neither an ethically nor politically sound alternative. The recent resurgence of Russian immigration into Israel, its renewed ties with the United States, the weakening of Soviet power, the escalating U.S. presence in the Middle East, the support of worldwide Jewry for Israel, the might and determination of Israel itself—all suggest that the Palestinians must find a modus vivendi with the Israelis. And there are indications that they are leaning in that direction by modifying their demands for a peaceful settlement, seeking an accommodation with Israel, rather than annihilation of the state.

THE SECOND PRINCIPLE

The second principle, common to most conflicts, is this: the stronger party must reject force and reach toward a settlement.

Israel's might and Palestine's relative vulnerability seem apparent. As by far the superior force, Israel must take the initiative. The greatest obstacle to any conflict resolution is the threat of coercion, and it is up to Israel to foster conditions in which the two sides can begin to communicate in an atmosphere relatively free of coercion and threats. But before doing this, Israel will need to understand the continuing cost of the conflict as demonstrated, for example, by its internal political strife and flagging economy. Recent attempts at peace negotiations are encouraging, but both sides have a long way to go.

Israel's victim mentality, so thoroughly understandable, must be replaced by a greater awareness of Israel's dominant position. Israel cannot, of course, trust its old enemies; but it can trust itself and its own power sufficiently to initiate a more egalitarian dialog. It can start out with a willingness to offer *understanding* of the Palestinian viewpoint. This should not be difficult, since the basic needs of the Palestinians are similar to those of the Israelis; their outcast role in the Middle East, as we have seen, is somewhat similar, including a fundamentally hostile relationship with the rest of the Arab world. The recent assault by the Lebanese army on PLO-controlled areas of Lebanon confirms the plight of the Palestinians.

LIBERTY AND THE LIMITS OF ECONOMIC EXCHANGE

Before Intifada, relations between Palestinians and Israelis were in some ways improving. While the West Bank was by no means an autonomous region, its economic relations with Israel created a free-trade zone between the two communities from which both benefitted. The mutual advantages of free trade between Israel and the West Bank—as well as divided Jerusalem and the Gaza strip—was addressed by Shawn Tully in the May 20, 1991 *Fortune*. In an article entitled "The Best Cause of Mideast Peace," Tully wrote:

What they [those seeking peace] too often ignore are the immense
economic benefits of peace—and the staggering costs of prolong-
ing the struggle. A settlement would help bring Israel the invest-
ment capital needed to absorb Soviet immigrants. It would
unleash the Palestinians' formidable business talents, planting a
budding Hong Kong in the Middle East. The result could be a
new generation of Arabs and Jews with a stake in prosperity, not
war. If ever two people could benefit from each other by working
together, it is the Arabs and the Jews.

Calling for an Arab-Israeli "common market," Tully declares "Any
settlement above all must be built on free trade."

Tully points out that after Israel seized the West Bank from Jordan and Gaza from Egypt during the 1967 war, it opened the
borders between itself and the captured territories. Israeli capital
and technology combined with Palestinian cheap labor resulted in
an economic boost to all involved. In the eight years following the
war, the economy of Israel grew at 7 percent, while the rate in the
occupied territories exceeded 14 percent.

As Israel's economy stagnated in the mid-1970s, it then became
more protectionist, banning many products from the occupied territories. Intifada resulted in the further suppression of trade by
both sides, and then the PLO's support of Iraq against Israel during the Gulf war led to the closing of borders by Israel. While
limited trade and labor exchange has been reestablished, nothing
like the original free trade seems likely to be reinstituted, even
though both sides continue to suffer the loss.

Tully concludes that the occupied territories could become
"booming capitalist enclaves" at the heart of both economic recovery and cooperation between Arabs and Jews. He quotes an Israeli
manufacturer who uses Arab labor: "In our plants and offices, Arabs
and Jews work side by side to make products instead of mischief."
Thus capitalism hopefully leads to cooperation and mutuality.

As useful as it is, something is clearly missing in Tully's analysis.
Psychosocial needs frequently dwarf pure economic interest. So do
other political issues. The desire for political freedom, self-esteem,
and cultural identity motivated the Palestinians to resist the Israelis. Furthermore, despite vigorous trade and the thousands of Arabs crossing into Israel to provide much-needed cheap labor, there

was little impulse on either side for social integration. Arabs and Jews did trade and work together, but they did not make friends with each other. Politically, Arabs were barred from joining the powerful Israeli labor federation, Histadrut. Thus, economic ties that benefitted both did little to bring the two sides closer together.

BACK TO THE FUTURE: JIMMY CARTER AT CAMP DAVID

At the June 1991 National Conference on Peacemaking and Conflict Resolution (NCPCR) in Charlotte, North Carolina, former president Jimmy Carter was interviewed in front of a plenary session by James Laue. With the main topic peacemaking, Carter talked extensively about the Camp David accords in which he brought together Anwar Sadat and Menachem Begin to forge a blueprint for peace between Egypt and Israel. Carter believes that the accords, which were officially endorsed by the Israeli and Egyptian parliaments, still provide the basic principles for an overall Arab-Israeli peace. The Arabs must end the embargo and reject the destruction of Israel, and the Israelis must grant "full autonomy" to the Palestinians and give up Jewish settlements in the Arab territories.

The Arab-Israeli negotiations were unique in that the United States was willing to reward both sides with enormous financial aid, and perhaps to punish them diplomatically if they failed. But in addition to the inducements, and perhaps threats, peace required a complex process of genuine conflict resolution led by Carter.

In analyzing the Camp David success, Carter described the importance of bringing participants together in an inspiring natural surrounding, such as Camp David, and the need for setting deadlines for the negotiations. He talked about the moment when both sides believe that peace is to their advantage, and the importance of a win-win outcome. He helped the process by providing Begin with polls of his own citizens, confirming that they would make concessions, including withdrawal from the newly formed settlements in the Sinai. In regard to Sadat, he emphasized their personal ties and their mutual love and trust. Many of these issues are discussed in Carter's book, *Keeping the Faith* (1982).

Several points stood out in Carter's presentation. One was his conviction that the Arab and Israeli *people,* in contrast to much of their leadership, wanted peace. This confirms the metaphor of the Conflict Tree. Ordinary people are often nearer to their common roots than are their more polarized leaders. Second, although Carter did not emphasize it, I was impressed by hints that the Arab and Israeli people could celebrate each other. This was suggested by the joyous welcome given to Sadat when he made his first visit to Israel. But what interested me the most was the role that love played in the actual negotiations between Begin and Sadat.

At first glance, the assertion that love played any role at all in the negotiations would seem absurd. After all, Begin and Sadat could not get along, and for the last ten days of the negotiations, they never saw each other. And while Carter unreservedly loved Sadat, he did not express much affection for Begin. What impressed me was *Carter's overall loving attitude*. I believe that Jimmy Carter infused love into the whole negotiation process.

Of course, the negotiation and conflict-resolution process involves more than love. Specific conditions must be set up and specific steps must be taken. As summarized in chapter 1, the third party must create a voluntary setting in which power is forsaken as a means of attaining goals; basic needs and vital interests must be identified and rationally addressed by analytic methods; collaborative problem-solving must redefine win-lose conflicts in a way that permits both sides to win; the cost of the conflict must become clear to both parties; and help may be needed in generating alternative mutually satisfying solutions (Burton, 1990).

Most of these processes are related to Dynamic II: liberty. In keeping with the principles of liberty, to begin a negotiation process, the individuals involved must show respect for each other. However, to more fully resolve their differences, they must ultimately collaborate toward understanding and satisfying each other's basic needs. That takes place most thoroughly when motivated by love.

When a third party, such as Carter, intervenes in a conflict, love creates and motivates the forum for conflict resolution. Problem-solving then takes place within the caring context created by the intervener. Ultimately, valued and even loving relationships frequently emerge from the work of getting to know and to understand each other. Richard Rubenstein has pointed out to me that even in bitter political conflicts, such as those in Northern Ireland, conflict-resolution processes can create such rapport between the opposing leaders that they have difficulty being accepted by their constituents when they return home. Thus, there is little or no fundamental difference in the basic process of conflict resolution, whether it involves marital discord (see chapter 6) or national conflict.

At the NCPCR meeting, Carter described the last days of the meetings when he thought Begin would go home without accepting any compromise. As a part of leave-taking, Begin sent over a request for a signed portrait of the American president for his grandchildren. Meanwhile, Carter had obtained the names of all eight of Begin's grandchildren, and he was able to sign individual photos for each of them. When he handed the gifts to Begin, the old terrorist actually cried; and according to Carter, the President did, too. Within minutes after leaving the emotional encounter, Begin made a turnabout and sent word that he would agree in principle to the accords.

Did Carter's astute (if caring) "manipulation" of Begin's emotions bring about the Camp David accords? Of course, a lot more than that went into reaching an agreement: everything from the cost of all the previous wars, to the good intentions of Begin and Sadat, and especially, the political arm-twisting and financial rewards offered by the U.S. government. But I believe that Carter's loving attitude and demeanor played a role.

The anecdote about Begin's grandchildren illustrates an important principle: in the absence of love between adversaries in a conflict, a *loving mediator* can facilitate conflict resolution. The result may not be as thorough as if the parties to the conflict grew to love each other; but the outcome can be positive and pave the way for further gains. I know this to be true from my firsthand experience working with warring couples in psychotherapy, as well as friends, coworkers, and colleagues in my everyday life. It was gratifying to hear it confirmed in regard to warring heads of nations.

THE GREAT LESSON

In concluding this chapter, a fundamental principle of conflict resolution warrants repetition: all people are made of the same biological and spiritual stuff. Individuals born in one culture and raised in another will be the product of the culture that raises them. A child born to Arabs but raised as an Israeli Jew will become one. A child born to Israeli Jews but raised an Arab Moslem will become one. The same can be said of every nationality and religion. It is true of Soviets and Americans, of Chinese and Japanese, of warring African tribes.

When we look across the battle lines drawn on the basis of gender, race, religion, culture, or nationality, we are looking at ourselves. When we know this in our hearts, murderous conflict will be made impossible.

Is there hope that love can become a more pervasive value in the future? Only if people realize that it is the *only* hope for the future.

A potentially unified international movement is evolving from several divergent sources. The final chapter will examine this convergence of values within alternative movements. It could become a worldwide coalition of shared values inspired by the principles of liberty and love. The concluding chapter will also examine what may be the ultimate approach to conflict resolution for the world's most critical problems—Gandhi's "loving firmness."

Part III

Bringing About Change

CHAPTER 11

▼ ▼

What Kind of Community in Our Future?

Those of us living in large societies automatically assume that without "government" human societies would degenerate into uncivilized chaos. In their lack of "law and order," precivilized societies seem clearly deficient, lagging behind in the linear march of social "progress." What we forget is that our prehuman ancestors were social and formed stable social systems long before they were rational. . . . Strong social bonds, far from being something we create in a calculating, civilised manner, are something we deeply need and cannot help forming. We are not social because of rationally perceived individual benefits, such as economic gain or national security, but because our deepest emotional being does not allow us to be otherwise.

Mary Clark, **Ariadne's Thread** (*1989*)

The recognition that all men are persons and are not to be treated as things, has arisen slowly in the consciousness of mankind. It has made its way with difficulty against the recurrent testimony of immediate experience, against sophisticated argument, against the predatory and acquisitive instincts which men bring with them out of the animal struggle for existence. The passage from barbarism into civilization is long, halting, and unsure. It is a hard climb from the practice of devouring one's enemies to the injunction to love them. But in the long ascent there is a great divide which is reached when men discover, declare, and acknowledge, however much they may deny it in practice, that there is a Golden Rule which is the ultimate and universal criterion for human conduct. For then, and then only, is there a standard to which all can repair who seek to transform the incessant and indecisive struggle for domination and survival into the security of the Good Society.

Walter Lippmann, **The Good Society** (*1936*)

While no one can predict the future, it seems likely humanity's problems will continue to escalate dangerously unless we develop new and better ways of resolving conflict. We do not know how much time we have left, and we do not know how many years it will take to make the necessary transformations.

Doom has been predicted before. The need for a dramatic change in human attitudes has been announced at least as far back as the Hebrew prophets. The call for a more loving community has also been made many times before—seemingly to little avail.

Even if it is too late for our concerted efforts to prevent ultimate catastrophe—and I do not think that it is too late—I cannot imagine a life well-lived that does not involve trying. To live well, it seems to me, is to act in the world in an empathic and caring manner. Whatever the outcome, each individual can then feel that he or she has made a special effort and a unique contribution.

Life does not ask us to succeed; too many factors outside our control determine that. Life asks us to live ethically and to accept the consequences.

That's the dilemma of life. As individuals we can try as hard as we want, but without community effort little can be accomplished toward social change. The only hope is that sufficient numbers of individuals will transform themselves and their attitudes that community itself will be transformed.

The ultimate solution will require a great awakening of empathic caring throughout the world—an increasing awareness of love in every aspect of our lives, and a willingness to take risks toward implementing it in our own lives and lives of those around us.

TRIVIALIZING LOVE

As Gandhi, Schweitzer, and King will illustrate, political and intellectual leaders have on occasion elevated love to the central position in their lives. More often it appears in folk and pop music. From the Beatles and Bob Dylan to modern pop songs, themes of love abound, most often focused on romantic love, but sometimes directed at the yearning for peace.

The idea of love, as Ginger Ross-Breggin recently reminded me, has been marginalized and trivialized by relegating it to the domain of women. This book seeks to do that which should not need doing; it seeks to legitimize love among thinking people.

Is it naive and even foolhardy to imagine that people throughout the world might someday join in a common concern for each other and their home, Earth? Certainly we have the technological capacity to facilitate such a human community through communication and transportation. We can get to know each other well enough to feel kinship among ourselves. But can the human spirit rise to the occasion? And if so, through what sort of societal institutions?

PLACING HOPE IN RELIGION

It is easy enough to be skeptical and even cynical about religion. For those of us who are Jewish, it is difficult to imagine Christianity as a fountain of love. Historically, Christianity has victimized Jews and other non-Christians, and frequently instigated their outright slaughter. Christianity has also inspired mayhem and murder among competing versions of its own faith.

Nonetheless, the vision of this book has been in part inspired by the Judeo-Christian tradition. I have already cited two Christian psychiatrists, Smiley Blanton and M. Scott Peck, and later in the chapter I will favorably examine the ideas Gandhi, Albert Schweitzer, and Martin Luther King, Jr., three men deeply influenced by Judeo-Christian ideals.

Any Westerner who believes in the efficacy of love is likely to be borrowing from the Judeo-Christian tradition. The Golden Rule is the product of many different religions (Lippmann, 1937, quoted in chapter 2), but it comes to the West through Judaism and then Christianity. The central theme of Christ's teaching is to love God and to love each other. Nonviolence also finds some roots in Jewish and Christian teachings. Clearly many individuals and groups draw inspiration from these ideals.

Churches and synagogues frequently are community centers of caring and charity. American churches have in recent years sometimes spoken out against war and on behalf of the poor. The Catholic Church has been criticized by free-market advocates because of its call for state support of the poor.

On the other hand, organized religion rarely plays a positive role in societal or political conflict resolution. On issues of racism and sexism, for example, it too often reinforces suppressive ideas. Often religious fervor divides Jews, Roman Catholics, and Protestants, and often Protestants feud among themselves. In the political arena, religion tends to motivate and justify violent hatred, and in wartime religion almost always seeks to align God with its particular nation.

Overall, we can hope that Western religion will recall that its true faith is love. If so, organized religion could become a much more benevolent influence in society. Meanwhile, the *ideals* of Judeo-Christian tradition often inspire people to reject the very institutions that are supposed to epitomize and represent them.

PLACING HOPE IN THE STATE

Government-enforced policies cannot solve all of the problems that modern society faces. When government goes too far in suppressing freedom and the pursuit of self-interest, there are disastrous consequences.

Human beings need and want as much autonomy and personal freedom as possible in their lives. They want to determine the course of their own lives, and they resist attempts to thwart that intention. Only when liberty flourishes are people fully able to actualize their own lives and maximize their own chosen contributions to society. Liberty must become much *more* of a reality for all of the world's oppressed, including women and children; the poor, homeless, and hungry; and religious, racial, and ethnic minorities.

Free-market and anarchist critiques are correct in arguing that government should be limited in scope. Not only does the state threaten individual freedom, it frequently becomes the tool of the most oppressive groups in society. Motivated by mixtures of nationalism, racism, religious bigotry, and political ideology, modern governments have routinely become the instruments of violent oppression and unspeakable atrocities.

As described in chapter 9, the state, with its inherent coerciveness, has limits. Dynamic II: liberty is not about to belly up. Nor should it. We need to understand and to define it better; and to recognize the limits of what it can accomplish. We do not need to suppress liberty, but to help people understand the necessity of introducing more loving alternatives as well. We need benevolent ethics that—without suppressing liberty—offer something more. We need a world that respects liberty and promotes love within the context of modern, industrial society.

Government should focus on monitoring and controlling other power concentrations, while the people monitor and control the government. Government should also help to compensate and support those who have been exploited, lack autonomy, or otherwise cannot take care of themselves. Above all else, the state should be transformed as much as possible into an institution for voluntary conflict resolution. In effect, whenever possible, community must replace the state.

Usually, social critics and visionaries turn to the state as their hope for redemption. It is worth repeating that government is based on coercion and is therefore hamstrung when it comes to conflict resolution (see chapters 9 and 10). The state cannot be transformed into an institution for conflict resolution without transforming it into something other than a state. Voluntary, caring community must replace much of what now falls under the umbrella of government.

But how are we to achieve such a transformation, especially if it cannot come through the government itself?

PLACING HOPE IN PUBLIC EDUCATION

In *The Altruistic Personality,* Oliner and Oliner (1988) call for an educational system that will encourage empathy and love, and social responsibility.

Schools need to become caring institutions—institutions in which students, teachers, bus drivers, principals, and all others receive positive affirmation for kindness, empathy, and concern. Participants need opportunities to work and have fun together, develop intimacies, and share successes and pain. Students also need opportunities to consider broad universal principles that relate to justice and care in matters of public concern. . . . In short, caring schools will acknowledge diversity on the road to moral concern. (pp. 258–59.)

But there is a flaw in Oliner and Oliner's proposal. By their own description, it is the loving *family* that produced morally heroic, caring individuals.

Even if schools could fulfill such a basic moral and social function, how is society to develop such schools? Public schools and universities are instruments of the state. They cannot significantly transcend the values promoted by the state, which is itself based on coercion and obedience. For example, whenever a government declares war, it vigorously doctrinates violent patriotism into young citizens through their schools. In Nazi Germany, the educational establishment was quick to support the most vicious anti-Semitism. The educational model suggested by Oliner and Oliner becomes utopian (see chapter 9) because they cannot tell us how to bring it about without first transforming society.

THE NEW HOPE FOR LOVE

Ironically, it is recent international politics that provide the greatest inspiration for a more peace-loving world community. As I began this chapter, the media was filled with encouraging analyses of President Bush's summit meeting with President Gorbachev. The irony was not lost on anyone: from Reagan's "Evil Empire" to "Most Favored Nation" trade status in a few brief years. The Russian Bear that was going to "bury us" was now begging us for charity. As I am finishing the chapter, the USSR no longer exists. Russia, the country we once feared most in the world, is asking to be the recipient of our diplomatic and financial support.

Can there be any doubt about the readiness of masses of people to transform their attitudes from indifference or hatred to friendship and trust? If Russia can succeed in becoming more free, Russians and Americans may one day find themselves the closest of allies.

The earlier irony that our World War II enemies, West Germany and Japan, so quickly became our allies has often been remarked on. But the potential for reconciliation may even be greater between Americans and Russians. My friends and colleagues who visited the USSR regularly believe that Americans have much more natural affinity with Russians than with Germans or Japanese, or almost any other European nation.

Two peoples—whose conflict threatened to obliterate each other, themselves, and the whole world—could turn out to be best friends. Yet a few years ago, most people in both countries would have found such a prospect laughable—or *treasonous*. There have been times when supporting such a rapprochement would have cost you your life in the USSR, and cost you your reputation and your job in the USA.

Consider also the transformation taking place in the individual psyches of the peoples of Russia and other former communist countries. Many of them are rejecting the ideology that was crammed into their heads for so many decades, and calling for much more personal and economic liberty. They are doing so with more conviction than many Americans who remain cynical toward capitalism.

There's an important lesson in these events: dramatic *positive* social change and conflict resolution is possible, involving millions of individuals and whole societies. If today the United States and Russia, why not tomorrow the world? Toward that end, the United States should make every possible effort to support Russia and other newly liberated European nations.

SMALL COMMUNITIES, THE GLOBAL VILLAGE, AND THE MODERN INDUSTRIAL WORLD

What are the ingredients of a good society? Devotion to the principles of liberty is one of them.

As events in the former communist nations underscore, liberty *is* the engine of economic, scientific, and technological progress, at least as we know and define progress in the world today. Only when individuals and corporations are free to pursue their own self-interest, will they innovate at a rapid rate and keep an economy humming. Voices within the affluent nations are being raised in doubt about the wisdom of continued unfettered economic expansion and what they are saying merits attention (see chapter 9). But recent international events have confirmed once again that modern economies flourish only when individuals and groups are in part liberated to pursue their own self-interest.

Utopian solutions that urge a return to small communities often reject the benefits of the free market (Clark, 1989; Sale, 1985; van Andruss, Plant, Plant, and Wright, 1990; see also chapter 9). It is claimed that self-sustaining, cooperative communities could thrive without free-market competition and industrialization. Small communities could live off the land as native peoples have done or develop smaller, ecologically sound industries.

But smaller communities cannot survive outside the context of a peaceful global village, and the global villages requires modern technology, including the free market and industrialization. This proposition is so unfamiliar and yet important, that it requires further analysis.

The well-being of small communities requires peace and harmony throughout their region and even the globe, otherwise they would fall prey to larger, militant societies. Their survival requires a worldwide commitment to humanity as one family with universal respect for the rights of individual persons and each unique culture. Even those who promote small communities, while seeking to limit industrial growth, favor a global community. In *Blue Print for Survival* (1972), the editors of *The Ecologist* (Goldsmith, Allen, Allaby, Davoll, and Lawrence) point out:

There must be procedures whereby community actions that affect regions can be discussed at the regional level and regional actions with extraregional effects can be discussed at the global level. . . . We emphasize that our goal should be to create **community feeling** *and* **global awareness** *rather than that dangerous and sterile compromise which is nationalism. (pp. 40, 41.)*

A world organized around communities will require global awareness and communication.

Without a global village with widely shared agreement on peaceful conflict resolution, smaller communities would be swallowed up and overwhelmed by larger states much as they have been over the last 10,000 years. *But the global village depends upon the free market with its modern industrial achievements, especially international transportation and communication.*

For individuals and local communities to feel as if they are part of a worldwide society, they need contact with the wider world, including sufficient interaction and communication to evolve common ideals and an empathic devotion to each other's well-being. That worldwide contact requires modern industry and technology, especially transportation and communication. This dependent relationship between small communities, the global village, and modern industrialization has been missed by some of the most insightful and imaginative critics of modern society and requires further elaboration.

THE GLOBAL VILLAGE AND MODERN TECHNOLOGY

The global village, as originally proposed by Marshall McLuhan and Quentin Fiore (1967), is a product of modern methods of communication, such as the telephone, radio, and TV:

Electric circuity has overthrown the regime of "time" and "space" and pours upon us instantly and continuously the concerns of all other men. It has reconstituted dialogue on a global scale. Its message is Total Change, ending psychic, social, economic, and political parochialism. The old civic, state, and national groups have become unworkable. (p. 16.)

According to McLuhan and Fiore, not only electronic but print media are key to the global village:

Printing, a ditto device, confirmed and extended the new visual stress. It provided the first uniformly repeatable "commodity," the first assembly line—mass production.

It created the portable book, which men could read in privacy and isolation from others. Man could now inspire—and conspire. (p. 50.)

Although it depends upon modern technology, the global village returns us to a our tribal origins:

We now live in a global village . . . a simultaneous happening. We are back in acoustic space. We have begun again to structure primordial feelings, the tribal emotions . . . (p. 63.)

It is impossible to separate out the necessary technology for a global village from the remainder of the industrial complex. The global village requires telephones, radios, and TVs; photocopying and fax machines; computers and satellite communications; trains, planes, and buses. It requires energy sources and power stations for the production of electricity, and will probably require other fuels as well. We are a long way away from generating sufficient power from the sun, the wind, and the tides; and the development of these sustainable resources will in itself require advanced technology.

In addition to transportation and communication, the global village places other requirements on technology and industry. High-tech medical care is required to permit the free intermingling of peoples. Modern industrial methods of food production and transportation will be required for the foreseeable future for the feeding of populations in upheaval and transition. We cannot continue to ignore the massive loss of top soil and other problems caused by agri-business (Worldwatch Institute, 1990), but neither can we ignore the immediate dangers of famine.

Those who would wholly reject the free market, and hence modern industry and technology, do not realize that they are inadvertently rejecting world community. This reality needs more attention from those who hope for both local and world community. There is an inherent incompatibility between the small, close-knit *local* community and the industry required for a *global* village. The small, self-sustaining local community cannot produce the necessary technology to maintain the global village. The future of a loving world depends in part upon modern industry, as well as upon learning to mitigate its negative impact upon people and the environment.

THE FUTURE OF THE FREE MARKET

Even if it were possible to build a more united world without the extensive use of technology, it is highly unlikely that the next several generations will be willing to discard the advantages generated by the free market and modern industry. Americans aren't the only ones who believe in at least some degree of free enterprise. The trend in the Third World, including the former communist nations, is to want *more* capitalism. Even in Communist China, people were quick to grasp the opportunity to experiment with free enterprise, and like the Russians, were hungry to meet and to learn from Americans (see chapter 10). They did this despite the knowledge that a crackdown might come.

The so-called undeveloped nations will not tolerate outsiders putting a fuel governor on their sputtering engines while the Westernized nations roar along at full throttle. They will not hold back their own economies in the interest of the environment, nor will they limit their armies in the interest of world peace. At least, they will not consider these alternatives until the industrialized nations become willing to make it worth their while and until the people of the world adopt a new ethic.

To implement such a transformation in values will require enormous Dynamic I: generosity on the part of the industrialized nations toward the less developed nations. Ideally America would lead the way in offering incentives to other nations to preserve their environments and reduce their military budgets. This will require a radical shift in values worldwide.

"Small is beautiful" and "self-sustaining ecosystems" remain important ideals. But absent an earth-shaking catastrophe, the implementation of these ideals seems most unlikely on any large scale within the imaginable future. Industrialization is going to be with us for a long time. The goal must be to build more community-oriented values within existing modern society—values that will lead people to *want* to work together to overcome the hazards of the industrial age.

LOVING COMMUNITY

Is there any way to restrain the self-aggrandizing power of government and the monopolistic tendencies of the free market, and at the same time to encourage mercy, charity, and concern for each other and our world? Is there an organizing social principle beyond coercion (the state) and liberty (the free market)?

There is another principle—the energy of human community, love. We must find ways to mobilize the vast resources of love without turning to government or to the free market. Indeed, we must use these resources to help control the excesses of government and free enterprise. How to do that is the most pressing issue of our now and future time. It will require new viewpoints and new institutions as well as increased community involvement at a grassroots and individual level.

There are innumerable ways to mobilize loving community, but to be most effective love must be expressed in its most pure form as defined in the Three Dynamic Theory. It must be unconditional. It must lie outside both the state and the marketplace. It must not be distorted by coercion nor corrupted by the profit motive. By remaining independent of both the state and the market, the love expressed by new institutions could remain true to its essence as a spontaneous, joyful expression of "gifting."

Once people begin to focus on loving community, its expressions will flourish in ways we cannot now anticipate. As possible models, I will describe two potential directions: First, a developing coalition of independent reform groups that share and promote a more loving attitude toward people and the planet; and second, a renewal of civil disobedience in the form of Gandhi's "loving firmness." These two alternatives can embrace both the personal and the political.

LOVING COMMUNITY AND THE THIRD SECTOR

In *The New Realities* (1989), Peter Drucker describes the vast array of voluntary activities that are "non-business, non-government, 'human change agencies,' the nonprofit organizations of the so-called third sector." To illustrate the third sector, he cites the Boy Scouts and Girl Scouts, the Salvation Army, the American Red Cross, American Lung Association, American Heart Association, American Mental Health Association, Urban League, innumerable church activities, a wide variety of cultural activities (museums, symphony orchestras), and community chest activities such as "Meals on Wheels." He does not mention the infinite number of groups that support ethnic identities and the enormous number that support athletics, including Little League. More striking, he makes no note of the great variety of reform-minded or radical counterculture activities (see below).

Drucker points out that "the third sector is actually the country's largest employer," even though it is not reflected in gross national product and labor statistics. One out of every two adult Americans, ninety-million people, contribute to the third sector, most of them in addition to a full-time job.

The third sector, according to Drucker, plays a vital role in building community and bridging the socioeconomic gap between volunteers and less-educated classes:

America's third-sector institutions are rapidly becoming creators of new bonds of community and a bridge between knowledge workers and the "other half." Increasingly they create a sphere of effective citizenship. (p. 204.)

These activities benefit the volunteer as well as the recipients. The new America, which he calls the knowledge society, "needs community, freely chosen yet acting as a bond." Thus the third sector combines what I am calling Dynamics I and II. He concludes in that vein:

It [the knowledge society] needs a sphere where the individual can become a master through serving. It needs a sphere where freedom is not just being passive, not just being left alone rather than being ordered around—a sphere that requires active involvement and responsibility. (p. 206.)

Drucker's analysis is helpful, but the Three Dynamic Theory sheds more light on this vast social activity. The third sector has the *potential* to become loving community, Dynamic I activities that could transform society.

Drucker contrasts the third sector with "business" and with "government." The Three Dynamic Theory helps focus on the basic needs and social relations characteristic of each of these different institutions. What Drucker calls business is actually "free enterprise"—the profit-motivated sector. What he calls "government" is state coercion—the use of organized, legitimized force to obtain certain ends. What he calls the third sector is to a great extent "love"—freely given gifts or gifting as a way of relating.

Drucker characterizes the third sector as consisting of

"human-change agencies." But state and federal governments also support many human-change agencies, including prisons, mental hospitals, museums, art and cultural activities, and innumerable forms of educational and service agencies that aim at human-change, from the public schools to poverty programs. The free enterprise system as well is often involved in human change. It offers alternatives to many government services, including schools, prisons, hospitals, museums, and those services covered by welfare and social security, such as health and disability insurance. The profession of psychotherapy, the epitome of human-change activities, is typically a free-enterprise activity. So are the many management consultants and training programs that aim at transforming both individual managers and their corporations. The difference is that the third sector is based on love—the desire to give gifts to others, to serve for the fundamental purpose of serving, to care for caring's sake. Because it is motivated by ideals, and potentially unencumbered by ties to establishment institutions and to earning a living, the third sector is potentially very radical.

Of course, third sector agencies can easily become distorted or corrupted. Also, those who volunteer may get advantages beyond the joy of giving, such as prestige, useful training experiences, and social or professional contacts. But the basic need and the basic method of social relationship for third sector volunteers is Dynamic I: love.

Drucker calls the third sector "counter cultural" but his reason for doing so is not clear to me. All of the activities he lists are rather conservative in nature, implementing established, time-honored American values. In his brief survey of third sector organizations, he does not include movements that support feminism, civil rights, children's rights, peace, the environment, or other more nearly countercultural groups. This is striking, because a great deal of radical social reform, for better or worse, originates in the third sector, including the whole spectrum from the Ku Klux Klan to the Jewish Defense League and the Black Muslims. Even if they want it, radical approaches usually cannot obtain government or business support. If they do not begin with sufficient Dynamic I energy they cannot survive.

Not every group that falls into the third sector or even the loving community will necessarily express love at its most ideal. Most third sector organizations are likely to be rather limited or focused.

But since they exist outside both the government and the free-enterprise system, their membership is likely to be driven by an ideal of some sort and by a need for community. Even the most cultist and seemingly antisocial third sector groups almost always maintain an intense community experience within themselves, while other people are being excluded or even targeted as enemies. The love shared or promoted by these groups remains corrupted but nonetheless recognizable. The cult often offers the most loving experience in the lifetime of its members, who frequently come from deprived and abused backgrounds. Thus, individuals frequently join hate-mongering groups not only to express their negative emotions, but also to share in the caring community which these groups provide their members.

I am reminded of my shock when, as a young psychiatrist, one of my first clients told me that the most caring and morale-building experience of his life had been in the Hitler youth. Compared to the authoritarian, oppressive family life he had known, the devoted leadership and seemingly high ideals of the Hitler youth became a genuine Dynamic I experience for him.

It is of course commonplace for soldiers of every army to share an intense and often overtly loving experience among themselves, even while they are fighting and killing other human beings. Fear of the enemy facilitates the community among the soldiers, much as it does among cult group members. While acting violently toward others, they allow themselves to become more vulnerable to each other. Men in particular may feel more comfortable in showing and fulfilling their more "needy" feelings when they are, at the same time, "proving themselves" in sports, on the battlefield, or in other seemingly "manly" ways.

Drucker gives us insight into the enormous human energy being poured into the third sector in the United States. As a basically Dynamic I influence, it has tremendous potential to become an energy that uplifts society beyond the institutions of liberty (political freedom and the marketplace) and coercion (the state). To some extent, the third sector already does this, and as Drucker notes, is a great source of community spirit. With so many people willing to donate their time to public service, imagine what might happen if large numbers of them focused their efforts more consciously upon love for *all* Americans and, eventually, for *all* people. The third sector could become the loving community, and the country could quickly begin moving much closer toward the solution of its most difficult problems and conflicts.

BECOMING EACH OTHER'S ANSWERS

In a paper entitled "Becoming Each Other's Answers," Ginger Ross-Breggin has described a number of alternative or minority traditions that have recently begun converging toward a common set of values. All of them are largely third sector or loving community groups. Among these she includes:

1. *Environmentalism,* especially deep ecology.
2. *Conflict resolution,* especially peacemaking.
3. *Feminism,* with its rejection of patriarchy in favor of mutuality, and its growing focus on the male abuse of women and children.
4. *Social justice,* including groups devoted to civil rights and the eradication of racism, children's rights, reform of prisons and the criminal justice system, health care reform, and the amelioration of hunger and poverty.

My own major area of human rights activism has been psychiatric reform, including a great deal of networking with the psychiatric survivor movement (Breggin, 1991). Nearly all the people I work with in reform activities have a strong sense of bonding among themselves and with human beings in general. A high degree of empathic awareness frequently motivates their work.

In the United States, the Native American revival—inspired by growing general appreciation of its philosophy and religion—also holds many values in common with the other groups.

As already noted, the *ideals* of the Judeo-Christian tradition continue to encourage people to love each other as equals in God's eyes. These ideals are the source of much that is positive in this book. The problem is how to bring the institutions of religion up to the standard of their own spiritual principles.

The "shared values" that Ross-Breggin identifies within these alternative movements provide a starting point for a Dynamic I: love coalition. Ross-Breggin has isolated four basic shared values:

1. *Abhorrence of violence.*

2. *Equality of all human beings.*

3. *Inter-connectedness of human beings with the earth.*

4. *The creation of community on both a personal and a global level.*

Each of these values reflect, Dynamic I and can be found in the Three Dynamic Table (see page 261). In addition, Ross-Breggin and I have also discussed in our seminars the emergence of four additional values which cut across Dynamic I: love and Dynamic II: liberty. These are:

5. *Comprehensive thinking and communicating.* Scholars and activists alike are breaking down the traditional barriers between disciplines such as psychology, philosophy, economics, politics, and religion. They are adopting plain English, rather than specialized jargon, and interrelating the various isolated academic disciplines into a holistic conception of humanity and nature.

6. *Personal growth or self-realization as an aspect of political reform.* Personal growth becomes inseparable from making efforts for the common good of humanity and the planet. Personal change leads to societal change and, conversely, working toward the improvement of society improves oneself.

7. *Distrust of statism.* Solutions are evolving through individual actions, small groups, communities, and so-called grassroots efforts. This anarchistic theme is usually unstated and by no means consistent within the reform groups; but individualism and antistatism are closely aligned with the concept of grass roots. It is captured in the slogan of environmental groups, "Think globally, act locally."

8. *Feminism.* Despite the overall emphasis on the equality of all beings, the equality of *women* is by no means a frequent enough theme within the reform movements. But there is increasing recognition of feminism's intellectual

contribution. Patriarchal, hierarchical values of "power over" and competitive exploitation, help explain many contemporary problems, from war and the despoiling of the environment to wife and child abuse.

Many educators, activists, and concerned people from around the world have expressed to us their own sense of a coming together of shared values. Many of the newsletters and journals of these diverse alternative movements are making connections among feminism, peace, social justice, and environmentalism. Numerous critiques of the Gulf war, for example, addressed each of these issues. If this international "Shared Values Movement" could identify itself and draw together in a more orchestrated fashion, it could rapidly discard its minority status. It could become *the* major influence in the course of human events. We could have the potential for a "World Coalition of Shared Values" aimed at educating people and transforming the world into more loving community—Riane Eisler's "partnership future."

The hope for the future lies not only in individual and small-group activities, but in a great coming together of people throughout the world around a common set of values and meanings based on liberty and especially on love.

STANDING FIRM ON LOVE

If the loving community cannot and will not express itself through government or the free market, how will it influence people? In addition to individual actions, education, and other well-known activities, what *mechanism* for change could be used by the loving community, including the proposed "World Coalition of Shared Values"?

The thoughts and actions of three Twentieth Century leaders— Gandhi, Schweitzer, and King—are especially compatible with the Three Dynamic Theory emphasis on both individual liberty and bonding through love. The political and religious principles of these three men especially exemplify the theme of love. Each developed a method of conflict resolution based on love: Schweitzer as a doctor treating African tribal people far from civilization, and

Gandhi and King as political activists through public nonviolent confrontation.

GANDHI'S SATYAGRAHA

Perhaps no one has examined and lived more deeply the issues of severe conflict and its resolution than Gandhi. In *The Conquest of Violence: The Gandhian Philosophy of Conflict* (1988), Joan Bondurant explores *satyagraha*, Gandhi's method of conflict resolution. Of special interest, she focuses her book specifically on Gandhi as a conflict resolver. For Bondurant, Gandhi's major contribution lay not in his overall philosophical, religious, or economic theory, but in his approach to resolving conflict.

What makes Gandhi's vision so important is its spiritual content—the ideal of love—and his determination to be guided by love in confronting life-threatening political conflict. Gandhi gave up his earlier phrase "passive resistance" in favor of satyagraha, which he defined as "the Force which is born of Truth and love or nonviolence," (p. 8). According to Gandhi, God is truth, and "the nearest approach to truth was through love," (p. 18). Conflict is resolved through the search for truth, and the method must be loving.

Satyagraha requires always striving to see the other's viewpoint. The other persons in the conflict must be treated with dignity and they must be treasured.

Satyagraha further requires that every attempt be made to avoid injuring those who are being confronted. The ancient Hindu, Jain, and Buddhist ethical precept, *ahimsa*, means nonviolence or noninjury. Gandhi equates it with love, and Bondurant compares it to Christian charity and Greek *agape*. The refusal to do harm, even in self-defense, became the center of Gandhi's philosophy and methodology. It is love's abhorrence of violence in its more consistent expression. One refuses to *acquiesce* to wrong deeds, and one refuses to *perpetrate* them either.

In conflict, the individual satyagraha may have to undergo suffering, rather than inflict it on others. Through this "self-suffering" the individual hopes to persuade by touching the conscience of one's seeming opponent.

It is a mistake to think of Gandhi as either an inspired idealist *or* a pragmatic politician. He was both. Satyagraha was the highest moral principle, and the *most effective* technique for bringing about the just resolution of conflict.

Because Gandhi was thoroughly committed to civil disobedience, a distinct streak of Dynamic II individualism runs through his philosophy. According to Bondurant, "For Gandhi, society must provide opportunities for the individual, and the final decision as to what constitutes that growth lies with the individual," (p. 162). Bondurant quotes Gandhi, "No society can possibly be built on denial of individual freedom. It is contrary to the very nature of man. . . . Even those who do not believe in the liberty of the individual believe in their own," (p. 162).

Gandhi's moral individualism lent his thoughts and actions, at times, an aura of anarchism or even conservatism. Gandhi did not aim at overturning existing institutions as much as he favored limiting government power and correcting its more grievous moral flaws. Always, however, the ultimate source of morality remained individual conscience. Thus his thought drew upon both liberty and love.

Bondurant identifies the roots of Gandhi's philosophy not only in conscience but in basic needs. For Gandhi, the "criteria of truth lay in the meeting of human needs" and "concern for human needs lies at the core of Gandhian teaching," (p. 193). Thus Gandhi's approach to conflict corresponds very closely with the Three Dynamic Theory.

THE MIRROR LIT WITH LOVE

At first glance it seems surprising to identify Gandhi, as Bondurant has done, as a man devoted to conflict *resolution*. From the viewpoint of the British or the South African government, he was an instigator and provocateur. That is because the British and the South Africans wished to suppress the conflicts that their policies created. From Gandhi's viewpoint as a young Indian lawyer living in South Africa, he was responding to the conflict created by injustice.

It is misleading to think of conflict resolution as a kind of smoothing over of the waters. As Gandhi exemplifies, conflict resolution can be a confrontation of its own: love's confrontation with hatred and strife.

To confront conflict in the light of love is to see it more clearly, more starkly, and more realistically. The person devoted to resolving conflict must first understand its destructiveness and then reflect it back upon the participants.

When a man and woman, for example, have turned their marriage into a battlefield, the loving therapist does not minimize or ignore the hatred and the pain. Instead, the therapist becomes a loving mirror who shows, in all its reality, the pain and hurt that the parties are inflicting on each other. Similarly, when the individual stands up with firmness and love against the evil that others are committing, he or she discloses the evil in its undisguised form.

I am not suggesting that the therapist or conflict resolver leap into the fray to bring out or underscore all its destructive elements. Usually the destructive aspects will come out soon enough on their own. In dealing with people, one must begin at the level of communication the participants can make use of. In therapy or conflict resolution, the task is to help the participants deal with what they are capable of dealing with, while encouraging them to take the next steps as soon as feasible.

If people in conflict seem ready to bolt from the office or the conference table at the first sign of confrontation, or if they seem ready to inflict irreparable damage on each other, of course the immediate goal is to calm everyone down. That may require proceeding as lightly as necessary. But the long-term task remains that of helping the participants recognize the damage that they are doing to each other, while helping them develop new and better principles for nonviolent, loving conflict resolution.

Only the mirror lit with love can accurately reflect the pain that it confronts, while putting that pain within the brighter perspective of future possibilities for liberty and love. The therapist or conflict resolver must be deeply rooted in two realities: the pain that people cause each other when they resort to coercion; and the joy and opportunity they create when they relate through the principles of liberty and love.

ALBERT SCHWEITZER

While Schweitzer was not completely in agreement with Gandhi, he supported the basic thrust of ahisma. In *Indian Thought and Its*

Development (1936), Schweitzer describes Gandhi as moving beyond the proscription of killing and causing hurt or pain. Ahisma in Gandhi's hands became "the complete exercise of compassion." In paraphrasing the principle more to his own liking, Schweitzer declared:

> *... that all worldly purposive action should be undertaken with the greatest possible avoidance of violence, and that ethical considerations should so dominate ourselves as to influence also the hearts of our opponents. ... that only activity in an ethical spirit can really accomplish anything. (pp. 233–34.)*

There is, of course, a sometimes thin line between passive resistance—even with the best of spiritual intentions—and coercion. Bondurant reports that Gandhi himself was concerned about his own tendencies to cross the line. In *Indian Thought and Its Development*, Schweitzer said of Gandhi with a seemingly sympathetic chiding, "He has never succeeded in altogether controlling the agitator within his breast," (p. 232). Schweitzer, of course, was hardly the sort to walk the gauntlet of a rock-throwing crowd or to block the way of police mounted on galloping horses.

Schweitzer would eventually sum up his whole philosophy in the phrase "reverence for life" (see chapter 2). In *My Life and Thought* (1931), he wrote:

> *A man is ethical only when life, as such, is sacred to him, that of plants and animals as well as that of his fellow-men, and when he devotes himself helpfully to all life that is in need of help. (p. 188.)*

He referred to this psychospiritual impulse as "the universal ethic of the feeling of responsibility for an ever-widening sphere of all that lives." (p. 188).

In *The Philosophy of Civilization* (1951), Schweitzer spoke of the will-to-live which he saw operating in all life forms. His observation of this will-to-live led to his ultimate ethical axiom: "Devotion to life resulting from reverence for life," (p. 306). According to Schweitzer:

In ethical conflicts man can arrive only at subjective decisions. No one can decide for him at what point, on each occasion, lies the extreme limit of possibility for his persistence in the preservation and furtherance of life. He alone has to judge this issue, by letting himself be guided by a feeling of the highest possible responsibility towards other life.

We must never let ourselves become blunted. We are living in truth, when we experience these conflicts more profoundly. The good conscience is an invention of the devil. (pp. 317–18.)

For Schweitzer, conflict resolution is an ongoing process of spiritual consciousness in which the individual strives ever harder to be aware of other life and to take responsibility for its furtherance. This is conflict resolution through love.

Like Gandhi, Schweitzer remained devoted to the individual and to liberty. His writings reflect a profound desire to live life exactly as he himself chose to. Consistent with Dynamic II: liberty, in *My Life and Thought* he promoted the Western traditions of "rationality" and "inalienable human rights," (p. 257), advocated "the rights of human personality," (p. 113), and cited his own desire to pursue "an absolutely personal and independent activity . . . to which I could devote myself as an individual and as wholly free," (p. 106).

That Schweitzer and Gandhi chose *service* to humanity should not confuse us about their determination to make their own choices. Nor should their devotion to serving others be understood as a sacrifice. For Schweitzer and for Gandhi, individual freedom, human conscience, and love are inextricable; each *consciously chose* to live a life based on love. They demonstrate the principle that "gifting" is a joy in itself and therefore entails no sacrifice. Thus, love transcends distinctions between selfishness and altruism (see chapter 2).

Schweitzer believed more in individual acts than in political activity as a method of implementing love in society. From political confrontation to tending people in the jungle or raising children in a family, there are many ways to serve, and many ways to devote oneself to resolving conflict.

MARTIN LUTHER KING, JR.

Martin Luther King, Jr. drew upon Gandhi for hope and inspiration. Commenting on "My Trip to the Land of Gandhi" (Washington, 1986), King wrote:

The way of acquiescence leads to moral and spiritual suicide. The way of violence leads to bitterness in the survivors and brutality in the destroyers. But, the way of nonviolence leads to redemption and the creation of the beloved community. (p. 25.)

Using principles identical to those of Gandhi, King described nonviolent resistance as "a courageous confrontation of evil by the power of love, in the faith that it is better to be the recipient of violence than the inflictor of it." By accepting rather than delivering injury, the nonviolent resister "may develop a sense of shame in the opponent, and thereby bring about a transformation and change of heart," (p. 26).

THE FUTURE OF LOVING FIRMNESS

The nonviolent methods of Gandhi and King exemplify loving community: implementing love on a societal level. It is important to explicitly separate loving community from the two dominant institutions of our society, government (state coercion) and the marketplace (the profit motive). Otherwise we fail to identify exactly how we need to proceed. People must become so convinced that love is the best and only hope that they will *voluntarily* and *out of love* band together to express it as a method of conflict resolution. They must *intend* to create a loving community through voluntary relationships among people for the purpose of solving conflicts through love.

Hopefully, the proliferating reform movements that share

Dynamic I values will converge into "The Shared Values Movement." They will be able to speak out against and educate people about the outrages perpetrated in the name of the state, socialism, communism, or the free enterprise system. But then, at a critical moment, there will be a need to take more definitive action—to lay oneself on the line, so to speak.

Often the decision to act results from personal anguish and outrage over the pain inflicted upon others. An injury against people or the planet becomes personally unendurable. At that moment, when words have failed to make a difference, individuals and groups can turn for inspiration to Gandhi and to Martin Luther King, Jr. They may wish to help others gather together to witness the injury and to refuse to participate in the perpetration.

It all begins with personal feelings of empathy and conscience. What seems to offend me to the core may hardly offend you at all, and what horrifies you may seem the least among many horrors to me. Some may wish to stand up with loving firmness against abuses being directed against themselves within the home by a family member. Or perhaps they can no longer tolerate the injustices done to them at work or school or in church. Many people may be more highly motivated by the injuries inflicted upon others, such as a family member, neighbor, or friends; a pet, a local woods, or park. Still others may feel it most deeply when they consider the outrages perpetrated against larger groups: battered women, abused children, the poor, the hungry, the homeless, the chronically ill, the survivors of psychiatric or penal abuse, racial or religious minorities, animals, nature, the earth. Some may take individual actions, others may join groups. Two things can be said with certainty: there is no end of injuries and injustices inflicted by people upon each other and upon nature; there is no end to the need for more action in the name of liberty and love in this world.

SEARCHING FOR BALANCE AND TAKING A STAND

It is not easy to find an ideal interaction or balance among coercion, liberty, and love. Few people are willing, for example, to wholly reject coercive state interventions aimed at redistributing wealth in the interest of caring for the poorest in our midst. Many environmental problems seem to demand government action. We do conclude, however, that in all areas of life coercion must be kept to a minimum.

Liberty, while not the ultimate value in life, is an important one, and provides the best context for developing love. It also generates what we have come to view as material and economic progress. Whether or not this is positive progress, however, has come under increasing scrutiny; but technological progress seems a necessary component of peaceful global dialog.

Love, the only dynamic that is ethically complete, abhors coercion and violence, takes joy in all expressions of life, and wishes for mutual satisfaction and happiness. Whenever possible, love should be our standard.

Human beings throughout the world need an infinitely more loving attitude toward each other, nature, and the earth itself. Helping ourselves and others to find this love in our hearts is our shared duty. Meanwhile, the ways of going about this are as varied as human relationship and imagination.

Love can be expressed and shared among friends and family, with children, toward animals, in recreational pursuits, in the workplace, in clubs and philanthropic organizations, in the arts and sciences, in schools and places of religious worship, and through groups working toward reform of society. It can be shared and inspired by popular movies and music; and, much too rarely, it can be found in universities and in scholarly publications. I have found it on occasion in the courts, in legislative bodies, and on radio and television. Often I have found and shared it at conferences of people devoted to reform and the improvement of society. Meanwhile, love is always there in nature, ready for the giving and the receiving.

When love is felt and expressed, it can usually be recognized with ease. Some of the basic expressions of love are identified in this chapter in the description of the "Shared Values Movement" and others are listed as short phrases in the Three Dynamics Table. But there is more direct access to love than that—within the place in our hearts that feels joyfully aware of other people, all life forms, and existence itself. We can find love there, and know it by the treasuring, reverence, charity, and forgiveness that it radiates. Then we can encourage it to grow.

When we feel ready as individuals to confront conflict with love, neither the free market nor the government will be wholly on our side. The loving firmness of Gandhi and King may be the only hope. At some point, a sufficient number of people must refuse to participate in the destructiveness that tortures human society, nature, and our earth. In the long run, nothing can substitute for the actions of individuals dedicated to both the preservation of liberty and the furtherance of love. Above all, we need without embarrassment to embrace love as our best approach to resolving conflict and, beyond that, as our way of life.

THE THREE DYNAMICS OF HUMAN PROGRESS FOR INDIVIDUALS, INSTITUTIONS, AND SOCIETIES

▼ ▼

INDIVIDUAL SPIRITUAL STATE	MODE OF INTERACTION

DYNAMIC I: LOVE—THE HIGHEST PRINCIPLE OF LIFE

Beingness	*Loving Affiliation or Gifting*
The Human as a Being or Soul	Abhorrence of Force
Self as Source of Love	Mutual Unconditional Love
Reverence for Self	Treasuring of All People
Acceptance of Self & Life	Peace & Harmony with Life
Spiritual Self-fulfillment	Kindness, Empathy, & Generosity
Equal Worth of All Selves	Concern for Human Destiny
Communality of All Selves	Humanity as One Family
Integrity, Wholeness of Self	Oneness with Nature, God, Life
Devotion to Higher Values	Promotion of Liberty & Love
Love of Truth & Knowledge	Enlightenment

DYNAMIC II: LIBERTY— THE NECESSARY PRINCIPLE FOR PROGRESS

Doingness	*Voluntary Exchange*
The Human as Agent or Doer	Force Limited to Self-defense
Self as Creator of Effects	Control over Physical Universe
Uniqueness of Self	Concern with Personal Satisfaction
Responsibility; Honesty	Contracts & Agreements
Egoism & Self-interest	Competition; Limited Cooperation
Respect for Self	Personal and Business Ethics
Self-direction; Autonomy	Bargaining and Free Enterprise
Reliance on Reason	Scientific & Technical Progress
Individualism	Respect for Rights & Freedoms
Personal Success	Personal & Socioeconomic Progress
Antiauthoritarianism	Open, Pluralistic Society

DYNAMIC III: COERCION—THE MOST DESTRUCTIVE PRINCIPLE OF LIFE

Thingness	*Involuntary Relationships*
The Human as Object or Thing	Arbitrary or Unlimited Force
Self as a Reaction or Effect	Prediction & Social Control
Self-hate & Self-oppression	Hatred & Violence to Attain Ends
Selfishness & Egomania	Envy & Distrust; No Cooperation
Dishonesty toward Self	Lying, Cheating, & Fraud
Out of Touch with Self	Alienation, Remoteness
Anti-individualistic	Adjustment & Survival Values
Biological View of Self	Physical Theories & Therapies
Behavioral View of Self	Behavioral Theories & Therapies
Mechanistic View of Self	Scientism
Personal Failure; Psychosis	Socioeconomic Decline
Authoritarianism	Closed, Totalitarian Society

BIBLIOGRAPHY

▼ ▼

Adler, Alfred. *The Science of Living*, New York: Doubleday & Company, Inc., 1969.

Allport, Gordon. *Becoming: Basic Considerations for a Psychology of Personality*, Yale University Press, 1955.

Anderson, Terry L. and Leal, Donald R. *Free Market Environmentalism*, Westview Press, Inc., 1991.

Andruss, Van; Christopher Plant, Judith Plant, and Eleanor Wright . *Home! A Bioregional Reader*, New Society Publishers, 1990.

Ansbacher, Heinz and Rowena Ansbacher. *The Individual Psychology of Alfred Adler*. Basic Books, Inc., 1956.

Arieti, Silvano. *American Handbook of Psychiatry*. Basic Books, Inc., 1960.

Artiss, Kenneth L. *Therapeutic Studies*. Psychiatric Books, 1985.

Athens, Lonnie. *The Creation of Dangerous Violent Criminals*. Routledge, 1989.

Bastiat, Frederic. *The Law*. The Foundation for Economic Education, Inc., 1981.

Bellah, Robert N.; R. Madsen, A. Sullivan, W. Swidler, and S. Tipton, *Habits of the Heart: Individualism and Commitment in American Life*. Harper & Row, Publishers, 1985.

Berry, Wendell. *A Continuous Harmony*. Harcourt Brace, 1972.

Berry, Wendell. *The Unsettling of American Culture and Agriculture*. Sierra Club Books, 1977.

Berry, Wendell. *Home Economics*. North Point Press, 1987.

Blanton, Smiley. *Love or Perish*. Simon & Schuster, 1956.

Block, Sidney and Peter Reddaway. *Psychiatric Terror: How Soviet Psychiatry Is Used to Suppress Dissent*. Basic Books, Inc., 1977.

Boetie, Etienne de la. *The Politics of Obedience: The Discourse of Voluntary Servitude*. Free Life Editions, 1975.

Bondurant, Joan V. *Conquest of Violence: The Gandhian Philosophy of Conflict*. Princeton University Press, 1988.

Boulding, Kenneth E. *Beyond Economics: Essays on Society, Religion and Ethics*. Ann Arbor Paperbacks, 1968.

Boulding, Kenneth E. *Ecodynamics: A New Theory of Societal Evolution*. Sage Publications, 1978.

Bowlby, John. *Attachment and Loss Volume II: Separation Anxiety and Anger*. Basic Books, Inc., 1973.

Branden, Barbara. *The Passion of Ayn Rand.* Doubleday & Company, Inc., 1986.

Branden, Nathaniel. *The Psychology of Self-Esteem,* Bantam Books, 1969.

Breggin, Ginger and Peter Breggin. "Feminist Paradigms and Conflict Resolution." *ICAR* Newsletter (Institute for Conflict Analysis and Resolution, George Mason University) Spring 1992.

Breggin, Peter R. 1964. "Coercion of Voluntary Patients in an Open Hospital." *Arch Gen Psychiatry* 10:173–181, reprinted with a new introduction in Edwards RB (ed), *Psychiatry and Ethics.* Prometheus Books, 1982.

Breggin, Peter R. *Electroshock: Its Brain-Disabling Effects.* Springer Publishing Co., 1979.

Breggin, Peter R. "Evaluating Human Progress: A Unified Approach to Psychology, Economics, and Politics." In Konstantin Kolenda, ed., *Organizations and Ethical Individualism.* Praeger Books, 1988.

Breggin, Peter R. "How and Why Psychiatry Became a Death Machine." Paper presented at *Medicine Without Compassion,* a conference on the history of medicine during Nazi Germany, Koln, Germany, 1988.

Breggin, Peter R. "Iatrogenic Helplessness in Authoritarian Psychiatry." In Morgan RF (ed), *The Iatrogenics Handbook,* IPI Publishing Co., 1983.

Breggin, Peter R. *Psychiatric Drugs: Hazards to the Brain.* Springer Publishing Co., 1983.

Breggin, Peter R. "Psychiatry and Psychotherapy as Political Processes." *American Journal of Psychotherapy.* 29:369–382, 1975.

Breggin, Peter R. *The Psychology of Freedom.* Prometheus Books, 1980.

Breggin, Peter R. "Psychotherapy as Applied Ethics." *Psychiatry: Journal for the Study of Interpersonal Processes.* Vol. 34, No. 1, Feb., 1971.

Breggin, Peter and E. Mark Stern (Eds.). *Psychotherapy of the Psychotic Patient.* Haworth Press, in press, 1993–94. Will also appear as a volume of the journal, *The Psychotherapy Patient,* in press, 1993–94.

Breggin, Peter R. "Sex and Love: Sexual Dysfunction as a Spiritual Disorder." In Shelp EE (ed), *Sexuality and Medicine.* D. Reidel, 1987.

Breggin, Peter R. (1992–3, in press) "The Three Stages of Human Progress." *Review of Existential Psychology and Psychiatry.*

Breggin, Peter R. *Toxic Psychiatry: Why Empathy and Love Must Replace the Drugs, Electroshock and Biochemical Theories of the "New Psychiatry."* St. Martin's Press, 1991.

Breton, Denise and Christopher Largent. *The Soul of Economies: Spiritual Evolution Goes to the Marketplace.* Idea House Publishing Company, 1991.

Brown, Charles J. and Armando Lago. *The Politics of Psychiatry in Revolutionary Cuba.* Transaction Publishers, 1991.

Brown, Phil. *Transfer of Care*. Routledge, Chapman, and Hill, 1988.

Buber, Martin. *I and Thou*. Charles Scribner's Sons, 1958.

Burton, John, ed. *Conflict: Human Needs Theory*. St. Martin's Press, 1990.

Burton, John. *Conflict: Resolution and Provention*. St. Martin's Press, 1990.

Burton, John. *Resolving Deep-Rooted Conflict*. University Press of America, 1987.

Burton, John. *Separation: Anxiety and Anger*. Basic Books, Inc., 1973.

Carnegie Council on Adolescent Development. *Turning Points: Preparing American Youth for the 21st Century*. Carnegie Corporation of New York, 1989.

Carter, Jimmy. *Keeping the Faith*. Bantam Books, 1982.

Chesler, Phyllis. *Women and Madness*. Doubleday & Company, Inc., 1972.

Clark, Mary E. *Ariadne's Thread: The Search for New Modes of Thinking*. St. Martin's Press, 1989.

Clark, Ronald W. *Einstein: The Life and Times*. Avon Books, 1984.

Coate, Roger A. and Jerel A. Rosati, eds. *The Power of Human Needs in World Society*. Lynne Rienner Publishers, 1988.

Cohen, David, ed. "Challenging the Therapeutic State: Critical Perspectives on Psychiatry and the Mental Health System." The Journal of Mind and Behavior. Vol. 11, Nos. 3 and 4. Also in book form. Haworth Press, 1990.

Coleman, Lee. *The Reign of Error: Psychiatry, Authority, and Law*. Boston: Beacon Press, 1984.

Costello, Judy. "Beyond Gandhi: An American Feminist's Approach to Nonviolence." In Pam McAllister, ed., *Reweaving the Web of Life: Feminism and Nonviolence*. New Society Publishers, 1982.

Cousins, Norman. *Albert Schweitzer's Mission: Healing and Peace*. W.W. Norton & Co., 1985.

Csikszentmihalyi, Mihaly and Isabella Selega Csikszentmihalyi. *Optimal Experience: Psychological Studies of Flow in Consciousness*. Cambridge University Press, 1988.

Dalai Lama. *Ocean of Wisdom: Guidelines for Living*. Harper & Row Publishers, 1989.

Daly, Herman E. and Cobb, John B. Jr. *For the Common Good*. Beacon Press, 1989.

Davies, James Chowning. "The Existence of Human Needs." In Roger A. Coate and Jerel A.Rosati, eds., *The Power of Human Needs in World Society*. Lynne Rienner Publishers, 1988.

de Waal, Frans. *Peacemaking Among Primates.* Harvard University Press, 1989.

Dewey, John. *Freedom and Culture.* Prometheus Books, 1989.

Drucker, Peter F. *The New Realities.* Harper & Row Publishers, 1989.

Dyal, James A. *Education for Survival: The New Security Paradigm.* Paper presented at the annual meeting of the American Psychological Association, August 19, 1991.

Egeland, Byron and Martha Farrell Erickson. "Rising Above the Past: Strategies for Helping New Mothers Break the Cycle of Abuse and Neglect." *Zero to Three.* 11(2), 1990.

Eisenberg, Leon and Leo Kanner, "Early Infantile Autism, 1943–1955." In Charles Reed, Irving Alexander, and Silvan Tomkins, *Psychopathology: A Source Book* Harvard University Press, 1958.

Eisenberg, Nancy and Janet Strayer. *Empathy and Its Development.* Cambridge University Press, 1990.

Eisler, Riane. *The Challice and the Blade.* Harper & Row Publishers, 1987.

Ellis, Havelock. *Studies in the Psychology of Sex: Volume II.* Random House, 1937.

Erdoes, Richard. *Crying for a Dream.* Bear & Company, 1989.

Erikson, Erik. *Childhood and Society.* W.W. Norton & Co., 1963.

Etzioni, Amitai. *The Moral Dimension.* Free Press, 1988.

Fausto-Sterling, Anne. *Myths of Gender.* Basic Books, Inc., 1985.

Feather, Frank. *G-Forces: The 35 Global Forces Restructuring Our Future.* William Morrow and Co., 1989.

Fireside, Harvey. *Soviet Psychoprisms.* W.W. Norton & Co., 1979.

Fischer, Louis, ed. *The Essential Gandhi.* Random House, 1962.

Fisher, Roger and Scott Brown. *Getting Together: Building Relationships As We Negotiate.* Penguin Books, 1988.

Fossey, Dian. *Gorillas in the Mist.* Houghton Mifflin Company, 1983.

Foucault, Michel. *Madness and Civilization: A History of Insanity in the Age of Reason.* Vintage Books, 1965.

Frank, Leonard. *The History of Shock Treatment.* Available from L. Frank, 2300 Webster Street, San Francisco, CA 94115, 1978.

French, Marilyn. *Beyond Power: On Women, Men, and Morals.* Ballantine Books, 1985.

Freud, Sigmund. *The Problem of Anxiety.* W.W. Norton & Co., 1936.

Friedman, Thomas L. *From Beirut to Jerusalem*. Doubleday & Co., Inc., 1989.

Fromm, Erich. *The Art of Loving*. Harper & Row Publishers, 1956.

Fromm, Erich. *Escape from Freedom*. Farrar and Rinehart, 1941.

Fromm, Erich. *To Have or To Be?*. Harper & Row Publishers, 1976.

Galbraith, John K. *The Affluent Society*. Houghton Mifflin Company, 1958.

Galbraith, John K. *Annals of an Abiding Liberal*. Meridian Books, 1980.

Gandhi, Mohandas K. *Gandhi: An Autiobiography*. Beacon Press, 1957.

Gelles, Richard and Murray Straus, *Intimate Violence: The Causes and Consequences of Abuse in the American Family*. Simon & Schuster, 1988.

Gilligan, Carol. *In a Different Voice*. Harvard University Press, 1982.

Goffman, Erving. *Asylums: Essays on the Social Situation of Mental Patients and Other Inmates*. Doubleday & Company, Inc., 1961.

Goldsmith, Edward; Robert Allen, Michael Allaby, John Davoll, and Sam Lawrence, eds. *Blueprint for Survival*. New American Library, 1972.

Goodall, Jane. *The Chimpanzees of Gombe*. Harvard University Press, 1986.

Gould, Stephen J. *The Mismeasure of Man*. W.W. Norton & Co., 1989.

Green, Arthur. "Physical and Sexual Abuse of Children." In Harold Kaplan and Benjamin Sadock, eds., *Comprehensive Textbook of Psychiatry*. Williams and Wilkins, 1989.

Hanh, Thich Nhat. *Peace Is Every Step: The Path of Mindfulness in Everyday Life*. Bantam Books, 1991.

Harris, Adrienne and Ynestra King. *Rocking the Ship of State: Toward a Feminist Peace Politics*. Westview Press, Inc., 1989.

Hart, David K. "Management and Benevolence: The Fatal Flaw in Theory Y." In Konstantin Kolenda, ed. *Organizations and Ethical Individualism*. Praeger Books, 1988.

Hart, David K. "Public Administration, the Thoughtless Functionary, and 'Feelinglessness.' " In Robert B. Denhardt and Edward T. Jennings, Jr., eds. *The Revitalization of the Public Service*. University of Missouri–Columbia Press, 1987.

Haworth, Lawrence. *Autonomy: An Essay in Philosophical Psychology and Ethics*. Yale University Press, 1986.

Hayek, Friedrich A. *The Counter-Revolution of Science: Studies on the Abuse of Reason*. Liberty Press, 1952.

Hayek, Friedrich A. *The Road to Serfdom*. The University of Chicago Press, 1944.

Helgesen, Sally. *The Female Advantage: Women's Ways of Leadership.* Doubleday Currency, 1990.

Hertz, J.H. *The Pentateuch and Haftorahs.* Soncino Press, 1960.

Hess, Karl. *Dear America.* William Morrow & Co., 1975.

Hoffman, Martin L. "The Contribution of Empathy to Justice and Moral Judgment." In Nancy Eisenberg and Janet Strayer, eds., *Empathy and Its Development.* Cambridge University Press, 1987.

Horney, Karen. *Neurosis and Human Growth.* W.W. Norton & Co., 1950.

Horney, Karen. *Our Inner Conflicts.* W.W. Norton & Co., 1945.

Hudson, Michael C. *The Palestinians: New Directions.* Center for Contemporary Arab Studies, 1990.

Hunt, Morton. *The Compassionate Beast: What Science Is Discovering About the Humane Side of Mankind.* William Morrow & Co., 1990.

Jaffe, Peter; David Wolfe, and Susan Wilson. *Children of Battered Women.* Sage Publications, 1990.

James, William. *The Principles of Psychology.* Vol. I & II. Henry Holt & Co., 1890.

James, William. *Varieties of Religious Experience.* The Modern Library, 1929.

Jenkins, Bruce. "Einstein Institution Delegation Discusses Civilian-Based Defense with Lithuanian Officials." *Nonviolent Sanctions: News from the Albert Einstein Institution,* Vol. II, No. 4, p. 4., Spring 1991.

Karon, Bertram. "Psychotherapy Versus Medication for Schizophrenia: Empirical Comparisons." In Seymour Fisher and Roger Greenberg, eds., *The Limits of Biological Treatments for Psychological Distress,* Lawrence Erlbaum Associates, 1989.

Kaufman, Gershen. *The Psychology of Shame.* Springer Publishing Company, Inc., 1989.

Kaufman, Les and Kenneth Mallory, eds. *The Last Extinction.* MIT Press, 1986.

Keirsey, David and Marilyn Bates. *Please Understand Me.* Prometheus Nemesis Book Company, 1984.

King, Jr., Martin Luther. *Strength to Love.* Pocket Books, 1963.

Kohn, Alfie. *The Brighter Side of Human Nature: Altruism and Empathy in Everyday Life.* Basic Books, Inc., 1990.

Kohn, Alfie. *No Contest: The Case Against Competition.* New York: Houghton Mifflin Company, 1986.

Kolenda, Konstantin, ed. *Organizations and Ethical Individualism.* Praeger Books, 1988.

Kropotkin, Petr. *Ethics: Origin and Development.* Dial Press, 1924.

Kropotkin, Petr. *Mutual Aid: A Factor of Evolution.* Porter Sargent Publishers, Inc., 1914.

Kruegler, Christopher. "A Bold Initiative in Lithuanian Defense." *Nonviolent Sanctions: News from the Albert Einstein Institution.* Vol II, No. 4, p. 1, Spring 1991.

Laing, R.D. *The Politics of Experience.* Ballantine Books, 1967.

Lamont, Corliss. *The Philosophy of Humanism.* Frederick Ungar Publishing Co, 1977.

Lee, Dorothy. *Freedom and Culture.* Waveland Press, 1959, reprinted in 1987.

Leifer, Ron. *In the Name of Psychiatry.* Science House, 1969.

Lennon, Randy and Nancy Eisenberg. "Gender and Age Difference in Empathy and Sympathy." In Nancy Eisenberg and Janet Strayer, eds. *Empathy and Its Development.* Cambridge University Press, 1987.

Lepp, Ignace. *The Psychology of Loving.* Helicon Press, Inc., 1963.

Leritz, Len. *No-Fault Negotiating: A Practical Guide to the New Dealmaking Strategy That Lets Both Sides Win.* Warner Books, 1987.

Lerner, Gerda. *The Creation of Patriarchy.* Oxford University Press, 1986.

Liebert, Robert; Rita Wicks-Nelson, Robert Kail. *Developmental Psychology, 4th edition.* Prentice-Hall, 1986.

Lippmann, Walter. *The Good Society.* Little Brown and Company, 1937.

Mack, Phyllis. "Feminine Behavior and Radical Action: Franciscans, Quakers, and the Followers of Gandhi." In Adrienne Harris and Ynestra King, eds., *Rocking the Ship of State: Towart a Feminist Peace Politics.* Westview Press, 1989.

Mahler, Margaret S.; Manuel Furer, and Calvin F. Settlage. "Severe Emotional Disturbances in Childhood: Psychosis." In Silvano Arieti, ed., *American Handbook of Psychiatry.* Basic Books, Inc., 1959.

Marx, Karl. *The Economic and Philosophic Manuscripts of 1844.* International Publishers, 1959.

Maslow, Abraham H. *The Farther Reaches of Human Nature.* Viking Press, 1971.

Masson, Jeffrey Moussaieff. *Against Therapy: Emotional Tyranny and the Myth of Psychological Healing.* Atheneum, 1988.

Masson, Jeffrey Moussaieff. *The Assault on Truth: Freud's Suppression of the Seduction Theory.* Faber and Faber, 1984.

May, Rollo; Ernest Angel and Henri F. Ellenberge, eds. *Existence: A New Dimension in Psychiatry and Psychology.* Basic Books, Inc., 1958.

McAllister, Pam. *Reweaving the Web of Life: Feminism and Nonviolence*. New Society Publishers, 1982.

McLuhan, Marshall and Quentin Fiore. *The Medium is the Massage: An Inventory of Effects*. Bantam Books, 1967.

McConnell, James V. *Understanding Human Behavior*. Holt, Rinehart and Winston, 1989.

McCullough, Christopher and Mann, Robert Woods *Managing Your Anxiety*, Jeremy Tarcher, 1985.

McKibben, Bill. *The End of Nature*. Random House, 1989.

McKnight, Gerald. *Verdict on Schweitzer*. The John Day Company, 1965.

Merton,Thomas, ed. *Gandhi on Non-violence*. New Directions Publishing Company, 1965.

Mill, John Stuart and , Harriet Mill Taylor. *Essays on Sex Equality*. University of Chicago Press, 1970.

Miller, Alice. *Thou Shalt Not Be Aware*. New American Library, 1984.

Millett, Kate. *Sexual Politics*. Ballantine Books, 1978.

Mitscherlich, Alexander and Fred Mielke *Doctors of Infamy: The Story of Nazi Medical Crimes*. Henry Schuman, 1949.

Montagu, Ashley. *Touching: the Human Significance of the Skin*. Harper & Row Publishers, 1978.

Morrison, Andrew P. *Shame: The Underside of Narcissism*. The Analytic Press, 1989.

Mosher, Loren and Lorenzo Burti. *Community Mental Health: Principles and Practice*. W.W. Norton and Co., 1989.

Muller-Hill, Beno. *Murderous Science: Elimination by Scientific Selection of Jews, Gypsies, and Others, Germany, 1933–1945*. Oxford University Press, 1988.

Naisbitt, John and Patricia Aburdene. *Re-inventing the Corporation*. New York: Warner Books, 1985.

Nock, Albert Jay. *Our Enemy the State*. Free Life Editions, 1973.

Norton, David L. "Social Organization and Individual Initiative: A Eudaimonistic Model." In Konstantin Kolenda, ed., *Organizations and Ethical Individualism*. Praeger Books, 1988.

Nozick, Robert. *Anarchy, State, and Utopia*. Basic Books, Inc., 1974.

Okin, Susan Moller. *Justice, Gender and the Family*, Basic Books, Inc., 1987.

Oliner, Samuel P. and Oliner, Pearl M. *The Altruistic Personality, Rescuers of Jews in Nazi Europe: What Led Ordinary Men and Women to Risk Their Lives on Behalf of Others?*. The Free Press, 1988.

Oppenheimer, Franz. *The State*. Free Life Editions, 1975.

Ouchi, William G. *Theory Z: How American Business Can Meet the Japanese Challenger*. Avon Books, 1981.

Pavlov, I.P. *Experimental Psychology and Other Essays*. Philosophical Library, 1957.

Peck, M. Scott. *The Road Less Traveled*. Simon & Schuster, 1978.

Peters, Thomas J. and Robert H. Waterman, Jr. *In Search of Excellence: Lessons from America's Best-Run Companies*. Warner Books, 1982.

Phillips, Kevin. *The Politics of Rich and Poor: Wealth and the American Electorate in the Reagan Aftermath*. Random House, 1990.

Piven, Frances Fox and Richard A. Cloward. *The New Class War: Reagan's Attack on the Welfare State and Its Consequences*. Pantheon Books, 1985.

Plutchik, Robert. "Evolutionary Bases of Empathy." In Nancy Eisenberg and Janet Strayer, eds., *Empathy and Its Development*. Cambridge University Press, 1987.

Podvoll, Edward M. *The Seduction of Madness*. HarperCollins Publishers, 1990.

Rand, Ayn. *Atlas Shrugged*. Random House, 1957.

Rand, Ayn. *For the New Intellectual: The Philosophy of Ayn Rand*. Random House, 1961.

Rand, Ayn. *The Fountainhead*. The Bobbs-Merrill Company, 1943.

Rand, Ayn. *Introduction to Objectivist Epistemology*. New American Library, 1979.

Robitscher, Jonas. *The Powers of Psychiatry*. Houghton Mifflin Company, 1980.

Rogers, Carl R. *On Becoming a Person: A Therapist's View of Psychotherapy*. Houghton Mifflin Company, 1961.

Ross-Breggin, Ginger. "Becoming Each Other's Answers." Unpublished, 1990.

Rothbard, Murray N. *The Ethics of Liberty*. Humanities Press, 1982.

Rothbard, Murray N. *For a New Liberty*. Macmillan Company, 1973.

Ruskin, John. *Unto This Last and Other Writings*. Penguin Books, 1985.

Ryan, William. *Blaming the Victim*. Vintage Books, 1976.

Sale, Kirkpatrick. *Dwellers in the Land: The Bioregional Vision*. Sierra Club Books, 1985.

Scheffer, Victor B. *The Shaping of Environmentalism in America*. University of Washington Press, 1991.

Scheflin, Alan and Edward Opton, Jr. *The Mind Manipulators*, Paddington, 1978.

Schmookler, Andrew Bard. *Out of Weakness: Healing the Wounds That Drive Us to War.* Bantam Books Inc., 1988.

Schneider, Isidor, ed. *The World of Love.* Volumes I & II. George Braziller, 1964.

Schoeck, Helmut and James Wiggins, eds. *Scientism and Values.* D. Van Nostrand, 1960.

Schoeck, Helmut. *Envy: A Theory of Social Behavior.* Harcourt, Brace & World, 1966.

Schweitzer, Albert. *Indian Thought and Its Development.* Henry Holt & Company, Inc., 1936.

Schweitzer, Albert. *The Philosophy of Civilization.* The Macmillan Company, 1951.

Schweitzer, Albert. *My Life and Thought: An Autobiography.* George Allen & Unwin Ltd., 1933.

Scott, William G. and David K. Hart. "The Moral Nature of Man in Organizations." *Academy of Management Journal.* June, 1971.

Scott, William G. and David K. Hart. *Organizational America.* Houghton Mifflin, 1979.

Scott, William G. and Terence R. Mitchell. "The Problem or Mystery of Evil and Virtue in Organizations." In Konstantin Kolenda, ed., *Organizations and Ethical Individualism.* Praeger Books, 1988.

Seeley, Robert A. *The Handbook of Non-Violence, Including Aldous Huxley's An Encyclopedia of Pacifism.* Lawrence Hill & Company, 1986.

Seligman, Martin E.P. *Learned Optimism.* Alfred A. Knopf, 1991.

Sharp, Gene. *The Politics of Nonviolent Action* (3 volumes). Porter Sargent Publishers, 1973.

Shelp, Earl E. *Sexuality and Medicine: Volume I: Conceptual Roots.* D. Reidel Publishing Company, 1987.

Shipler, David K. *Arab and Jew: Wounded Spirits in a Promised Land.* Penguin Books, 1986.

Shivers, Lynne. "An Open Letter to Gandhi." In Pam McAllister, ed., *Reweaving the Web of Life: Feminism and Nonviolence.* New Society Publishers, 1982.

Sites, Paul. "Needs As Analogues of Emotions," In Burton, John, ed., *Conflict: Human Needs Theory.* St. Martin's Press, 1990.

Skinner, B.F. *Beyond Freedom and Dignity.* Alfred A. Knopf, 1971.

Smith, Adam. *The Theory of Moral Sentiments*. Liberty Classics, 1976.

Smith, Adam. *The Wealth of Nations*. Penguin Books, 1982.

Spencer, Herbert. *The Man Versus the State*. Mitchell Kennerley, 1916.

Spitz, R.A. "Anaclitic Depression," *Psychoanalitic Study of the Child*. 2: 313–42, 1946.

Spooner, Lysander. *No Treason: The Constitution of No Authority (1870)* and *A Letter to Thomas F. Bayard (1882)*. Ralph Myles Publisher, 1973.

Stone, Merlin. *When God Was a Woman*. Dorset Press, 1976.

Sullivan, Harry Stack. *The Interpersonal Theory of Psychiatry*. W.W. Norton & Co., 1953.

Thompson, Ross A. "Empathy and Emotional Understanding: the Early Development of Empathy." In Nancy Eisenberg and Janet Strayer, eds., *Empathy and Its Development*. Cambridge University Press, 1987.

Thoreau, Henry David. "An Essay on Civil Disobedience." *The Portable Thoreau*, Carl Bode, ed. Viking Press, 1980.

Tolstoy, Leo. *The Kingdom of God Is Within You* (1894). University of Nebraska Press, 1894.

Tournier, Paul. *The Meaning of Persons*. Harper & Row Publishers, 1957.

Trattner, Walter I. *From Poor Law to Welfare State: A History of Social Welfare in America*. The Free Press, 1984.

Von Mises, Ludwig. *The Anti-Capitalistic Mentality*. Libertarian Press, 1972.

Von Mises, Ludwig. *Human Action: A Treatise on Economics*. Contemporary Books, Inc., 1966.

Von Mises, Ludwig. *Omnipotent Government: The Rise of the Total State and Total War*. Arlington House, 1969.

Von Mises, Ludwig. *Planned Chaos*. The Foundation for Economic Education, 1947.

Wachtel, Paul L. *The Poverty of Affluence*. New Society Publishers, 1989.

Walker, Lenore E. *Terrifying Love: Why Battered Women Kill and How Society Responds*. Harper & Row Publishers, 1989.

Waring, Marilyn. *If Women Counted: A New Feminist Economics*. Harper & Row Publishers, 1988.

Washington, James Melvin. *A Testament of Hope: The Essential Writings of Martin Luther King, Jr*. Harper & Row Publishers, 1986.

Waterman, Alan S. "Psychological Individualism and Organizational Functioning: A Cost-benefit Analysis." In Konstantin Kolenda, ed., *Organizations and Ethical Individualism*. Praeger Books, 1988.

Weatherford, Jack. *Indian Givers: How the Indians of the Americas Transformed the World.* Fawcett Columbine, 1988.

Weaver, Henry Grady. *The Mainspring of Human Progress.* Foundation for Economic Education, 1947.

Weaver, Paul H. *The Suicidal Corporation: How Big Business Fails America.* Simon & Shuster, 1988.

Wilson, Edward O. *On Human Nature.* Harvard University Press, 1978.

Wolfe, David A. *Child Abuse: Implications for Child Development and Psychopathology.* Sage Publications, 1987.

Worchel, Stephen; Joel Cooper, and George R. Goethals. *Understanding Social Psychology.* Dorsey Press, 1988.

Worldwatch Institute. *State of the World.* W.W. Norton & Co., 1990.

Wyatt, Gail Elizabeth and Gloria Johnson Powell. *Lasting Effects of Child Sexual Abuse.* Sage Publications, 1988.

Yllo, Kersti, and Michele Bogard. *Feminist Pespectives on Wife Abuse.* Sage Publications, 1988.

ABOUT THE AUTHOR
▼ ▼

Peter R. Breggin, M.D., a Harvard College and Case Western Reserve School of Medicine graduate, and former teaching fellow at Harvard Medical School, was full-time consultant for the National Institute of Mental Health before going into the private practice of psychiatry in Bethesda, Maryland, from 1968 to the present. He is the director of the center for the Study of Psychiatry and Professor (Adjunct) of Conflict Analysis and Resolution at George Mason University, as well as the author of numerous books and articles dealing with psychiatry. Dr. Breggin frequently lectures and gives seminars to lay and professional audiences and appears on national television as an expert on psychiatric and conflict-resolution issues. He has been a consultant in landmark and federal legislation on behalf of patients' rights and psychiatric reform. Dr. Breggin's most comprehensive book on the subject of psychiatry is entitled *Toxic Psychiatry: Why Therapy, Empathy, and Love Must Replace the Drugs, Electroshock, and Biochemical Theories of the "New Psychiatry"*, and is also published by St. Martin's Press.